*To the Relatives of the Author and Illustrator*

*and*

*The Commission of the European Communities*
*(Enviromental Division)*

# THE HISTORIC RIVER

## rivers and culture down the ages

**S.M. Haslam, M.A., Sc.D.,**

Botany School, University of Cambridge,
Cambridge, U.K.

*Illustrated by*
**Y. Bower**

*COBDEN OF CAMBRIDGE PRESS*

47 Newnham Road, Cambridge, England

First published in Great Britain in 1991 by
Cobden of Cambridge Press
47 Newnham Road, Cambridge CB3 9EY, United Kingdom

British Library Cataloguing in Publication Data
Haslam, S.M. (Sylvia Mary), *1934-*
*The Historic River: rivers and culture down the ages*
1. Title
910

S.M. Haslam: illustrated by Y. Bower - 1st Edition
Includes bibliographical references.
*Rivers and culture*
*Water — People — Landscape archaeology — Environmental aspects*

1991

ISBN 0 9517963 0 5

Printed and bound in Great Britain by Piggott Printers, Cambridge

# Contents

# Acknowledgements

When the author wished to learn about the historical environment of rivers, Mrs D. Phipps provided guidance, information and direction to sources. In a large measure this book is due to her expertise in this.

This research was partly funded by the Commission of the European Communities (under Contracts 079-71-1 FNV UK, 105-76 EWV UK and ENY-710-UK(H)) and the Department of the Environment: whose funding for river botany enabled the author also to see other aspects of rivers, and so whose help, like that of the University of Cambridge Botany School, is most gratefully acknowledged.

Permission to use illustrations by Mrs Y. Bower and Mrs P.A. Wolseley from the writer's earlier books has been most graciously given by the illustrators, Cambridge University Press, and Belhaven Press. Mrs M Bolaney most kindly provided some new illustrations, and Miss P. Burges, neat copies of drawings.

Chapter 8 is mostly by Mrs Bower, who also supplied the section on Stock in Chapter 12.

I am much indebted to those who provided the technical expertise needed to convert manuscript and figures to a book suitable for printing: Mrs T. Bone, and Miss J. Hodgart in particular; and also to Mrs M. Stokes for sorting material.

Permission to use copyright material was very helpfully given by Blackwells; Broads Authority; The Master and Fellows of St Catharine's College, Cambridge; Elsevier; Field Studies Council; Fitzwilliam Museum, Cambridge; Professor A. Köhler; Mid-Kent Water Co.; National Collection of Malta, Museum of Fine Arts, Valletta, Malta; National Gallery, London; Mr D. Pannett; The Society for the Protection of Ancient Buildings; Tate Gallery, London; the Master and Fellows of Trinity College, Cambridge; University of Durham Botany Department; University Library, Cambridge; University of Oxford Department for External Studies; Victoria and Albert Museum, London.

Many people have very kindly answered — often peculiar — queries about waters. They are too numerous to list, but special thanks go to Dr M. Block, Dr H.W. Haslam, Mr R.M. Haslam, Mid-Kent Water Co., Trinity College (Cambridge), Miss A. Tyndale, Wells Cathedral and the University College of North Wales Library.

# Preface

**This book is about the wealth of heritage around our rivers, that which has been transmitted from our ancestors, from past ages. Rivers have been used by man since time immemorial, and much still remains, of the use of the past few centuries at least. Much of this past is unrecognised — so is liable to unnecessary destruction.**

This is a European book. Quite as fascinating material is surely found elsewhere (the author has seen some, in USA). Fieldwork has been principally in Belgium, Britain, Czechoslovakia, Denmark, France, Germany, Gozo, Guernsey, Luxembourg, Madeira, Mallorca, Malta, Menorca and The Netherlands. It is a book to interpret and, it is hoped, illuminate the rivers as they can now be seen. It is not a book on deep history; it gives only as much past history as is needed to appreciate the present rivers. Here pictures are quite as important as written records: illuminations, principally from the fifteenth and sixteen centuries, woodcuts, principally from the sixteenth and seventeenth centuries, paintings from the seventeenth century and photographs from the nineteenth century. Anyone can start studying with a visit to the local river and local art gallery. It is not a subject restricted to specialists or experts, it is an awareness of the human environment of rivers. Anyone becoming interested in pollution and vegetation aspects of rivers may wish to read the other books by the author cited in the Bibliography (n.b., *River Plants of Western Europe* (Haslam, 1987) is a very academic text!).

Dividing the material into chapters has proved exceptionally difficult — one man's transport is another man's invasion, a riverside garden may be an ornament and a health hazard. I apologise to all who disagree with my solutions to these knotty problems.

The book is not a full and final treatise on navigation, drainage, wells, floods or whatever. These are individually covered in many books. It is, rather, an introduction to the general historic environment of the river.

The text refers to the *Domesday Book*. For non-English readers, in 1066 Duke William of Normandy conquered England, and became King William I, William the Conqueror. To determine the resources of the kingdom, he instituted a survey — described in the *Anglo-Saxon Chronicle* for 1086, as surveying the country so carefully that there was not a hide (a measure of land) in England of which he did not know who held it and how much it was worth. This was used as the ultimate reference for centuries and soon became known as *Domesday Book*. A doom was a decree, a judgement, and the book judged all impartially, as the Lord will on Judgement Day. There was no appeal against the Book.

The author recommends that, after reaching the end of the book, readers return to Chapter 2 and see, in particular, the illustrations: which will then be more illuminating.

S.M.H.
June 1991

Fig. 1.1  A Logging River: wood cut in the hills sent downstream to sawmills.

Most line drawings have been sufficiently reduced to show much depth, perspective, when looked at through a magnifying glass. Readers are recommended to try this! (Not Fig. 1.1, though.)

# 1

# Water: an Essential Element

A dry and thirsty land, where no water is. (Ps 63.1)

Concerning rivers: there be so many wonders reported and written of them, and of the several creatures that be bred and live in them; and those by authors of so good credit, that we need not to deny them an historical faith. (Walton, 1653)

## Introduction

Living organisms are composed mainly of water: the living contain more water than anything else. Man's body contains around 67% water, a baby's at least 70%. The more watery fruits and vegetables, like strawberries and lettuce, contain above 90%, even reaching 98%. Water is constantly being lost from the living, and this water content must be constantly replaced. The water content of animal tissue must stay within strictly defined limits, where the dilution of various chemicals cannot change without serious consequences. Salt content echoes the salinity of primaeval oceans. Man can live without food for perhaps forty days and more, but without water he perishes fast — after only a few hours in a tropical desert (with high temperatures and low humidity), though lasting several days in colder climates (with a higher humidity).

Many animals require fresh water only to replenish that which is lost from their bodies. Some also use it for washing, though usually to a much lesser extent than does man. Others use it as the medium of existence, like fish and fresh-water shrimps, or as the medium for part of their life, like dragon-flies or amphibians. Some animals use water as a surface to live on, like duck, or as a habitat for hunting, either hunting within the water, like cormorants, or from shore, like heron. Although this list could continue, it pales into insignificance beside the uses of waters by man (Table 1.1). This book is concerned with rivers, not the salt-water seas or the major inland lakes.

The varied, weird and wonderful ways in which man has used the rivers have changed over the centuries, but the use, and the need, remain. No wonder that in so many cultures deities of some kind, usually female, were believed to live in springs, wells, fountains and streams: the nymphs (including Egeria), the Woman of the Wells, and Anahita, for instance. The sources of water — the places of living water as they were so aptly named — were surely worthy of reverence and worship. Indeed, though worship is now absent, the lack of the former respect is bringing ecological imbalance, if not worse: water supplies are being depleted, more being taken out than is being put in, ground-water levels are lower; springs and brooks have gone; rivers have too often become even shallower and more uniform channels

*Table 1.1*
*Some past and present river uses for man*

**Drinking:** people; farm, travel and domestic animals
**Cooking**
**Cleaning:** clothes, people and animals (sheep-dip); homes; farmyards, stables, etc.; roads and other built-up surfaces.
**Other domestic supply:** fire engines, hydrants; heating by volcanic water (Reykjavik); water-meters, etc.
**Food and drink:** fishing (rivers, man-made fishponds), waterfowl, watercress (rivers, man-made cress beds); irrigation, drainage, grazing; alcoholic and other drinks.
Major ingredient of food and drink.
**Materials** (source, or processing in the river itself): osiers and withies (baskets, poles, etc.); rushes (chairs, matting, lights), reeds (thatch, etc.), strewing-plants (floors), tussock sedges (stools).
Soaking flax, hemp, fleeces.
Extraction of gravel, sand, etc.
**Medicinal:** springs, spas.
Plants.
**Religion:** holy wells, baptism, ritual cleansing; pilgrimages to holy rivers, springs.
Forming remote places for hermits and religious communities.
**Magic:** rain-making, rain- and flood-removing; fertility; other magic fountains and waters, various.
**Industry:**   *Power* — Watermills driving machinery for grinding corn, other grain, olives, other plants; fashioning armour, jewellery, etc.; tanning, fulling, dyeing; making paper, gunpowder, metal products, boilers for steam engines; sawing wood,etc;
Hydroelectricity; cooling water for other forms of electricity generation.
   *Processing and washing* — mines: coal, tin, gold, lead, silver and other ores.
Most industry, ancient and modern, matting, tanning, paper-making, tempering iron, metal products, textiles, foods and drinks, etc.
**Transport:** boats for trade, business and pleasure activities, river-bed transport, ice transport.
Boilers for steam engines, boats, trains.
**Recreation and ornament:** ornamental fountains and rivers, water-gardens, etc.; water-spectacles, river parties.
Fishing, coarse and salmonid (conserving spawning-grounds and migration routes when changing rivers).
Walking, picnicking and parking beside a river, living in temporary tents or caravans.
Swimming, paddling, SCUBA-diving, water-skiing, etc. Model boats, Pooh-sticks, etc.
Water-clocks and other mechanical machines.
Watering (land), gardens.
**Waste disposal:** sewage, factory, mine and farm effluents; run-off from farmland and roads; general waste.
Drowning unwanted animals.
Murder and suicide of persons.
**Punishment for crime:** ducking, drowning.
**Defence from attack:** river bends, marshes, moats; stakes in river, chains, fortified bridges, forts, etc.
**Attack:** by boat (e.g. Vikings); across river.

---

for removing 'unwanted' water quickly. Water is being polluted, polluted even before it reaches the springs, by fertilisers and biocides percolating through from farmed land above, sometimes by even worse; and polluted on its way to the seas by dirty water from sewage and sewage-treatment works, and from factories, motorways and mines etc. Long-term damage to the river does not just kill fish and eliminate otter: it lowers the quality of life for all, including man.

## Human Ecology of Rivers

In the eighth century B.C., the Prophet Isaiah (Is. 19.5-10) described the devastation resulting from the loss of the river: 'And the waters shall fail from the sea, and the river shall be wasted and dried up. And they shall turn the rivers far away; and the brooks of defence shall be emptied and dried up: the reeds and the flags [marsh grasses?] shall wither. The paper reeds by the brooks, by the mouth of the brooks, shall wither, be driven away, and be no more. The fishers also shall mourn, and all they that spread nets upon the waters shall languish. Moreover, they that work in fine flax, and they that weave, shall be confounded. And they shall be broken in the purposes thereof, all that make sluices and ponds for fish.'

Here we have a description of the total dependence of a community on the river. The river is used for water supply, for defence (moats), to support the reed-swamp plants used for thatch, walls and paper, for treating the flax used for clothing and ornamental weaves, and for supplying food. Fish are both netted from the river and grown in specially constructed fishponds fed from the river.

But how much remains! The old course of the river bed, the new course, the pollen from the swamp plants (so that erstwhile swamp communities can be identified), the sluices and the fishponds. All may have gone, but also all may remain, and indeed may have been renewed, time after time. The present saltponds of Malta were originally Roman. A mill with late-Roman granite millstones was working near Jerash in Jordan in the 1930s (Morton, 1934).

So, much remains, and it is high time this fascinating record of human ingenuity and endeavour was rediscovered. Indeed, if it is not to be lost under massive modern redevelopment, it must quickly be given its rightful importance.

This book is most concerned with post-fourteenth-century water uses and structures, these now being the most easily seen on the ground. Ancient civilisations, it must always be remembered, though, could be highly developed in their use of water. Roman (Pisidian) Antioch, for instance, had plumbing to most houses, the public fountains therefore flowing just for ornament, according to Libianus; there were washing-machines with water and mineral soap, swimming pools, automatic dispensers of holy water outside temples, a fire-safety water-sprinkler system operating by water pressure, and waterwheels for driving water (Morton, 1936). Eshinuro, in 2,500 B.C. had brick-lined sewage pits with outlets to covered street drains (Warren, 1971). The Romans attributed the invention of drains — and of regular town-planning — to the Etruscans; but the Romans themselves were in general more successful with providing good water supplies (aqueducts, etc.) than with solving the problem of good waste disposal via sewers.

When civilisations decay, civilised arts are lost. Home comforts equivalent to those of the Roman period were not again known in Europe until the turn of the twentieth century. Other cultural phases have come and gone also. To name but a few, there was the holiness and literature of the Celtic Church, which peaked from the fifth century (in Ireland) to the seventh century A.D.; the vigour of the Vikings, in the ninth to eleventh century, which was followed by that of their Norman descendants in the eleventh and twelfth centuries; then there was the Elizabethan explosion in the civilised arts of literature. None of these included high standards of cleanliness and indoor use of water. In England, it took a dandy, Beau Brummel, in the early nineteenth century, to make personal cleanliness fashionable again (his influence persists also, in European dress, men still being less brightly coloured in their clothes than women). Florence Nightingale pushed personal cleanliness wider, and included the cleanliness of towns, armies and hospitals among her achievements. The thousands who cleansed their nations in the past one and a half centuries, often in the face of ridicule and worse, deserve much honour. But cleanliness was not first invented in 1800. It had merely been forgotten.

Use of water varies with the general thrust of a culture, as well as with technology. Fountains and tinkling water were important in the gardens of Arab Europe (e.g. Sicily) even though the Mediterranean drought discourages non–essential use of water. Modern Scotland and Norway, with ample water, lay no such emphasis on its ornamental value. However, the eighteenth-century nobility specialised in water-gardens throughout Europe. This is clearly a cultural phenomenon, a question of taste and fashion, not necessarily related to wealth or technology.

Use also depends on geographical and geological factors; these determine the lie and size of the natural rivers. In turn, those determine potential use. Navigation requires a certain quantity of water and a reasonable absence of Alpine torrential flows. The development of power from water requires a sufficient flow. Physical factors determine the available types of recreation, whether to watch cascades or go SCUBA-diving, etc., though in general recreational use depends more on human factors, increasing with numbers and leisure time, as well as varying with culture.

Looking more widely, trading-centres are necessarily centres of good communications, though cultural pattern determines whether the reverse is true. Scandinavia is traditionally outward-looking, but so were many more southern river-ports such as Antwerp on the Scheld, Hamburg on the Elbe, London on the Thames, Nantes on the Loire, and Bordeaux on the Garonne, as well as smaller places like Wisbech on the Nene/Great Ouse. The land divides, the water unites, to mis-quote

Fig. 1.2 The river for recreation (from Haslam, 1990).

an old saying. Before railways, aeroplanes or good roads, the carriage of freight was difficult and dangerous whether by land or by water, but it was cheaper, and frequently easier, by water. Culture, again, is important: the Dutch made far more use of their waterways than, say, the pastoral Irish, and became a trading nation.

Early industry to some extent must be in or near where people have settled for some other reason, perhaps for good farmland, for defence, or for trading. In a more developed state, however, industry is determined by the available raw materials: the iron outcrop, woods for charcoal, rivers for power. Later, the seams of coal (the pumps to extract water from which could be placed anywhere) became the sites for heavy industry, and finally in the twentieth century the power is electrical, easily supplied throughout the Continent, and raw materials are likewise movable. We turn a tap rather than go to the well, turn a switch rather than visit a watermill, and telephone an order for Swedish furniture from a London shop: the logs may have come down from forest to factory by river (Fig. 1.1), but other direct contact with rivers is little. This industry is more separate from the river than before but, as will be seen in the following pages, its dependence on the rivers is no less.

Fig. 1.3 Lion's head fountains. a) at the head of the Wignacourt Aqueduct, Valletta, Malta, recently re-built. b) Lydyeard St Lawrence, England, also recent.

Consequently, much of the direct use of rivers is forgotten. The direct use of Fig. 1.2 is indeed known to all, but how many recognise the old area of town that bore the water-based industry? And, when passing the Watermill Industrial Estate, how many consider that it is exactly that, modern industry on the same site the watermill had industriously used for centuries? That little old bridge, for pack-laden horses, permitted small, essential goods to pass over storm-flooded streams? And that fountain with the lion's head (Fig. 1.3): its forebears date from at least the fifth century B.C. (Morton, 1936). Horses, dogs and bears have been equally known to man: the continued choice has rested on the lion. (It was chosen, for instance, in Malta to commemorate the coming of clean water to Balluta in 1882.) The line of old pollards winding down the field (Fig. 1.4) — who looks closely to find the stream? These are harvested trees, harvested above the level of grazing stock, and were typically cultivated along streams. If no stream is present now, because of abstraction and drainage, a little study will usually show the depression from which it is now lost.

The type and thrust of river use has altered, over the centuries, but the dependence on the river has not altered. The three principal early uses were (1)

Fig. 1.4 Pollards along the streamline. a) Old course marked by old pollarded willows, Belgium. b) Less-old course with less-old pollards (compare Fig. 4.21, more disturbed), England.

watering man, stock and land from springs, wells or rivers or, in larger places, perhaps from a water-carrier or water-cart; (2) transporting freight, and often people as well; and (3) the development of power from watermills. These watermills were introduced by the Romans in the late first century B.C., and quickly spread over and beyond the Empire, remaining the main (mechanical) source of power until the Industrial Revolution.

Domestic water supply is now from a tap, originating in a river or a source that would otherwise have reached a river, and it may have been transported 100km or more from its water source (industrial cities of the English Midlands such as Birmingham and Manchester developed nineteenth century reservoirs in far-off hills, and the twentieth-century adds schemes for transferring water from one river to another over long distances). Water supply, though, remains the first of the three most important modern uses. The second is waste disposal, the use of rivers to dispose of sewage, farm and industrial waste. Waste has increased enormously over the centuries, partly because population has increased, the population of England for instance rising from 1 to nearly 60 millions from Norman times to the 1990s; but also because consumer and business goods have increased almost as dramatically (think of the industrial by-products involved in constructing not one, but millions, of television sets and then the disposal of those sets themselves, when discarded (and also consider the same for the millions of the other 'essential' goods now used!). Much waste goes to rivers, and is seldom cleaned to a satisfactory standard (see Table 1.2). Drainage is the third most important modern use of rivers — the removal of water from farmland to improve crop yield.

### Table 1.2
#### State of water-pollution control in various countries
##### (From Water Research Centre, 1977)

|  | Belgium | Denmark | Eire | France | Germany (FDR) | Italy | Luxembourg | Netherlands | United Kingdom | Sweden | USA |
|---|---|---|---|---|---|---|---|---|---|---|---|
| total population (millions) | 9.7 | 5.0 | 3.0 | 52.0 | 60.8 | 55.0 | 0.35 | 13.6 | 55.3 | 8.1 | 271.8 |
| % sewerage | 30 | 84 | 61 | 44 | 79 | 58 | ? | 92 | 94 | .83 | 73.5 |
| % sewage with primary treatment only | 1 | 20 | 28.2 | ? | 20.4 | 8 | 20 | 6 | <10 | 5 | 18 |
| % with secondary treatment | 6 | 33 | 4 | <40 | 44.1 | 7 | 70 | 54 | 780 | 77.2 | 50 |
| effectiveness of law enforcement | ? | ✓ | ✗ | ✓ | ✓ | - | ✓ | ✓ | ✓ | ✓ | ✓ |

Primary treatment is the removal of solids, by settlement and filtration.
Secondary treatments include the use of activated sludge and biological filters.
Tertiary treatments include sand filters, microstrainers and further chemical or biological processes.
Treatment patterns vary widely between countries. The amount of sewerage and of treatment is not necessarily related to its effectiveness: Britain's rivers are no better than France's or Germany's, and worse than Denmark's or Eire's. In the latter, for instance, the poor treatment is compensated for by the population being small and mainly coastal, so that the total waste discharge to rivers is low. To a lesser extent the same is found in Denmark: where also much waste is discharged to lakes, which act as purifiers before it reaches rivers.

These aspects can all be seen and studied. The river, however, also shows its heritage, as well as its present purposes, to those who look.

## The Portrayal of Rivers

Much can be learnt about the history of rivers by looking at paintings or drawings in the past. Details are usually extremely accurate. Water plants are identifiable. In the earlier pictures, rivers are an active and central part of life. In the twelfth century (Fig. 1.5), for instance, the river bears fish and fowl and has many small boats on it (bearing, e.g., two to eighteen people). The watergate to the Hall is as important as the landgate. In the fifteenth century (Fig. 1.6) the accent is more on buildings, on the settlement as a whole, whether walled village, castle or watermill: the homely, civilised places. Here the people live and work—and close by it they farm. Here are the uses of the water: the steps for supply and access, the boats, for business and pleasure — and the bridges, and defences against attack by bridge or water. The individual is not important; the focus is on settlement and community. The river stretches off into the distance, it is outside the pale of home, where few except the adventurous watermen have any interest. Over the sixteenth (Fig. 1.7), seventeenth (Fig. 1.8) and eighteenth (Fig. 1.9) centuries the emphasis on the inhabitants increases, the sites increasingly revolve around man, rather than concentrating on sites. The eighteenth-century portraits show man proudly dominating some small part of a riverscape. A portrait must, of course, show its subject large and clear. When the subject dominates, though, rather than being part of the natural world, this is done by choice. The landscape gardening of the eighteenth century may come from romanticising the lost agricultural sites. The Victorians did subdue nature on a large scale. Their works, bridges, factories and busy towns spoke for themselves, and their riverscape pictures are less man-

Fig. 1.5 Twelfth century river picture from the Canterbury Psalter (by permission of the Master and Fellows of Trinity College, Cambridge).

Maguncia

Fig. 1.6 Fifteenth century river picture (German woodcut, *Nuremburg Chronicle*, by permission of the Master and Fellows of St Catharine's College, Cambridge).

dominated (Fig. 1.10). Victorian landscape painting could have been a direct result of man's mastery over nature and his consequent loss of it. A pretty meadow on the wall helps to make up for an industrial vista from the window.

Finally, the twentieth century (Fig. 1.11) exhibits the complete domination of the river by man. These are caged rivers, with zookeepers to keep them so — or for the public to gape at .

The study of old pictures, and that of present streams, is complementary. Illuminations are of most value in the fifteenth century and woodcuts in the sixteenth century, with landscape painters coming into their own in the seventeenth century, and photographs in the later nineteenth century. A visit to a local museum or art gallery is usually most productive for river history — once the eye is acclimatised to studying the river, not the ostensible subject of the painting, or the talent of the artist.

These pictures show many uses of the river: supply, power, transport and many others. It is a telling comment on the state of the roads that hard-bottomed streams were used for horse-borne traffic! Near settlements, larger streams, those over *c.* 3m wide, bore little vegetation. This was due to disturbance from many causes, including transport, as will be discussed later. The causes of disturbance can be obtained from written records: their severity and effect on river ecology, only from pictorial ones.

Fig. 1.7 Sixteenth century river picture (German woodcut).

Fig. 1.8 Seventeenth century river picture (landscape with rainbow, Henley on Thames, J. Siberechts (by permission of the Tate Gallery)). Village of meal and maltsters. Note barges at wharf, barge being towed. Lost in reduction is a row-boat by village.

# River Rights

The word 'rival', according to the *Oxford English Dictionary*, early meant one who uses the same river as another. The development into 'competitor' was by no accident!

Rodgers (1947-8) describes the complicated system of river rights which grew up. There was the right to use the stream for navigation; milling, fishing and setting up nets and eel traps, throwing rubbish into it, taking the water out for different purposes; the right to construct weirs and locks; and the right of the riparian owners to the use of their land without obstruction or unnecessary flooding. Two other rights can be added to Rodgers' list: swan-keeping and drainage. Many of these rights obviously conflict: the mill-owners and the fishermen obstructed the passage of boats, the weirs sometimes caused land to flood, and the disposal of sewage and refuse killed the fish and could cause epidemics among the people who lived on the banks. As a result of

Fig. 1.9 Eighteenth century river picture. (Sir Benjamin Truman, Gainsborough. By permission of the Tate Gallery). Formal river.

much dissension, considerable legislation was passed until 'methods of control and management were gradually evolved.... In early days there was no more fruitful source of contention than river rights', and books can be filled with these contentions, English records being numerous from the thirteenth century — but contentions assuredly being frequent for many centuries previously.

Magna Carta, the Great Charter of Rights wrested from King John by his barons in 1215, had much to say on rivers: London and other ports were to retain their traditional trading-rights by land and by water (for the benefit of merchants and trade). Fishweirs (kiddles or kidels) were to be removed from the Thames and Medway (the former a royal river) and throughout England, except along the seacoast (this protected trade rather than fisheries, but as kiddles continued to

Fig. 1.10 Nineteenth century river picture (from *Girls Own Paper* 1880s).

Fig. 1.11 Twentieth century river. (from Haslam, 1990).

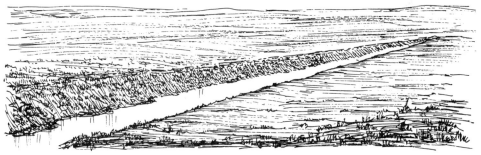

obstruct ships, some measure of justice presumably resulted). All merchants were given safe and unmolested passage during their travels by land and water throughout the country, except when war provisions applied (note that travel by water inland was considered normal for merchants). River banks which were reserved for the King's sport during King John's reign were again thrown open (the previously numerous local rights for livelihood were to prevail over this King's sport). All oppressive practices relating to river banks and the malpractices of riverbank keepers were to be enquired into and abuses rectified (a complex system and liable to abuse). No town or individual would be forced to build bridges at river crossings except those under a customary and legal obligation to do so (this idea of separate and reluctant responsibility is less in line with twentieth-century thinking. Notions of public responsibility for the travelling public developed later).

Apart from demonstrating grievances, this comprehensive list shows that Central Government was very conscious of the importance of water-borne trade, and that locally owners of fisheries, etc., although they might agree as to the principle of easy passage by boats, considered their own livelihood more important. Human nature changes little!

Arundel Bridge in Sussex, England can be cited as an example of the development of civic responsibility for travellers (Rodgers, 1947-8). There was possibly a Roman bridge (military) here. When King Henry I died in 1135, his widow, Queen Adeliza, founded a priory and made the canons custodians of the bridge, which she may have had built or rebuilt (an act of pious royal charity). Upkeep of the bridge passed to the town when the priory was dissolved in 1525, and the town neglected it (no civic responsibility). The bridge was rebuilt in 1593, two mayors having left annuities for its upkeep, and donations having come from the neighbourhood. Another appeal was needed for rebuilding in 1641. Both times the magistrates refused to levy a local tax (those who most wanted the bridge, paid). In 1724 a stone bridge replaced the again-decaying wooden one, built with the aid of the Duke of Norfolk, a wealthy noble with his seat at Arundel. (Responsible aristocracy, and those wanting the bridge, paid.) The bridge is now maintained by taxes, maintenance being — at last — seen as a public duty.

The constant conflict of rights over rivers was doubtless very expensive in money, time and temper. However, the other side is that on average rivers were conserved. No one had the power to do anything drastic to long stretches of river. As late as the eighteenth century Cowper's 'I am monarch of all I survey, my right there is none to dispute' was written for a man on a desert island, not for one in well-populated, lowland western Europe, where disputes and restrictions were the norm! The twentieth century trend in western Europe, though, has perhaps been convenient for man but has certainly been destructive to the river. Most rights and powers have accrued to new water authorities, removing the old checks and balances between powers. And the right that has been put foremost by most lowland authorities is drainage. As freedom from flood has always been desired, flood-protection works have followed. But the massive drainage — not of wetlands but of lowlands — is recent and, overall, has superseded the other rights. In 1989 in England, some separation of river uses was made, dividing rights between water companies and the National Rivers Authority. Interestingly the latter now has 'flood protection' divisions, not 'drainage' ones. Drainage keeps farmland dry, dry enough to need irrigation in drought. It involves speeding flow by straightening and deepening rivers, removing all obstructions and lowering the general water level (Fig. 1.11). This is to the great detriment of the river ecology: ecology not being a historical river right, or a commercially profitable use. Regrettably there is no conflict between drainage and pollution (the right to put waste in the river), so the incentives to keep rivers clean have been low. Conservation versus Any Other Interest is therefore a modern conflict, with Any Other Interest usually winning.

The remains of old conflicts still surface, and new ones to do with recreation appear, such as pollution versus anglers, canoeists versus riparian owners, and canoeists versus anglers.

## English Place Names

Place names reflect the preoccupations of those giving the names, and English place names show the importance of fresh waters to (mainly) the Anglo-Saxons. Tables 1.3-1.7 give some examples of this — the elements describing different kinds of waters, such as *burna* (stream) and *celde* (spring); those describing the use of the

*Table 1.3*

*English place names connected with streams, etc.*

Some examples of origins of names, from Ekwall (1960) which book should be consulted for details. (See Table 7.1 for names associated with crossings.)

*aewelm:* OE (Old English) 'river source', e.g. Ewen (Glos.)

*a:* ON (Old Norse) 'river', e.g. Aby (Lincs.), Ambleside (Cumbria).

*baece, bece:* OE 'stream', 'valley', e.g. Beachampton (Bucks.), Evesbatch (Herefordshire).

*baeth, bathum:* OE 'bath', e.g. Bath (Avon), from at least 796 A.D.; Moorbath Dorset).

*bekkr:* ON 'stream', 'beck', e.g. Caldbeck, Beckermet ('stream junction') (Cumbria).

*broc:* OE, 'brook', 'stream', in place names after 730 A.D.; earlier, only in river and field names, e.g. Begbroke (Oxon).

*burna:* OE 'stream' pre-730 A.D., (earlier, *brunna*), e.g. Burnham (Essex), Bourne (Cambs.), Washbourne (Glos.).

*celde:* OE 'spring', e.g. Bapchild (Kent).

*ea:* OE 'river', e.g. Eton (Bucks.), Pevensey (Sussex), Eamont ('river junction') (Cumbria).

*fleot, fleote:* OE 'estuary', 'small stream', e.g. Fleet (Dorset), Swinefleet (Yorks.).

*flode:* OE 'channel of water', e.g. Cheselade (Somerset)

*funta:* OE 'spring', from Latin *fons, fontis*, and apparently used for a spring with Roman building-work, differing from those to which OE *well* was applied, e.g. Chalfont (Bucks.).

*gemythe:* OE 'river junction', e.g. Eamont (Cumbria).

*hyth:* OE 'landing-place on a river', 'inland port', e.g. Lambeth, Chelsea (London), Earith (Cambs.).

*kelda:* ON 'spring', in northern counties and Scotland, e.g. Keldhome (Yorks.), Threlkeld (Cumbria).

*lad:* OE, *lode:* ME (Middle English) one meaning is 'watercourse', 'aqueduct', open drain in fenny districts, e.g. Whaplode (Lincs.).

*laecc, laece:* OE 'stream', 'bog', e.g. Lache (Cheshire).

*loekr:* ON 'brook', e.g. Leake (Notts.)

*pol, pull:* OE 'pool'; *pyll* OE 'tidal creek', ?'small stream', e.g. Pool (Cheshire), Walpole (Suffolk: 'oxbow pool', besid the stream during a flood).

*rith, rithig:* OE 'small stream', e.g. Ryde (Isle of Wight), Sawtry (Hyde), Reed (Yorks.).

*sic:* OE 'small stream', tiny watercourse, common in fields, but too small to be more than rare in minor settlement names, e.g. Sitch, Seech (as names of fields).

*sik:* ON as last, e.g. Sykehouse (Yorks.).

*staeth:* OE 'landing place', e.g. Stathe (Somerset), Statham (Cheshire).

*waeter:* OE 'water', 'river', 'lake', e.g. Bourton-on-the-Water (on R.Windrush, Glos.).

*well, wella, welle:* OE 'spring', 'stream', e.g. Well-under-Heywood (Salop), Upwell (Cambs.).

land by the waters, such as 'the stream where commerce took place' and 'the landing-place where cattle were shipped'; and those describing particularly clean or (probably) dirty waters, such as 'bright stream' and 'dirty river'.

## Conclusion

The usefulness and importance of the river to man have, it is hoped, now been demonstrated. Different aspects of this importance are taken up in the following chapters. The titles and the division thereunder are arbitrary; the stream is a unity but categories are necessary to understanding it.

A spring, dedicated of old to a saint, reputed to heal sore eyes, supplying a hamlet with domestic and farm water; the same stream a little distance below, bearing a fishery, irrigating watermeadows, and turning a polluting fullingmill — under what heading should it be described? The writer can but hope the reader finds most of the classifications that follow acceptable.

---

*Table 1.4*

*English place names to do with land use by water*

(Some examples from Ekwall (1960))

Aldreth (Cambs.): 'landing place by the alders'.

Barnwell (Cambs.): 'spring (stream) of the warriors'.

Birdforth (Yorks.), Bridford (Devon): 'ford of the brides'.

Chillwall (Lancs.), Chilwell (Notts.): 'stream of the children'.

Chopwell (Durham): 'stream where commerce took place'.

Coleford (Glos.): 'charcoal ford'.

Creekson (Essex): 'landing-place at the creek'.

Glandford (Norfolk): 'ford where sports were held'.

Harford (Devon), Hereford (Herefordshire): 'army ford'.

Harpswell (Lincs.): 'harpers' spring'.

Honeybourne (Glos.): 'stream in whose banks honey was gathered'.

Hungerford (Berks.): 'stream where there was starvation'.

Huntingford (Dorset): 'huntsmen's ford'.

Kilburn (Yorks.): 'stream by a kiln'.

Langwathby (Cumbria): 'homestead at long ford'.

Lathford (Som.): 'beggars ford'.

Leconfield (Yorks.): 'people at the brook'.

Lotherton (Yorks.): 'people at a clean spring'.

Matlock (Derbys.) 'oak where a moot (official gathering) was held'.

Matlask (Norfolk): 'ash where a moot was held'.

Melverly (Salop): 'land by the mill ford'.

Montford (Salop): 'men's ford'.

Mottisfont (Hants.): 'spring where moots were held'.

Mutford (Suffolk): 'ford where moots were held'.

Playford (Staffs.): 'ford where sports were held'.

Quarnford (Staffs.): 'ford by a mill'.

Rotherhithe (Surrey): 'landing-place where cattle were shipped'.

Oxford (Oxon): 'ford for oxen'.

Salford (Oxon): 'ford over which salt was carried'.

Salterford (Northants.), Salterforth (Yorks.): 'salt-sellers ford'.

Salterhebble (Yorks.): 'salt-seller's footbridge'.

Sawtry (Hunts.): 'landing-place at the salt-sellers'.

Sheepy, Magna, and Sheepy Parva (Leics.): 'sheep river' and 'sheep island'.

Shefford (Beds.): 'sheep ford'.

Shipbourne (Kent), Shiplake (Oxon), Shiplate (Somerset): 'sheep wash'.

Shipston on Stour (Warks.): 'tun (settlement) at a sheep wash'.

Stafford (Staffs.): 'ford by a landing-place'.

Stathe (Somerset), Toxteth (Lancs.): 'landing place'.

Sykehouse (Yorks.): 'house on a stream'.

Treville (Herefordshire): 'mill (?with a hamlet)'.

Walbrook (London) Walburn (Yorks.): 'Welsh brook' or 'serf's brook'.

Walkerith (Lincs.): 'landing-place of the fullers'.

Walkern (Herts.): 'fulling-mill or fuller's house'.

Wansford (Yorks.): 'ford of the mobs'.

Washingborough (Lincs.): 'burg (settlement) of the people at the whirlpool'.

Westmill (Herts.): 'west mill'.

Whorlton (Durham): 'tun by the mill stream'.

Windsor (Berks.): 'bank with landing-place'.

---

*Table 1.5*

*English place names to do with river use*

(Some examples from Ekwall (1960))

**1. Watercress**

Bilbrook (Som.), Carlswall (Glos.), Carshalton (Surrey), Carswell (Berks.), Caswell (Northants.), Craiseland (Lincs.), Cresswall (Herefordshire), Cresswell (Derby), Kearsley (Lancs.), Kearnsey (Kent), Kerswell (Devon), Rib (river, Herts.), Ribbesford (Worcs.).

**2. Waterfowl**

(a) *Ducks:* Andwell (Hants.), Emborne (Berks.), Enford (Wilts.), Entwhistle (Lancs.), Hendred (Berks.)

(b) *Goose:* Gosbed (Suffolk), Gosford (Derby, etc.), Gosforth (Cumbria, etc.).

**3. Fish**
- (a) *Crayfish:* Crabwell (Cheshire).
- (b) *Eel:* Ely (Cambs.), Whaplode (Lincs.).
- (c) *Fish, general:* Fangdale (Yorks.), Fishbourne (Sussex), Fishburn (Durham), Fishlake (Yorks.), (?)Wembdon (Som.); structure for catching: Yarpole (Herefordshire), Yarm (Yorks.), Yarwell (Northants.).
- (d) *Gudgeon:* Blandford (Dorset).
- (e) *Trout:* Farnham (Suffolk), (?)Rawtrey (Yorks. etc.)(?). Shottersbrook, (Berks.), Troutbeck (Cumbria), Trouts Dale (Yorks.).

**4 Watering of stock**
- (a) *Bulls:* Bulwell (Notts.).
- (b) *Cows:* Cole (Wilts.).
- (c) *Goats:* Gateford (Notts.), Gateforth (Notts.).
- (d) *Horse:* Bayswater (Middx)
- (e) *Oxen:* Oxford (Oxon).

**5. Mill**
Curborough (Staffs.), Melbourne (Derby), Meldreth (Cambs.), Melford (Suffolk), Melplash (Dorset), Meltham (Yorks.), Millbeck (Cumbria), Millbrook (Beds., etc.).

**6. Weir, dam (and see 3c above)**
Weare (Derby), Ware (Herts.), Wareham (Dorset), Warford (Cheshire), Wargrave (Berks.), Warehorne (Kent), Warleigh (Som., etc.), Edgeware (London).

**7. Fulling**
Washburn (Yorks.).

**8. Sheepwash**
Washbourne (Glos.), Washbrooke (Suffolk) (or washing clothes).

**9. Criminals, felons, and where they were executed (drowned)**
Weybourne (Surrey), Wreigh Burn (Northants., etc.), Warnborough (Hants.), (?)Wheldrake (Yorks.).

**10. Supernatural (see also Chapter 14)**
- (a) *Wishing-well:* Elwell (Dorset), Frithwell (Oxon), Holywell (Lincs.).
- (b) *Troll, goblin, water-sprite:* Flawith (Yorks.), Puckeridge (Herts.), Purbrook (Hants.), Shobrooke (Devon), Shocklach (Cheshire).
- (c) *Holy:* Holiwell (Middx), Hakwell, Halwill (Derby), Holwell (Dorset), Holybourne (Hants.), Holywell (Hunts., etc.) Winford (Som.) (or 'white', 'happy').
- (d) *Prophetic:* Ladbrook (Warks.).

**11. Miscellaneous**
- (a) *Thralls (slaves):* Threlkeld (Cumbria).
- (b) *Nuns:* Nunwells Park (Isle of Wight).
- (c) *Bathing:* Bath (Avon).

*Table 1.6*
*English place names indicating clean water*
(Some examples from Ekwall (1960))

*(N.B.: since clean water was the norm, the fact that it was not mentioned does not mean the water was dirty.)*

Arkendale (Yorks.): 'pure, clear stream'.
Brightwell, Britwell (Berks.): 'bright spring'.
Errington (Northumberland): 'enclosure on a bright stream'.
Fairford (Glos.): 'clear ford'.
Farewell (Staffs.): 'beautiful stream'.
Harwell (Notts.): 'pleasant stream'.
Limebrook, Lingen (Herefordshire): 'clear, beautiful stream'.
Rother (river, Sussex): 'bright river'.
Sherborne (Dorset, Glos., Hants., Yorks.): 'bright stream'.

Sherford (Norfolk, Devon): 'clear ford'.
Shirebrook (Derby): 'bright stream'.
Shirwell (Devon): 'clear spring'.
Skerne (river, Yorks.): 'bright, clear'.
Skinfare (river, Yorks.): 'bright stream'.
Skirbeck (Lincs.): 'bright brook'.
Tanat (river, Salop): 'brilliant river'.
Wendover (Berks.): 'white river'.
Whimple (Devon): 'white stream'.
Whitford (Devon): 'white ford'.
Winford (Som.): 'white (holy, happy)' with 'stream torrent'.
Worf (river, Salop): 'turbid' (possibly 'winding').

*Table 1.7*
*English place names indicating coloured water*
*(Some examples from Ekwall (1960))*

*(N.B. Coloured water is not necessarily dirty, but polluted waters will be included in the list.)*

Blackburn (Lancs.): 'dark stream'.
Blackford (Som.): 'black ford'.
Blackfordby (Leics.): 'homestead at black ford'.
Blackwater (Dorset, Hants.): 'dark stream'.
Coldrey (Hants.): 'coal (black) brook'.
Doulting (Som.): 'dirty river'.
Drybeck (Westmorland): 'dirty stream'.
Fotherley (Staffs.): 'slope by the dirty stream'.
Fulbeck (Lincs.), Fulbrook (Berks.): 'foul/dirty brook'.
Fulford (Som., etc.): 'dirty ford'.
Fulready (Warks.): 'foul/dirty brook'.
Fulwell (Durham): 'foul/dirty stream'.
Glazebrook (Lancs.): 'blue, green, grey brook'.
Harborne (Staffs.): 'dirty stream'.

Radford (Beds.): 'red-soil ford' (usually).
Radwell (Beds.): 'red spring/stream'.
Retford (Northants.): 'red ford'.
Shambrook (Beds.), Shamford (Leics.): 'muddy brook/ford'.
Shernborne (Norfolk): 'muddy brook and tun (settlement)'.
Skeckburn (Northumbria): 'muddy stream'.
Slimbridge (Glos.): 'bridge in a muddy place'.
Surfleet (Lincs.): 'sour stream'.
Tame, Thames, Teme (Oxon, etc.), Taff (Wales): 'dark river'.
Wennington (Lancs.): 'dark river'.

# 2
# The Past in the Present

Rivers ...were made for wise men to contemplate, and fools to pass by without
consideration. (Cited in Walton, 1653)

## Introduction

This chapter describes a town and six contrasting rivers. It introduces many
concepts further developed in later chapters, and shows, unlike those later
chapters, the unity as well as diversity of river use. No examples are described in
full: that would require a volume for each. A few of the salient points, merely, are
described, and even fewer are illustrated. (Most illustrations, here and later are
accurate representations of single, identifiable sites. A few, however, incorporate
features from other nearby places, space not permitting the separate portrayal of
each in full.)

## Megève  *(Fig. 2.1)*

Megève used to be a small town in the French Alps, a local capital and centre. It has
recently much expanded with tourism. It exhibits the standard European town
pattern (also see Chapter 8), with one curious twist.

On my first morning in Megève I walked into the town centre. I found the
stream, around 4m wide with a flow adequate for mills and industry and I went
upstream to the old bridge (Fig. 2.1a). That was my first check: industry should
have been downstream of an old bridge like that, and it was not there. Of course it
is always possible for old sectors of towns to be removed early, and without trace.
A quarter of Cambridge was, in the fifteenth century;  but this is rare. Most
removals are modern, with, e.g., new houses or car parks instead, and none such
were here. Bewildered, I went to the Square, and found the church to my right, not
facing me as it should have been when I entered from the stream. I was now
thoroughly muddled. I pottered around, wondering whether the general European
town plan could possibly be absent from a town in the Alps.

My doubts were short-lived. Megève has two streams, and the west one, the
main Arly, is exactly as expected. Downstream of the Square, there is the industry,
where it has been for centuries, and where, on the same site it has been rebuilt and
modernised also for centuries, earlier using the river for supply and power.
Upstream of the Square, industry is absent. A pleasing French note is added by the
floral decorations to the further-upstream bridge. As usual, the civic building, here
the *Mairie*, faces the church. There are two main entrances to the Square. One is
the north road from Geneva and Chamonix. There is no old bridge where this
crosses the river. Instead the river is underground, indicating an early ford or
replacement of a too-small bridge. This comes in not quite opposite the church.
Straight opposite the church, though, is the flight of steps leading up from the Arly.

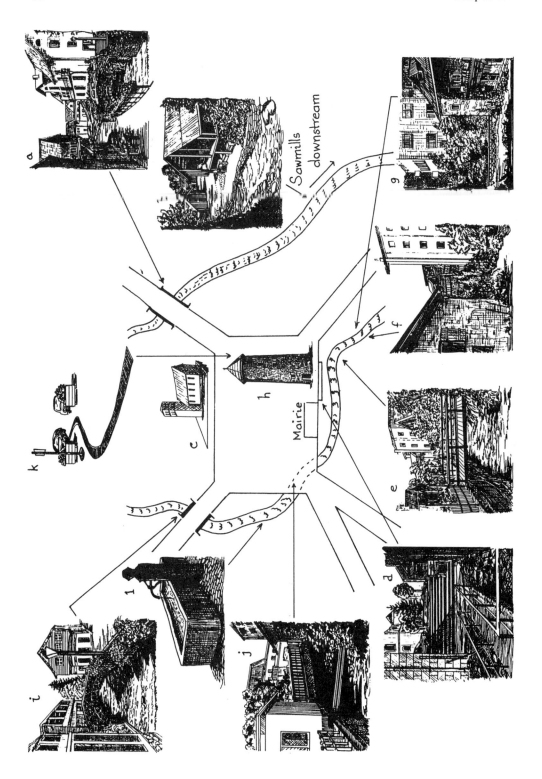

This is the main entrance, therefore — by water, and along the tiny Arly, all the way from the river Isère (*c.* 30km)! (See Tuddenham, Fig. 6.6, for old transport on unlikely streams.) The steps are in two portions, the grand wharf steps (which will be met again later) and the side ones, for collecting water for supply. Guarding the port — closer to this than to the north road — is the Old Tower (of 'Rapunzel, Rapunzel let down your hair' type, thus dating both). Since Megève is such a small centre (yet a Centre), access and Old Tower are actually in the Square itself. Larger places have a Water Street leading from the river to the Square (Fig. 8.4).

There are a number of fountains of both ornamental and useful types, often ornamented with flower-boxes. In the past, horse-troughs were, of course, necessary to land transport. Horse-traps in Megève are still used for tourists and horses still need to drink. Where these traps wait is a drain in the road. Well downstream of the old centre, sawmills are now found along the Arly. The second (east) stream is not used — except for a small modern farm downstream of Fig. 2.1a. Megève is a standard small European Centre: these are built on one stream, not two. The stream has industry. It has accesses to the Square, the wharf being formerly guarded by a tower. The church is opposite the access and the civic building is opposite the church.

## River Gelster, N.C. Germany *(Fig. 2.2)*
### *(Information supplied by A. Tyndale)*

The Gelster is a small rural stream, chosen here to illustrate on the main stream village life and industry, and on the side stream an uninhabited valley with changes in land and stream use.

The Gelster rises in steep hills, and runs through Grossalmeröde village in the valley below. The Fahrbach tributary is rural. In Grossalmeröde the stream is now underground in the newer upstream part of the town, emerging in the old village, which includes fourteenth century houses. The village developed on both sides of the stream (a typically *heim* pattern, see Chapter 9). Older houses still discharge into the Gelster, which is also polluted by road run-off and other waste. These village streams were used for all purposes: drinking, washing, cooking, home industry — and waste disposal. With the earth-closet (before the water-closet) there was much less liquid waste, and much less chance that — in a village — it would reach the river. Mains water further increased the quantity of dirty water leaving the home — much more water is used when it does not have to be carried.

Fig. 2.1 Megève, French Alps. a) Old bridge to east. Note no industry either side, restaurant to left, downstream; open to right. b) Downstream east river, recent farm, with fowl etc. using stream. c) Church. Opposite Mairie, and old steps, sub-opposite road to north. d) Old steps. To square, facing church. Note differing ages. Pattern indicates old access for boats, more recent access for supply. Upstream of industry; would have been ponded for mills. River leads south to R. Isère. e) f) g) Downstream of steps. Industrial developments of varying ages, up to twentieth century. The long-time Industrial Estate, with much former use of river. h) The old tower at the side of the square, sited to guard primarily this and the old steps. i) Upstream along the west — used — stream. Old bridge, but residential area. Decorated. j) West stream, underground (rather than bridged) under the main north road. k) Drain where pony-traps wait. l) One of the more functional fountains of the town — old-type pump with trough. Decorated with flower boxes (not shown).

Note, here and elsewhere, the many other riverside features depicted.

Consequently the role of the village stream as a sewer greatly increased, and though in Grossalmeröde the newer houses are on mains drainage, stream pollution is causing community concern.

Downstream of the centre, the stream is still small, only 2-3m wide. It runs at the side of the road with little bridges to the houses on that side: a very common pattern seen over much of Europe (Fig. 9.15). These downstream, newer houses were also built on the road. It is incidental and accidental that a stream is there too. In contrast, the old central houses needed the water and were sited on the stream to use it. The two patterns are different, and the difference can be seen and will be found repeatedly over Europe.

Bridges may be decorated, as in France.

An even smaller stream, the Scheidquelle, rises in clay cliffs to the side and flows to join the Gelster. The cleft, the *Scheid*, is still there, running between the oldest houses, which used the stream for supply, etc. The bed is now mostly dry, though the potteries were based here.

Grossalmeröde, especially with the help of this clay — and available water — has been an industrial village. There was a glass trade in the twelfth century; this and pottery expanded in the fourteenth century. The small industry now includes a printer, woodyard, coachwork factory and carpenter.

Downstream, where the water flow is doubled by the inflow of the Fahrbach, water could turn wheels easily, and the four remaining ex-mills are there. One has been redeveloped as a factory, one is a private house and the others (Thomas mill and Pea mill) are parts of farms. Upstream, therefore, there was industry needing water but not power, while downstream, power was developed.

Grossalmeröde has some nice fountains, old and new, now ornamental. (Water was needed for stock and traveller's horses, and for domestic supply for those not drinking at the stream — see Fig. 10.2 for good German standards of hygiene.)

There are swimming-pools on the hillside, in meadows used for sunbathing, the leisure-meadows (*liege Wiese*). In the past, German meadows close to rivers were often used for the Great Annual Wash in the river after the snowmelt floods in spring (when the river was clean), and put out on the grass to bleach. It was a great social event, lasting about a week.

The Fahrbach tributary rises in a pond, within the woods of a Water Protection Zone (*Wasser Schutzegebiet*). The pond (and the woods) is now managed by the Forestry Commission but it used to be a fishpond: the fishing-platform and net-stakes, though decayed, can still be seen. Downstream are meadows but until recently the fields bore vegetables and pasture for the village (so the fishpond was less isolated from general work than it is now). A good water supply was needed, and the irrigation channels are still seen — channels taken off the natural stream (which is in the valley centre). These run along the contour, dropping only slowly, with the watering-channels running straight into the valley at intervals. The remains of the system are clear. Straight streams are man-made or man-altered, while natural streams wind.

Here, as often happens elsewhere, the diverted channel got most of the water, as it was essential to maintain it, while the natural stream did not matter. Sometimes, as the water table dropped with drainage, the natural stream bed

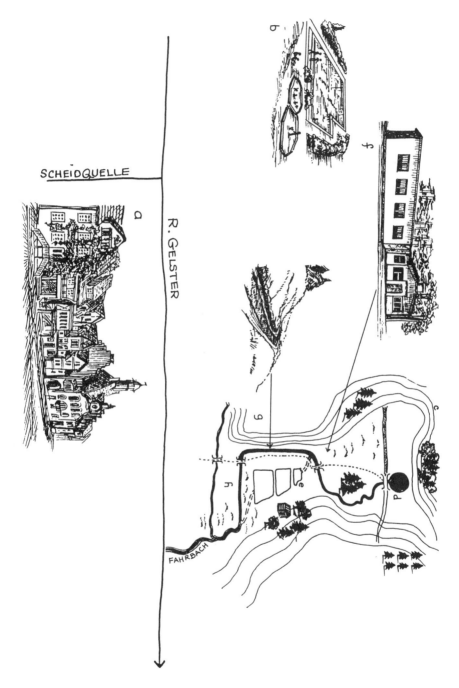

Fig. 2.2 River Gelster, Germany. a) Grössalmerode centre. b) Swimming pool on slope above Grössalmerode. c) Water Protection Zone woods. d) Old fish pond upstream. e) New fishponds with smoking-shed. f) New restaurant. g) Old Watering Channel, now a track along contour. h) Car park by Old Watering Channel and stream.

became dry, leaving only the artificial one lying above the base of the valley floor. Here the maintenance of the top channel meant that when a large track was needed up the valley, this nice straight channel made an obvious site. This track goes up to the restaurant though, apart from Land-rovers, cars are left in a stream-enclosed space (an old field), with its hard ground made by spoil from the new fishponds (see below). Cars reach here along a lane — presumably the site of a former, and now dry, channel.

The restaurant owner has diverted (or re-diverted?) water himself to supply washing-water for guests: a repeat of an old pattern for a new age.

The first and lowest of the new fishponds was started in 1964, the rest following. The lowest bears 3,000 adult trout, the middle one, younger fish, and the top one, char of a few months. The fish are caught before the winter frosts, a few being left to hibernate under the ice. This is a sporting venture by the local angling association, not currently a commercial one. However, there is a hut for cleaning and smoking the fish, and here tourists come to buy. So the fish farm, the restaurant, the anglers and the tourists all thrive together.

This quiet country valley has, therefore, had much use. The two most recent are known: how many changes of pattern have occurred in the last thousand years? Note that the fishery remained but moved place, and that the growing of vegetables gave place to tourism.

Just in a nearby catchment is another use: the Health Wall (Fig. 2.3) of Bad Sooden Allendorf. A wall of twigs has stream water, with salt, trickled over it. This started when the local salt works went out of business — a new use for old salt in fact. The twigs become covered in salt, looking like coral, and smelling like a beach at low tide. Patients walk along the promenade of the Health Wall and sit in the grassland beside. My informant, to her surprise, found the wall benefited a persistent cough.

Fig. 2.3 Health Wall, Bad Sooden-Allendorf.

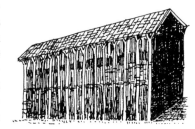

## River Rib, E.C. England *(Fig. 2.4)*

The Rib is a small rural river. Many villages lie on it, and its special features include the proximity of the Old North Road (London to Edinburgh, this part of it being the even more ancient Ermine Street); the main London waterway of the Lea, canalised in the eighteenth century, at its mouth; and watermills giving good and bad livings, developed to industry or left as dwellings. It suffers from water abstraction beside the river.

Four villages, from upstream Buntingford and Puckeridge (on the North Road), and Hare Street and Hay Street (on the Cambridge road), are road-based or Street villages, the houses being mostly on the main road. These see life. Before the twentieth century it was an advantage and interesting, not polluting and dangerous, to live on a main road. Hay Street is the smallest; it has a valley farm near the river and may have re-aligned itself with the road from an earlier 'hill-top' pattern.

Hare Street, slightly bigger, has a tiny tributary crossing it to the river (i.e. the village is parallel to, but away from, the main river, and at right angles to the tributary). Puckeridge, meaning 'the stream of the water-sprite', has a larger tributary, and the village has a centre, a cluster, based on the stream, as well as a street based on the road. Buntingford is the largest. At least five ways met here, giving it a local importance as well as that accruing from its position as a posting-stop on the North Road (which gave it numerous travellers and inns). Downstream there was a watermill, where now is the Watermill (industrial) Estate. The mill was the power source: people going there expected to find industry. Therefore when new, though non-water-based, industry appeared, the obvious place for it was the site of the old watermill. It would be interesting to know how often this decision (taken many times) was made intentionally? There are two pumping stations, one by the Watermill Estate and the other upstream of the village. The lowering of ground-water level for supply, removes the amount of that ground water available for the river. Near the main bridge is the Tannery, now new housing, but retaining the name of the old use of the area. The Street, the main village, is a field's width from the river, with a system of paths whose purpose has decayed. Upstream a minor 'bridge' is a causeway ford, with holes to carry low flows; it floods during high flows. The river here is walled. Buntingford, though surviving, has decayed with the loss of the post-route: cars, though far more numerous than coaches ever were, do not need such frequent service-stations and overnight stops.

The figures show the low water level which is the result of drainage and abstraction.

Westmill is a good example of a cluster-village close to, but with little interest in, the main river. The 'mill' was a windmill. (Windmills were only introduced in the twelfth century, quite late.) Aspenden, Nuthampstead and Dassels are small cluster-villages centred on tributaries, the usual pattern here for ancient villages.

Braughing was probably a royal domain, which would explain the importance given to this small village, later the centre of Braughing Rural District Council. It is a river cluster-village, with a new Street addition (with a garage, etc.) but, as is typical for Hertfordshire, it has a Maltings Lane. (Defoe, 1724-7, notes that Hertfordshire malt is esteemed the best in England. Hence the importance of shipping it south to London.) It has two ship (sheep) bridges, the sites of sheep-washing, and an old causeway. (Victoria County History 1902-14.) Waterfowl are still, as in ancient times, kept on the village river.

The downstream ford is typically East Anglian, with the high footbridge, and the gauging-post to measure water depth. Downstream in the 1940s were water-cress beds, quite possibly on the site of old fishponds.

As a local centre, Braughing was given the local sewage-treatment works, gathering sewage from a number of villages. Unusually, this is sited upstream of the village. Further upstream at Barkway is another sewage-treatment works where the Rib is now but a ditch. It is unfortunate for the river when more of its water comes from sewage-treatment works than from natural sources! Prior to water-closets and mains tapwater, much less waste would have gone to the stream, except from houses close to it. Even now, not all houses are connected to the sewage works. If the sewage works still, as when first planned, received little other than

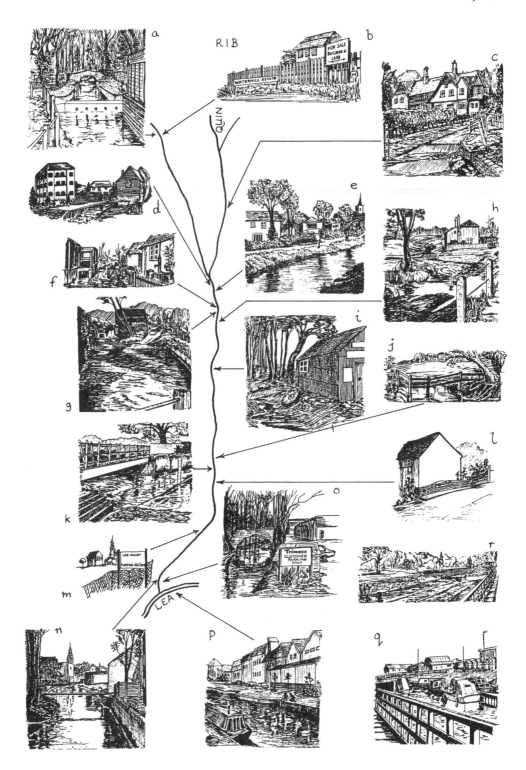

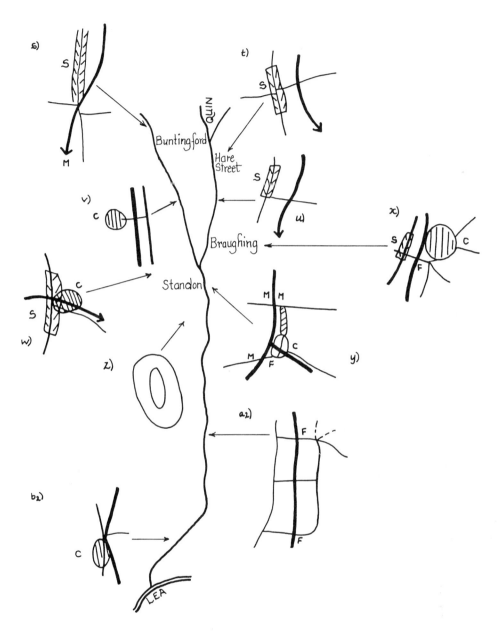

Fig. 2.4 River Rib, England. a) Upstream Buntingford. Old bridge, new-type ford. b) Downstream Buntingford. Watermill Industrial Estate on site of old watermill. c) Braughing, ford and The Maltings. Cluster village behind, Street Hamlet up hill ahead. d) Upstream Standon. Mills developed to nineteenth century industry. Works on left were built for steam. e) Standon High Street; riverside. Compare with the wharf in Fig. 1.8. Note ground level, and old access for supply leading from High Street centre (see y for tributary pattern). f) Downstream Standon. Wealthy mill now a dwelling. Note wheelhouse, dwelling opposite, former mill-weir, and garden pump. g) Downstream f), with old mill far. Long and deep ford, with footbridge. Formerly level controlled by mill. h) Larches.

sewage, the water would be in a much better state. Sewage breaks down and the treatment (see Chapter 11) is planned for this. Latterly, the sewage works have also received detergents, bleach, other disinfectants and cleaners, toothpaste, salt from winter roads, industrial spills, oil and petrol, and other substances too numerous to list. These are pollutants from dwellings and roads. Also, small industrial estates are spreading and adding their loads of poisons to the sewage treatment works (Table 2.1). They are not equipped to clean all the pollutants properly, and pollution in the river increases: the farming run-off adds yet more. The fertilisers and biocides leach happily to the river; silage liquor, slurry, sheep-wash and other chemicals ought never to reach the river, but too often do. This whole mix is new and poisonous — not violently poisonous, but just lowering river quality in quiet rural areas in a way which did not happen before.

---

*Table 2.1*
## Toxic substances present in industrial effluents
*(From Hellawell (1986))*

| | |
|---|---|
| **Acids** | Chemical industries, battery manufacture, minewaters, iron and copper pickling wastes, brewing, textiles, insecticide manufacture. |
| **Alkalis** | Cotton and straw processing, wool scouring laundries. |
| **Ammonia** | Gas and coke production, chemical industries. |
| **Arsenic** | Phosphate and fertiliser manufacture, sheep dipping. |
| **Cadmium** | Metal plating, phosphate fertilisers. |
| **Chlorine (free)** | Paper mills, textile bleaching, laundries. |
| **Chromium** | Metal plating, chrome tanning, anodising, rubber manufacture. |
| **Cyanide** | Iron and steel manufacture, gas production, plating, case hardening, non-ferrous metal production, metal cleaning. |
| **Fluoride** | Phosphate fertiliser production, flue gas scrubbing, glass etching. |
| **Formaldehyde** | Synthetic resin manufacture, antibiotic manufacture. |
| **Lead** | Paint manufacture, battery manufacture. |
| **Oils** | Petroleum refining, organic chemical manufacture, rubber manufacture, engineering works, textiles. |
| **Phenols** | Gas and coke production, synthetic resin manufacture, petroleum refining, tar distillation, chemical industries, textiles, tanning, iron and steel, glass manufacture, fossil fuel electricity generation, rubber processing. |
| **Sulphides** | Leather tanning and finishing, rubber processing, gas production, rayon manufacture, dyeing. |
| **Sulphites** | Pulp processing and paper mills, viscose film manufacture. |
| **Zinc** | Galvanising, plating, rubber processing, rayon manufacture, iron and steel production. |

---

The Gathering of Ways at an old ford. Far, paths from left and centre, road from right, dividing to go up hill to windmill; and near, roads from left and right. Ford unsurfaced. i) Barwick. Probable site of old inefficient Mill — inefficient from inadequate water. Millstone in ditch. j) Cattle watering area. Note variation in bank type. k) Barwicks Ford. Note gauging pole, and remains of earlier generations of crossings. l) West Mill. Wheelhouse on river, (wealthy) mill house, now a dwelling, on same side of river, beyond. m) Pumping station. Abstracting groundwater from the chalk, for domestic supply. n) Waterford. Cluster hamlet behind. Looking to industrial Hertford below. o) Dicker Mill Industrial Estate, near mouth of Rib. Canalised branch, with old Entrance Bridge. Buildings re-developed from watermill to Canal Age Industry to late twentieth century non-water based industrial estate. p) R. Lea Canal. Canal Age Industrial Hertford. q) R. Lea Canal. Downstream Hertford. r) Weir system controlling water level in R. Lea Canal. R. Lea to left.

s) Buntingford, S. t) Hare Street, S. u) Hay Street, S. v) Westmill, C. w) Puckeridge, C+S. x) Braughing, C (minor S). y) Standon, C. z) moated earthwork. a2) Larches. b2) Waterford, C. C = cluster village; S = street village; F = ford; M = former watermill; Thick line = river.

Between Braughing and Standon is the confluence of the Rib and the Quin, so the volume of water roughly doubles at Standon. Drainage and abstraction have much lessened the total available water, and for drainage, obstructions to flow are removed: the opposite of the earlier pattern of holding up water in order to turn wheels, hold boats and catch fish more easily. So in the past Standon would have had a good flow of water. There were mills upstream (now flour and plastics factories) and a small industrial lane. The flourmill building to the south of the upstream mill was a steam-operated mill connected to the older building opposite. There was another mill downstream, now a dwelling only. This last controlled what is now a long deep ford (and footbridge). Even now, with so much less water, cars cannot pass in high water and, though carts have a much higher clearance, in the past they surely could not have passed either. So what happened? The answer is seen in Constable's *The Hay Wain*, and in numerous similar pictures. Mills held up ponded water upstream for much of the time, to get a good head for power, and during this time the river could be crossed with ease. In other words, there was a part-time ford. Frequently, now, there are bridges — replacing old fords — downstream of mills, rather new bridges, as the ford, for long years, was adequate for sparse traffic. In the nineteenth century, the inhabitants of Standon mill knew better than to obtain drinking-water from the river: there is a good pump. The better-educated (and wealthier) usually change habits faster, including getting better water. For the main village the old supply was the little tributary now flowing (in wet weather) down the hill to the south.

Standon was an important village, becoming a borough by 1262, and held by great lords, including the Knights of St John of Jerusalem. There was an early (upstream) bridge, probably at the site of the present one, with a pre–Reformation Lady Chapel. Standon had a market which was encouraged by law at the expense of other villages, such as Buntingford (Victoria County History, 1902-14).

Standon is basically a cluster-village, also extending along the Rib, keeping to the south of the river. The old wharf, as well as the industry, contribute to this elongation. Fig. 2.4 shows the wharf clearly (compare, e.g., Henley, Fig. 1.8). The houses are set back from the river — but not to avoid flood, as the level is stable. Houses tend to be rebuilt on or about the same site, and this is a common wharf pattern. Standon is, after all, the upstream village before (from a navigation viewpoint) the river splits into two half-size channels, much less suitable for navigation. Remembering Magna Charta (Chapter 1) and similar Acts, it is reasonable to expect that Central Government would encourage trade to a village with water-borne freight. Standon had direct (however inconvenient) access to London and had malt and other products from the neighbourhood to send there. With this in mind the siting of the industry makes sense: the main village industry is upstream of the wharf, where the larger boats did not pass, and the downstream mill was one which controlled much water, allowing the passage of both boats (in flashes) and carts (while water was ponding). (The flash was a rush of water caused by the miller fully opening his gates.) The development of power was so important locally that boats were normally expected to suffer intermittent inconvenience.

Downstream there is an old moated oval earthwork, presumably a moated fort of some early date, but with no definite information available (V. Valentine, Royal

Commission on Historical Monuments, personal communication). This is in the alluvial valley, and was reshaped later to some degree.

The small hamlet of Larches is next downstream. Old lanes cross the Rib twice here. The upstream ford is a meeting of four old (small) ways, perhaps needed for access to the windmill (over the ford, up-hill to the right). The downstream crossing is even less suitable for cars. Cut into the winding old lane between the two fords is a straight road with a bridge going to a country house.

(Watermillers were traditionally considered pale, dour and bad tempered, windmillers, red-faced, jolly and stout. Considering the unhealthiness caused by floods and water-borne disease (Chapter 12), the descriptions are plausible.)

Barwick is a rather larger hamlet. It has an aged timber-company shed on a 1-2m tributary of the Rib. Two older nameplates refer to mechanical repairs, suggesting changes of ownership and use. A good living is obviously not forthcoming at this site. On its opposite bank there is a good–quality farmhouse. So the shed is on a site where a mill would be expected to be. And, indeed, hidden in the ditch is a millstone. The tiny brook, however, could turn a millwheel but seldom: creating the necessary head would take much time. It is likely, therefore, that a non-wealthy rural industry has been on this site for centuries, recently abandoning the use of water power. Such continuities occur often and are of much interest.

The next two pictures are downstream sites of interest, a cattle watering-site with fenced areas trodden down to make a gentle bank, and another ford. This site shows its history in the various remaining steps and posts, as well as in the current footbridge!

Downstream again are three more pumping-stations, taking yet more potential river water for domestic use. In the next village, Wades Mill is very fine. Further downstream is an isolated mill and country-house complex. West Mill was a wealthy mill with several buildings, and the family were able to afford a fine house, which was built away from the millhouse.

Several different mill patterns occur on the Rib. In Buntingford the old watermill site is a new Industrial Estate. In Standon the upstream mills were redeveloped and are still factories. The downstream mill gave a good living; the buildings are waterside and changed from mill use to just domestic use. The same happened at Wades Mill. At West Mill, however, a separate dwelling was later built away from the waterside mill. Again, a good living was provided. At Barwick the (presumed) mill was small, has been rebuilt and has no dwelling-space. Dicker Mill, below, shows yet another pattern.

The final village before the Rib reaches the Lea is the cluster-village of Waterford. This is not Rib-based (a tributary), but looks down to Hertford. From Hertford to London, the Lea has been a main waterway since at least Anglo-Saxon times (Chapter 12).

In one sense a 'navigation' is a journey by water (1527), the action or practice of passing on water in ships and other craft (1533), or a passage or course by which one may sail (1654) (Shorter Oxford *English Dictionary*): that is, any waterway carrying traffic or a journey thereon. However, when investors, mostly in the eighteenth and early nineteenth centuries (the Lea, after 1766), put much money into canalising rivers, making them easier for boats, they naturally charged tolls, and the rivers became Navigations, canalised stretches, whose rights to charge and duties of upkeep could be bought and sold. The two meanings of the word 'navigation' can often be distinguished only by context, or date of document, and confusion brings misunderstanding.

The Lea itself flows through Hertford. The navigation channel is to the north and east of the town. The port of Hertford, the terminus, has careful and complex water control, giving (still) easy boat passage. For a century (post-navigation, pre-railway) new industry sprang up to take advantage of this good, new route to London.

Hertford, Ware and Stansted Abbots all catered for the London trade in the Canal Age. Malt and other goods were made in waterside factories, and grain and other produce were collected from inland and sent by barge to the capital. These factories have been redeveloped to some extent, but the general pattern is still that of the Canal Age. The Barge Inn still exists, and so, pleasingly, do swans. Trade decayed but pleasure craft are now increasing to take its place. The Rib has an impounded branch canal, with an entrance bridge, and the new Dicker Mill Industrial Estate. What has happened? Dicker Mill was presumably on the original channel, ponding water upstream, with a parallel channel for surplus water and perhaps other uses. Then in the Canal Age the longer impoundment was created on it to join the Lea Canal. This short piece would have had an Industrial Estate, making the goods to convey on the canalised stretch to the main canal. The factories on the main canal came to have access to good roads. This little piece was isolated. Now, though, any industrial site is valuable, as adequate roads lead everywhere. So here there is a brand-new estate, with no interest in the river, and a decaying, impounded stream with an entrance bridge over it. The entrance bridge (also seen in Fig. 2.8) seems to have developed from the fortified bridge of earlier times; cf. Figs 8.2, 9.9, 9.15c. It marks the entrance to private property. The site has brought wealth as a watermill, through canal industry and, now, through non-water-based industry.

## River Hoyoux, Belgian Condroz (Ardennes) *(Fig. 2.5)*

This is an industrial catchment, the industry having moved downstream over the centuries. The Hoyoux rises on the Condroz plateau extending north from the Ardenne hills, where watermills provided ancient wealth to the settlements. This is unusual — in general the plateaux of Belgium-Luxembourg-Germany are recently-settled and impoverished, with wealth residing in the valleys below. Mills are also found where the stream runs off the hill, and there are farmhouses with slit windows, suggesting former fortification. The water flow is good, and the present millhouses wealthy — though surprisingly the millwheel is not enclosed. In the mill garden is an ancient controlled–level pond, for the industrial use of the mill.

Off the hill, however, the pattern changes from ancient milling to nineteenth-century iron works, now decaying. The river has weirs (mill sites?) which would have permitted barge access, but in the Railway Age a railway was obviously

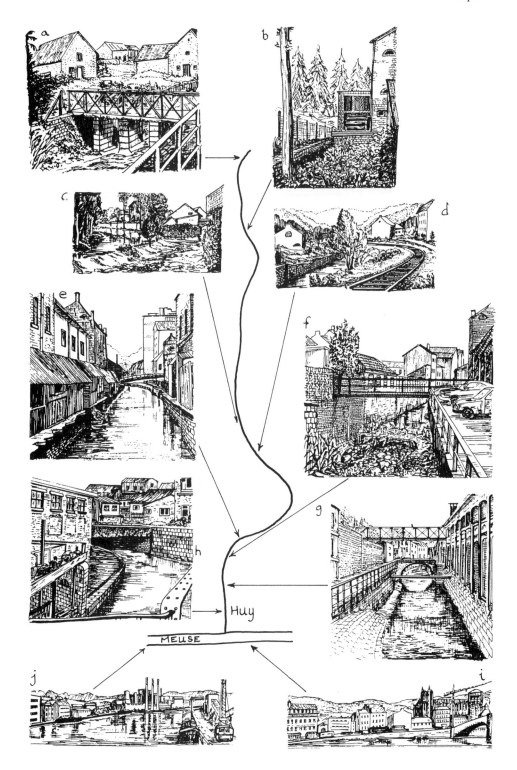

preferable for removing the ore and was built roughly parallel to the Hoyoux.

Huy is sited by the confluence of the Hoyoux and the Meuse, and the river was used for boats and industry throughout the town. Upstream there are ex-wharves but no industry; downstream there was much water-based industry: water-based in the sense of using water for processing and transport. Weirs to pond the water for navigation were frequent. The picture of the industrial area should be studied in detail, since here the interpretation is unmistakable: where the same pattern occurs elsewhere the same interpretation applies (see, e.g., Fig. 2.4: Hertford; and Fig. 9.1c, in the inland market town of Dorchester, where an old industrial canalised river comes as a surprise).

In Huy the small industrialists lived on the Hoyoux, which was insalubrious like so much water-based industry (see Fig. 11.3, Victorian Waterfront, and below). The wealthier (including traders) lived on the Meuse, which had the health problems arising from water but not those from pollution. Real wealth, however, escaped Huy (compare Fig. 9.4 showing the wealth of the nearby trading-town of Namur).

In the twentieth century commercial barges and commercial enterprises became much bigger. The Hoyoux was too small and was not redeveloped. Instead the industry moved to the Meuse, to land unbuilt-on previously outside the town.

Huy still has its old hill-fort, built to guard the town and the river crossing — the crossing now being a fine bridge.

The Hoyoux has for centuries provided much industrial wealth (but not to an outstanding degree) to those who lived near it.

## River Vazon, Guernsey (*Fig. 2.6*)

The Vazon is another small rural stream supplying various farms. It has been put partly underground. It turned a few mills (one, an 'overshot' mill, still turning), but water is now less, being taken off for domestic supply. There are an unusual number of cattle-troughs for the famous Guernsey cattle.

Guernsey is a small (*c.* 9 × 9km), rural, low–populated island (*c.* 55,000 residents being increased by nearly 10% by the *c.* 300,000 annual tourists). The Vazon is in the south, where formerly cows moved continually, necessitating innumerable watering-places beside the roads; in fact, these are almost wherever one of the many streams touches a road.

Upstream on the Talbot is an example of a small brook being diverted to supply a farm, and having a right-angle bend. When right-angle bends are created, they survive only where there is low flow and protection from scour, or, interestingly, in Denmark. There is a nice, decayed water-based cottage. Downstream of

Fig. 2.5 R. Hoyoux, Belgium. a) Old (wealthy) village on plateau (Mills). b) Old mill with open wheel, part-way down. c) d) Nineteenth century ironworks with railway. Industrial controls on river. e) f) g) h) Huy, downstream sequence on Hoyoux. e) above main industry. Wharf. f)-h) water-based industry, various. Note shapes of buildings, that barges could pull up along much, the water and its controls, and the various types of river crossings. i) Huy, from Meuse. Old Fort up hill on right (not shown). Compare frontage with e)-h), note bridge. j) Downstream Huy, on Meuse. New industry has now moved to the large river.

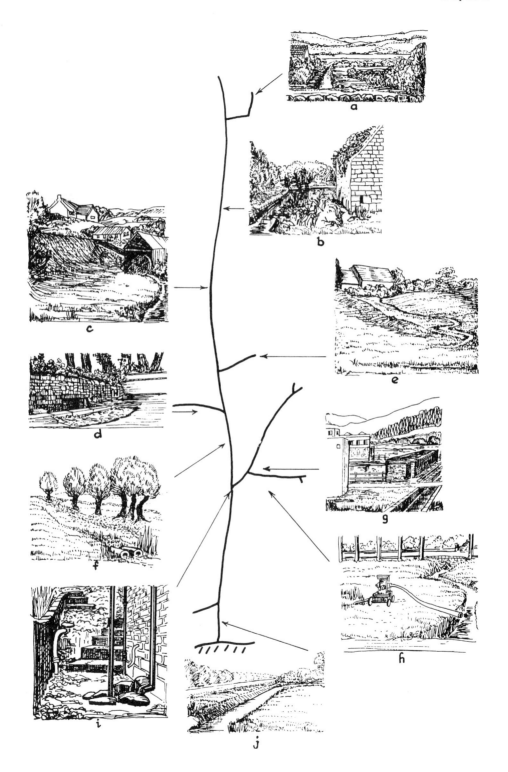

this a leat is taken off to the west side of the valley. The stream course, now with little water, winds along the valley base. The leat, with a much gentler slope, runs along what becomes a massive earthwork, raising its level to some 10m above the stream. This 10m head of water, even with so little water, is enough to turn an overshot mill, the Moulin des Niots. (An overshot wheel has the water hitting the top (not bottom) of the wheel. It requires a greater head, but less flow, than the undershot mills described above.) The Moulin des Niots is now used to generate electricity: it is a (small) hydroelectric plant. Downstream the water is returned to the main stream.

This 'main' stream is then put underground, the picture showing the point of emergence, in pipes. Guernsey streams are frequently underground for part of their length. The old pollard trees here enable the old course of the stream to be traced — as is typical (see Fig. 1.4). A tributary then joins: farms need much water, and old ones, as here, are often sited on small tributaries (also see Chapter 10). Another little tributary fills one of the many water-troughs on the lanes before joining the Talbot.

The Candie, another component stream of the Vazon, has roadside water-troughs, and an old wealthy farm complex, making full use (with diversions, etc.) of the water. The Les Grandes is shorter but has more water, and supplies a farm and an old mill.

There is a reservoir, where the tributaries join. Although Guernsey has over 1,000mm average annual rainfall, modern needs plus tourism strain the water supplies. Formerly, when all water went through the river, there were active watermills at Kings Mills. At the base the Vazon, now a small river, drains through a marsh to the sea.

## River Kbir (upstream), River Sewda (downstream), Malta

*(Figs 2.7, 2.8)*

*(Unfortunately, no one Maltese river shows all the most interesting features)*

In Malta, as in Arab lands further south, it is the valleys, the W*ieds*, rather than the rivers, which are considered important and named, and these valleys bear several names. Fig. 2.7 shows just the main rivers,

Fig. 2.7 Map of Malta.

Fig. 2.6 R. Vazon, Guernsey. a) Stream diverted to left of valley base, with a right-angle bend, to supply farm. b) Start of mill leat (stream is to the right) and decrepit stream-side cottage. c) Mill leat on earthwork to left, water turning overshot wheel of former mill, now hydro-electric plant. Stream in valley base. d) Water lane, tributary and cattle-watering trough. e) Farm on tributary to side of R. Vazon. Note natural winding stream course below. f) R. Vazon piped below ground. Note old pollards along original line. g) Reservoir on side-stream, water company buildings, channels etc. h) Upstream of reservoir, abstracting farmland water. i) King's Mills, part of old undershot water mills. j) Channellised river in flood plain near sea.

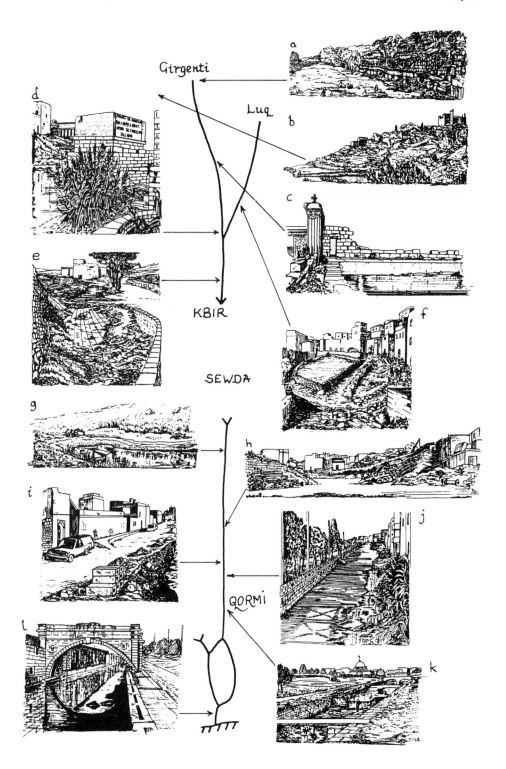

named after their lower valleys. In Mallorca, also Mediterranean, but further north with (mostly) drier rivers and less Arab influence, there is an intermediate pattern. The waters are named ('Torrente de …'), and have several names, but each named stretch is much longer than those in Malta. Malta, only 14 × 8km, has around 330,000 residents, plus the tourists (c. 50,000 beds), which mean a high demand for water.

Maltese streams contrast with the other examples here in being seasonal. Water supplies are inadequate, so pains are taken to save and re-use surface water and abstract ground water, thereby lowering river-water levels. Watering-channels occur, and rivers are used as defensive moats.

Malta has about 580mm rain in winter (average annual rainfall) and a dry, hot summer. The island consists of soft limestone into which rain sinks easily. The rivers flow after rain, reservoirs now having standing water for much of the time from October to May. The water remaining in spring is usually abstracted for the late potato and other crops — this sudden removal of water being much more destructive to aquatic life than the 'natural', slow drying-up would be.

In contrast to countries with temperate climates further north, rivers cannot supply drinking water all year in Malta. Therefore major settlements are on underground water supplies. For the same reason sewage cannot be disposed of via the rivers. The waste that does pollute the rivers, though, causes more damage than the same amount would further north, since there is little dilution and little flow to carry it out to sea. Much stays in the drying reservoirs. Rubbish remains until collected by government, unless it is washed out by major floods.

Almost at the top of the Girgenti tributary of the Kbir, the Great River, the channel is dry enough to be cultivated. Obviously only occasional storm flow reaches here. Interestingly, southern river beds are used for cultivation, which also occurs in Corsica, Mallorca, Menorca, etc., in suitable valleys. Such valleys are damper than the hillsides, though the crops remain at risk from spates. A little way downstream is an old bridge (out of sight on the picture). Here is the first indication of a lowered water table. A bridge is not built when a ford will suffice, particularly in such a rural place, so in the past the water must have been deeper. A further indication is the decayed water-channel on the far side of the channel. This watercourse actually starts just upstream, where its origin is now lost in rubble. These water-channels are common in dry Mediterranean countries such as Spain and Mallorca, and particularly so in Malta. The earliest, on rock, are Roman. Those of the early period of the Knights of St John of Jerusalem are like this one here.

Fig. 2.8 R. Kbir, upstream; and R. Sewda, downstream, Malta. a) Upstream. Decayed waterchannel right, originating just upstream, here above channel bed. Channel bed partly cultivated (dry). Decayed bridge across channel, far. b) Inquisitors' Palace right, water channel of a) continued round on wall to its outbuildings, centre. R. Kbir in valley, foreground. c) Water tank with shrine, above R. Kbir. Note steps down into tank. d) Junction of two streams of R. Kbir. Borehole, pumping station (Water Ministry temporarily combined with that of Sport). Enough water for water plants. Farms. e) River farm, R. Kbir. Note the frequent dams, the nearer one for the recent Valleys Good Luck Scheme. Road originated from a path within the Wied. f) R. Kkbir used for defence, Zebbug. Old village on right only. g) R. Sewda, frequent dams, water polluted from pig-farms, pipe in reservoir, decoy duck. h) R. Sewda. Upstream Qormi, water and road in same bed, scrap metal yard right, run-off polluting river. i) j) R. Sewda, Qormi. i) piping river underground in middle of road, j) road flooded. Note steps. k) R. Sewda, upstream Marsa, decayed old dams, land beside no longer intensively farmed. l) R. Sewda, near sea, looking upstream. Victoria bridge, the Entrance Bridge to a River Port (see R. Rib, R. Hoyoux, above).

Modern channels are concrete (see Chapter 3). They convey water by gravity, keeping near the contour lines and so using only a small head (though some modern channels may have fast flow). The channel mentioned runs to the outbuildings of the seventeenth-century Grand Inquisitors' Palace *c*. 0.3km away. To warrant this amount of trouble in building it, the channel must have flowed for a considerable part of the year. Now it could only be full for a few days. Therefore it must be concluded that the water table has fallen since the channel was built. Abstraction from the aquifer below has been exceeding input from rain. In lowland England, if it should be decided that the land is too dry, it is easy to put up weirs and stop the under-drainage and ditches. This would not replenish the deep water supplies, but would quickly raise the ground-water table. In Malta that option does not exist, and this much abstraction should be viewed with concern.

Similar water-channels are found in the nearby Luq stream, also built initially to supply a Knight's Palace. These are now also unusable, and there is a borehole to supply domestic demand. Where these two streams, the Girgenti and the Luq, meet, is the only part of the Maltese Islands with a cluster of river-farms —and, now, another borehole. Clearly these were the least seasonal rivers (or most-flowing accessible rivers) of the Island. The frequent weir-type farm bridges dam water above them, are crossable except during spate, and are shaped to diminish erosion. This type of dam was built in the Valleys Good Luck Scheme, following destructive floods in 1979. They are ingenious and effective (see Chapter 3 for other types). *Wieds*, being public property, were used for paths, as here for the farms off the road: the roads having developed from a *Wied* path anyway.

Upstream of the confluence on the hillside above the Girgenti, is a water-tank, fed by run-off water like many others, and with steps into it. Unusually, it has a shrine (most of Malta's many roadside shrines are land-based). This one, dated 1891, offers forty days' indulgence for reciting the *Salve Regina*.

The villages, as already noted, do not use the rivers for their main water supply or waste disposal. There are other uses: Zebbug is an example of the river used for defence, with the village sitting in the bend of the river. Although a partly dry river bed may not be as useful as the constantly-flooded ones of the north, it still forms a boundary into which the enemy must descend and then go up to meet the defenders securely waiting on the wall above. In the past, the greater general amount of water, with suitably placed weirs, could have kept the moat fuller. (Only one side was thus defended by moat, but manpower would have been released to guard the other side. Malta was for centuries subject to raids, and the population lived inland or in the fortified harbour, not in exposed fishing villages.) Zebbug has a fine old bridge and the river bed is again used as a track and, unfortunately, as a rubbish dump.

Water conservation is most important to farming such a dry and thirsty land (even though summer crops have not been grown since the cotton industry passed to Egypt in the late nineteenth century). Dams across the rivers are frequent, sometimes only 50m apart. The reservoir water may be removed by pipe (gravity or pump) or by lorry, either gradually or abruptly. Maltese stream water is saved.

The middle Sewda also has the same frequent dams, but two new features occur. The first is decoy ducks. Originally these were tame live birds (see Chapter

4) but here they are models. (Unfortunately, and in defiance of international pressure, Malta slaughters migrant and indigenous fowl in vast and depressing quantities.) The second, pig-farm slurry, makes the water badly polluted, smelly and discoloured. The consequent damage to flora and fauna is, of course, much enhanced by the low flow and the water-conserving dams: there is little opportunity for wash-out or purification. This is the longest polluted stretch of river in Malta. On the drying soil a polluted community of Chenopods (Goosefoots) may develop. The dams trap silt. Heavy rains on the dry, terraced hillsides above wash silt from the land into the river and here the dams block flow and cause silt deposition. Dredging is therefore necessary (slurry adds to the silting). Routine removal of accumulated silt is not ecologically damaging, but breaking the hard bed is, as it contains aquatic life, some of it dormant; such removal should be stopped.

The 'old' bridges here cross at right angles, the lane on either side being narrow. In the days of carts this was satisfactory but now a little turning space has to be given each side for cars and lorries.

Further down, the Sewda then reaches the village (now town) of Qormi. Qormi, unlike Zebbug, has expanded to the other side of the river, but the defensive pattern of the old centre enclosed by the river bed can still be seen. Along much of the course the river is also the road (a 'water lane'), and where it is a main road there is a newly made underground channel to carry low flows. Note the footbridge, and floodwater, on the picture. Some of the old houses — built when there was more water — have steps up to the doors. At the upstream end the water receives more pollution — a scrap-metal yard drains direct into the road-river (metal, paint, oil, etc.). Lower, old discharge pipes (run-off and sewer) lead into the channel.

Downstream, the river is again separate. It is now polluted and collects more urban run-off and waste as it passes to the sea. There are still frequent weirs but these are now only relics of the past when the area was still farmland — and when the water was possibly cleaner. Both weirs and bridges remain worthy of study.

Finally, almost at the sea, and now cut off from the sea by a road, is Malta's only river port. The provenance, with the Victoria Entrance Bridge (not a bridge for crossing the river) can be checked from Figs 2.4, 8.2, 9.9 and 9.15b.

## River Darent, S.E. England (*Fig. 2.9*)

This is another English (mainly) rural river, with former use for power (frequent mills), watermeadows and, more recently, good angling for trout. It is now important for general recreation. It has been included because it comes from Kent, traditionally known as the Garden of England, and shows a style of gracious living not seen in the examples above. It is visited for its beauty.

The Darent rises above and around the town of Sevenoaks, and then flows downstream onto chalk, becoming what is commonly known as a chalk-stream (though its vegetation, of course, also reflects the fertile sands above).

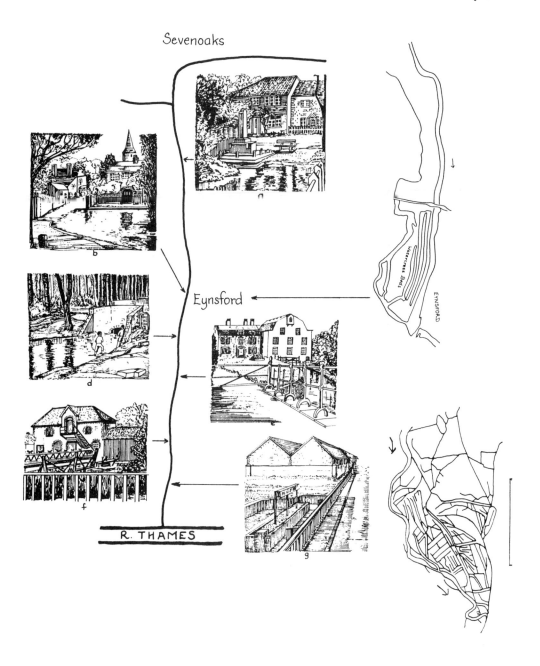

Fig. 2.9 River Darent, England. a) Shoreham. b) Eynsford. c) Larger water meadow channels near Eynsford in 1867 (bar = 1km). d) Horton Kirby. e) Farningham. f) South Darent. g) Nearer Dartford. h) Water meadow channels, only slightly decayed. Dorset. (bar = 1km).

The Darent, though less well-known than, for instance, the Test, was renowned for its trout fishing until the water level fell too far. Ponding due to controls for watermeadows and mills was removed, and water was abstracted from the chalk below. Water abstraction started in 1901 and was insignificant until the 1950s, but in 1988 was over 70% of the recharge water, from seven abstracting stations. Undoubtedly population has increased, but equally undoubtedly the Darent has been too much damaged.

The river even partly dries up in dry summers. This causes much concern to the local community, but little to the water authorities, charged with the duty of supplying water, and not concerned with retaining England's heritage. There are no cress beds or other enterprises which, by law, must have water. So let the river dry! A community group is currently trying to save the river. One idea at the time of writing was to narrow and so deepen the channel. The writer hopes not. Such a 2-1m channel becomes difficult to see, when flanked by ungrazed or woody vegetation. The visual impact and beauty is lost, and in a generation forgotten, so no one minds if the whole river then dies. A country as wealthy as Britain should pay to obtain water from other sources (e.g. reverse osmosis from seawater). The British, however, prefer their fitted kitchens and foreign holidays.

The Darent mills are objects of beauty, except close to Dartford, downstream (in the Outer London ambience), where they have been developed as unattractively as many other restructured mills. Mills occur both on the main river and on the side streams — for example at Sutton, where the mill was less wealthy, as was common where there was less water. (Where little water can be accumulated, the wheel cannot be kept turning for so long.) Until recently the wealth of an enterprise could be judged from its building. The master lived by, or over his Works, and the building showed the degree of prosperity. This contrasts with the present, where the wealth of the enterprises of Messrs Marks and Spencer or Boots cannot be judged with any accuracy either from their branches in any one town, or from the houses in which their heirs live — which are certainly not over their (many) shops. (In the Industrial Revolution, Masters lived in healthier places than their Works, but that was a different pattern: Marks and Spencers open branches in healthy places!). Mill uses included paper, gunpowder ('Powder Mill Lane') and cartridge filling (Victoria County History, 1908-32).

The river housing, large and small, exhibits that peculiarly English quality — regrettably not over all England — of living pleasantly and well in the countryside. Even where tourists congregate the quality of life is much higher than in, say, Fig. 1.11. To an extent not appreciated by modern planners, surroundings control behaviour. The Darent enhances the beauty of the buildings.

Watermeadows used to line the river. These, fully developed in the seventeenth century, provided among the most valuable grass in the land. However, they need much maintenance, and when fertilisers came to be used in large quantities in the late nineteenth and twentieth centuries, improving the grass from other fields, the watermeadows were gradually abandoned. Watermeadows are complex penned-water systems. The river has various controllable hatches and sluices, so that water can be taken off into carriers leading into the fields and there spread to many channels to flood or drain the meadows as required, surplus water running back to the river. When the flooding took place, it was a fine art to get water quantity, flow and timing exactly right. Silty water from late winter storms was used to fertilise the watermeadows. Although grassland still lines the river, there is no watermeadow and the channels have almost vanished. The Darent watermeadows, in fact, were lost early, late nineteenth-century maps showing incomplete feeder and draining streams. (There were, though, watercress beds (see Chapter 4) at Eynsford.)

# 3

# Water Supply

O traveller, stay thy weary feet,
Drink of this fountain, pure and sweet.
It flows for rich and poor the same.
Then go thy way, remembering still
The wayside well beneath the hill,
The cup of water in His name.
(Longfellow)

From that first tree flowed, as from a well
A trickling stream of Balme, most soveraine.
(Spencer, *The Faerie Queen*)

Rose stood on the low step cut in the fieldside, dipping a pitcher in the pond, then back again to the cottage. (Charlesworth, 1856)

## Introduction

Drinking-water may come from a river, from its source, or from deeper within the ground. To make the terms clear, a river is a stream of water flowing in its bed towards the sea. A spring is the place of rising, the source, of a well, stream or river, 'a flow of water rising naturally out of the earth'. Anciently a 'well' was a spring, a spring of water rising to the surface and forming a small pool or flowing stream. From this root come miracle, medicinal and healing springs and wells and names for settlements by such springs — Baden Baden, Wells, Wellingborough. Thirdly, and currently, a 'well' means a pit dug down to water and lined with masonry. 'Fountain' can also mean several things: a spring of water or river source, a spring with Roman masonry (Anglo-Saxon, Table 1.2), an erection in a public place for the constant supply of water for drinking, or a jet or stream of water made to rise artificially, or a structure built for such a jet or stream (*Shorter Oxford English Dictionary*). Readers please note!

## Development of water supply: the history of problems with, and attitudes to, clean water

A supply of fresh, clean drinking-water is of such importance to the health of a community that those providing it are worthy of — but seldom receive — the veneration of the community. The Wignacourt Aqueduct (Fig. 3.1a) in Malta, carrying water *c*. 5km to the capital, does commemorate the name of the Grand Master responsible for it in 1620, and His Excellency General Sir A. Barton is remembered on a — now ornamental — fountain recording his bringing of fresh water to Sliema, Malta, in 1882 (Fig. 3.1b).

Fig. 3.1 a) Wignacourt aqueduct, seventeenth century, Malta. b) Fountain commemorating bringing fresh water to Sliema, nineteenth century, Malta (note lion's head).

The bringing of water may have become the stuff of legend. Sir Francis Drake, to whom much in the English southwest was later attributed, was said to have brought fresh water to Plymouth — he rode to the Dartmoor hills, found a fine good spring, pronounced a magic word and galloped home, the spring following his horse's hooves all the way.

Fig. 3.2 Victorian slum (from Haslam, 1990).

In Wells, England, Bishop Beckynton (1443-64) granted to William Vowell, the brethren, fellow-citizens and burgesses to have and to hold for ever, a conduit with troughs and pipes above and underground, to be supplied from certain water within his Palace called St Andrews' Well (the waste-water to be for the episcopal mills). This supply is still used. Vowell and his fellow-citizens agreed to visit the Bishops' tomb annually (Heath 1911), and on or near January 14th, the Mayor and Council, Dean and Chapter of Wells still process to the tomb, for the customary prayers. Such acknowledgement is exceptional!

Dilute alcohol (Small Ale in England) was regularly drunk instead of water, and for good reason: distilled or boiled water was without bugs, even if filled with other contaminants. Such other contaminants were, however, much less dangerous before the Industrial Revolution than they are now. Most pollution was organic, sewage and manure, leachate from graveyards and slaughterhouses, etc. True, lead pipes conveyed water from Roman times even to now, and lead is poisonous, but the risks are low with fast-running water. In the nineteenth century industrial development increased chemical contamination (still only locally), and the population explosion increased the organic. Sewage percolates dreadfully — and mortally — from true slum conditions (Fig. 3.2). Typhoid, cholera and such-like became all too common, driving city fathers reluctantly to providing clean water. By the later nineteenth century, this process was well understood and normal (Table 11.1), but earlier it was neither understood nor accepted

The change is charted in the Public Records, and in such writings as the works of Charlotte Yonge, who, in the 1850s, considered drains of doubtful importance, but in the 1880s, told her readers never to drink water looking, smelling or tasting unpleasant. The old attitude is described by Ewing (1876). '[The fact that] the gentlemen who went round [a village, from the Sanitary Commission] felt it superfluous to have their orders carried out when strong men were no longer sickening and dying within two revolutions of the hands of the church clock, will surprise no one who has had to do with local sanitary officers. They are like the Children of Israel [before escaping from slavery in Egypt] and will only do their duty under pressure of a plague. The people themselves are more like the Egyptians. Plagues won't convince them. A mother, with all her own and her neighbour's children sickening about her, would walk miles in a burst shoe to fetch the doctor or a big bottle of medicine, but she won't walk three yards further than usual to draw her housewater from the well the sewer doesn't leak into.' And sewers did not only leak into wells, they could also lead into them, as can still be seen (e.g., in Horndon-on-the-Hill, England, where beautiful wrought iron work covers the well — which, inside, receives the drain. Y. Bower, personal communication).

It seemed at first as though all that was needed was to make water clear (filtered as necessary) and bacteriologically pure (disinfected, now usually with chlorine). Then came the twentieth-century spread of industry across the settlements, and of fertiliser and biocide across the land, all chemically contaminating the water supplies, and providing a new challenge. The search for cleaner water does not end with filters and disinfectants. Water supplied by pipe is the most convenient. Though remembered in, e.g., Byzantine culture, mains water became forgotten in Europe after Roman times, except in monasteries, the repositories of

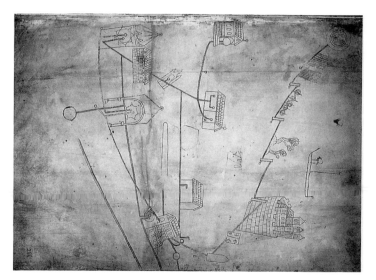

Fig. 3.3 Canterbury waterworks, pipes etc., twelfth century (England). (By permission of the Master and Fellows of Trinity College, Cambridge). Align by Cathedral.

Roman literature. Learning means water as well as Latin! In the twelfth century, Bernard of Clairvaux and Hildegard of the Rhine were designing monasteries. St Bernard's plan was widely copied. He had the river entering the abbey via a cornmill (which needs a head of water and does not pollute), to the boiler where beer was brewed and other supply, then to the polluting fullingmill, tannery and other industrial processes, finally leaving with the abbey waste (thus cleansing the abbey). Mechanical

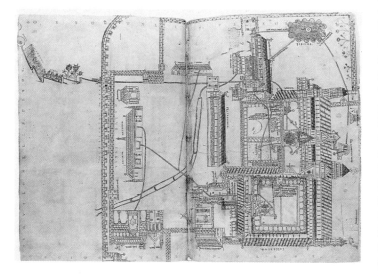

power was important in the monastery, to free the monks for prayer and intellectual work. Cleanliness was important to health (de Buitlear, 1985). St Hildegard had flowing water likewise, with water piped to all the offices (Thurston & Attwater, 1986).

Fig. 3.3 shows the twelfth-century waterworks of Canterbury, supplied by the Cathedral clergy, and Fig. 3.4 the vastly more complex but basically similar 1980s plan, with water supplied by the Mid-Kent Water Company (showing a shift from clerical to public responsibility). Parts of the original lead piping still exist.

Trinity fountain in Cambridge was supplied from a spring *c*. 2km away in 1327. This sufficed for what became the College until 1860, when it used the Cambridge Waterworks supply, which itself began in 1853. In 1907, though — as

Fig. 3.4 Canterbury waterworks, pipes, late twentieth century (England) (redrawn, by permission of the Mid-Kent Water Company). Align by Cathedral.

late as that — Trinity reverted to its own supply and used wells at the back of the chapel; it did not return to the Town supply until 1967 (Trinity College, personal communication). The fountain remained filled from the old spring. When Churchill College was built, the fountain supply to Trinity failed. Not connecting the two, and wishing to avoid the expense of re–laying the pipe, Trinity connected the fountain to the mains. However, Churchill basement flooded, and this was found to be through the breakage of the Trinity pipe, which was then restored (Trubshaw, *Cambridge Evening News,* 1988).

Gradually skills for piping were developed and spread. In Defoe's time (1724-7) London, according to him, had good water. It came partly from the Thames, which was still in adequate condition. With much trading, though, the river cannot have been perfect. London's water came also from the New River, from Ware (on the Lea, see Chapter 2: Fig. 3.5). The water was brought by an 'aqueduct' (we would now say 'artificial channel') and supplied the greater part of the city (and with better water than that from the Thames). A new basin had to be dug at Islington to give

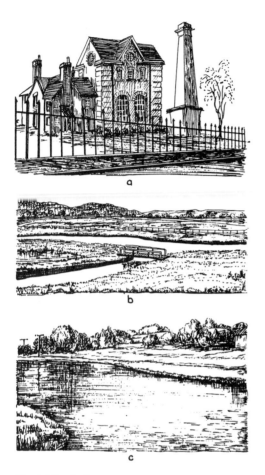

Fig. 3.5 London's water supply from Ware, England. a) Abstraction, Lea vale. b) Start of New River. c) Lower on New River.

a better head. This high basin was filled from the lower one by a great engine, formerly worked with six 'sails' (windmills) and in Defoe's time by many horses. With this they could supply the higher parts of the town, and more than the two Thames' engines could do. Everywhere water was laid in the streets in large timber pipes (healthy, but needing renewing often, unlike the 500-year old Cambridge lead pipes! Elm was good for this.). Every house had a pipe of running water, up to the uppermost story. Fire precautions were good. The timber pipes were furnished with fire plugs, for which the Parish Officers had the keys, and which, when opened, let a river of water into the streets giving immediate supply to the engines and firemen. (The Great Fire of 1666 was still a living memory, so fire precautions would be expected to be exceptionally good.) 'It cannot be denied', Defoe continues, 'that the City of London is the best supplied with water of any great city in the world.' What a pity that the ideal of pipes to each house was lost with the Industrial Revolution expansion when, for the poor, one tap per alley could be a luxury. In justice to the civic authorities, they were never intended to cope with such vast increases in population. In justice to the poor, they should have provided water.

Defoe describes Chester in 1690 as having no water supply apart from that carried from the River Dee in great leather vessels on horses and sold in the streets. These were of the same shape as those used for the same purpose in Constantinople, Turkey, Belgrade and Hungary. On his later visit to Chester, though, Defoe found a very good water-house in the river, and the city plentifully supplied by pipes, like London.

The Dutch, it must be said, were much in advance of Britain. They had good water supplies in the seventeenth century. When Queen Mary II (English-born wife of Dutch William of Orange, King William III) returned to England as Queen, she introduced a most peculiar Dutch custom into her bathroom at Hampton Court Palace: hot and cold running water (Chapman, 1953)!

The water-carrier and the water-cart have been familiar figures in larger settlements, selling water to all who did not wish to collect it for themselves. Piped water would have been fresher, cleaner and more convenient.

In the country, the ancient sources, rivers, wells, springs, etc. sufficed the population for longer but came under pressure from the same changes.

(1)    Increased numbers, which, as in towns, rendered the original sources inadequate. (Settlements began, of course, only where sufficient water was readily available.)

(2)    Increased contamination or increased recognition of contamination, which led to many traditional water sources being abandoned.

(3)    Lowering of the water table (through abstractions and drainage) so drying many wells and springs. This is a nineteenth- and twentieth-century phenomenon. Drainage adds to damage.

(4)    Increased demand per person. In less water-conscious times, especially when every drop (except that running off the roofs) had to be carried some way, demand was low. The Cambridge Water Company now estimate demand to be $c.$ 150 $l$ per head per day. Naval rations, until recently, were 13.6 $l$ (3 gallons) for all purposes, and this was considered ample. Half rations, 6.8 $l$, were a hardship.

*Table 3.1*

*Types of water supply in rural England (Leics.) in the late 1920s.*

*(A few examples, taken from Richardson (1931))*

**Villages**

*Barkstone:* the village depends on wells, most of which are fitted with pumps.

*Belvoir:* Many houses in the village are served by the Belvoir Estates Limited, with an undertaking from a spring in the Northampton Sand. Houses not so served depend on wells. Belvoir Spa: water in the upper bands of the lower Lias clays is locally saline. For some time there was a spa, from a well in this clay (as at Cheltenham Spa). Within living memory a woman walked regularly from a nearby village to drink from the well at the keeper's old house. (See also Chapter 14.)

*Bottesford:* the village depends on shallow wells.

*Croxton Kerrial:* the village has a piped supply, the property of Belvoir Estates Limited, and pumps. The piped supply comes from a spring in the Northamptonshire Sands. The water is raised by a ram to three tanks, from which it gravitates.

*Saltby:* the village has wells fitted with pumps, and the water in many wells in the upper part is good but hard. There is also a piped service, raised by a wind pump (with a ram for when wind is inadequate) to reservoirs from which it gravitates to standpipes.

*Sapcote:* a few cottages in this village are supplied by the Enderby and Stoney Stanton Granite Co. Ltd., the rest depend on wells. At Bath House, Bath Street, is a well known from time immemorial as Golden Well. The water is slightly chalybeate (iron-rich) and, according to an early nineteenth-century source, used to be highly recommended for nervous, consumptive (tubercular), scorbutic (scurvy-like) and scrofulous complaints, and for weak and sore eyes. It is still (in the 1920s) regarded as good for rheumatism. A bath house was erected in 1806, with hot and cold baths; it is now a stable. Near the village is a now-disused well called Soap well, formerly famed for having water so soft that no soap was needed for washing. (See also Chapter 14.)

*Sproxton:* part of this village has a piped service to standpipe, and part depends on wells fitted with pumps. The piped supply comes from a spring in the Marlstone in a valley.

**Town**

*Hinkley:* this town has an Urban District Council supply, the works being completed in 1891. This supplies (part of) Hinkley Urban District and parts of the parishes of Snowstone, Swepstone and Market Bosworth, and gives bulk supply to Hinkley Rural District Council for other villages. The supply comes from two shafts in the Triassic sandstone and conglomerate, and averages 400,000 gallons (over 18 million litres) per day. Owing to the increased demand and the decreased yield here, Nuneaton Corporation have been augmenting the supply since 1926.

Fig. 3.6 Springs. a) Schwarzwald, Germany. The formerly much-used village spring. Note surround and access. b)-d) Kent, England. Note abstraction in c). e)-g) Malta. e) Dried spring. f) Springs under limestone cap flowing in wet weather. g) Spring now shut away behind door — as frequent in South Europe. h) Fifteenth century. Note the high groundwater level and winding stream. Also the higher-level stream — irrigation channel?

The village brook of Foxton, England, sufficed for supply for many centuries — as was intended by the founders of the village. The seventeenth century saw a well at the Malthouse, and wells were numerous in the late eighteenth century. Searching deeper, some farms had bores and pumps in the mid-nineteenth century, others were still watering from the Brook. Then pumps came into general use. Two large bores, developed in 1873, gave better water, and water-carts carried the water round (Parker, 1975). Finally, mains water arrived. This history charts a gradual change from collecting surface water by householders to having underground water, from a distance, delivered to the house by an outside agency.

When meals were eaten on a platter of bread, no water was needed for washing up plates. When Queen Elizabeth I was considered fastidious for having a bath once a month, not much water was needed for washing the person. Indeed ladies on ships to and from India in the nineteenth century could wash satisfactorily — it is written — on a saucerful of water daily. Demand increased with modern conveniences. When mains water, easy drainage, water-closets and baths are available, they are used, with an enormous increase in daily consumption, added to by washing-machines, dish-washers, etc.

a

b

c

d

e

Fig. 3.6 contd.

f

Between the World Wars in England towns were on mains supplies. Villages, with smaller populations, more modest needs and less money, had a wide variety of sources of supply (Table 3.1). Piped water to villages was often through the good graces (or necessity) of a landed proprietor, gravel-works or other industrialist, or town nearby (or else the town's water supply came from a distance through the village). Wells, deep and shallow, pumped wells and small supplies abounded. It was only later that these went large-scale and came (mostly) under the control of government water authorities, though there is not yet a national grid for water like that for electricity. How much interesting variety of drinking-water we have lost, though! Compare Table 3.1 with the homogenised mix from the tap!

9

## Springs

Springs used to be abundant (e.g., Fig. 3.6), but with all the lowering of ground-water level of the past 150 years or so, many have been dried and lost. The writer has seen only two English villages with many natural springs (six or more near roads). The Quantock hills are a particularly rich area in damp weather. Before, and in mediaeval times, it was reputed that springs would well up in holy places, such as where saints were killed (see Chapter 14). Prior to drainage, it would have been very easy for the press of a pilgrim throng to alter the hydrology and produce small springs (cf. the occasion recorded by a writer on the Middle East, C.S. Jarvis, when a soldier hit a rock in the desert and, like Moses, produced abundant water).

Present springs may be used for mains supplies; they may have masonry surrounds if they were formerly the village water supply (surrounds so that the bank is not damaged nor the water dirtied by eroding banks). They may also, as in Malta, be for wash-places. These are described below.

h

Fig. 3.6 contd.

Fig. 3.7 Collecting water. a) Malta (note ford). b)
Malta. c) France. d) Czechoslovakia. e) Mallorca.
f) Malta.

# Wells

Wells, in the modern sense, have water
below ground level — sometimes only a
few decimetres, sometimes tens of metres.
The water, therefore, has to be raised and
Fig. 3.7 shows various ways of extracting
water. Women are most associated with
water, typically collecting the water for
the home (hence the goddesses of water?),
while men usually collect only to sell and
to water animals, and usually collect in
different containers (e.g., goatskins rather
than petrol-tins: Morton, 1934, in Israel).
Buckets have usually been used for water-
collection in Europe, whether dipped or
hauled (for mechanical raising, see 'Pumps'
below).

Wells vary greatly (Fig. 3.8). Field
wells are particularly common in the Mediterranean south, where every cultivated
field may need irrigating. These are usually plain. The Mediterranean is also where
animal-drawn wells are the most recently
in use or, indeed, are still in use. Mallorca
is still especially dependent on (simple)
wells. House wells are more ornate in
more wealthy or more ornamental cultures, but very plain ones may also occur
— often now represented just by a grating
on top preventing access to impure water.
Note the Roman one, which is not dissimi-
lar to more modern forms. Village wells
again vary, but can be objects of great
beauty, or very obviously functional (as

Fig. 3.8 Wells. a) Roman wellhead, Malta. b)
Roman fountain nymph with seashell, Malta. c)
Field well, Malta. d) animal-drawn well, Mallorca.
e) f) Well-houses, Menorca. g) Guernsey, modern
top. h) Guernsey, old supply for man and beast
(water at two levels). i) Menorca. j) Malta. k)
France.

the Mallorcan well with the wheel). Menorca is wind-swept, and the well-water is deep. Accordingly, unlike say Malta and Mallorca, it has numerous well-houses, providing shelter for man and beast. Some are simple, others elaborate affairs with plenty of space for animal-drawing of the water, and with, say, cattle-troughs, and irrigation water-channels (see Fig. 2.8) leading from the well-house perhaps to a storage water-tank.

Shallow wells are, of course, liable to dry in drought — which was sharply brought home to the English, particularly West Midlands, farmers in the 1976 drought, when there was great difficulty in watering stock. Having wells that were not liable to dry was a most valuable asset in the past. Gilbert White, in his *Natural History of Selborne* (1788), comments: 'Our wells at an average run to about 63ft [c. 20m], and when sunk to that depth seldom fail; but produce a fine limpid water, soft to the taste, and much commended by those who drink the pure element, but which does not lather well with soap.' (Was Gilbert White one who did not drink the pure element?)

Artesian wells are those in which the water rises under its own pressure, once the aquifer is reached. They are named from Artois, France, where they were early developed.

In arid lands, to own a well and to own the land around it meant the same, from ancient times. Water regimes based on cisterns (rainwater) and condensation water still exist, also.

## Pumps

When water is below ground, the other way to draw it is by pumps. Hand pumps are usually more functional than beautiful and bear a family resemblance across Europe (Fig. 3.9).

Wind pumps also draw water — rather different styles are typical in different places. Modern ones, usually for farm supply, are common in the Mediterranean, e.g., over much of Malta (where they were common by 1803), and more locally in Mallorca (N.E. and S.W. especially), where the water is deepest. Electric pumps may also be used, but many Mallorcans who tried these are reverting to the cheaper wind pumps. Wind pumps — windmills — have been well known in the north as drainers of wetlands, particularly in The Netherlands and the English Fenland.

## Fountains

In the classical world the cities had large public fountains: running water, with structures making for beauty and ease of collection (e.g., Corinth). Similar ones continued down the ages. Fountains can be on springs or have water piped to them. Indeed, it need not be only water. The old cathedral fountain in Lyons ran with wine in wine-festivals. Others did so for state occasions, e.g., in London for the second marriage of King Edward I; in Cambridge for the visit of Queen Anne — as late as

Fig. 3.9 Pumps. a) b) England. (b) pump-house). c) Czecho-slovakia. d) Germany. e) Mallorca.

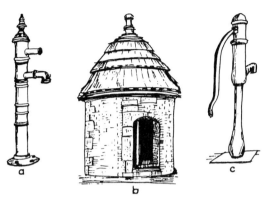

1705 (Green, 1970). Those in Fig. 3.10 are arbitrarily selected as being fountains for use, Fig. 13.2 showing ornamental ones — but there is no real distinction, the functional ones in wealthy or tasteful societies being ornamental. Like wells, fountains can become contaminated and be later closed. Two recent developments of the fountain — both getting into the definition above — are fire hydrants and drinking-fountains. In Malta, some village fountains were closed long ago: one rural one as lately as the past decade.

The cleanest water is that required for watering people, with the next cleanest being that required for laundry. Watering of stock and land (and cleaning of towns) is done, if need be, with water of a much lower standard. All the water may come from the same source, that is, the same tap, or else the sources may be separated: tap for people, stream for stock. In Valletta, Malta (Zammit, 1931), the fountain in the main square (1615) was for collection for dwellings: neither watering of animals nor laundry was permitted. Near the sea was the Neptune fountain (Fig. 3.11). Here all purposes were permitted — and the decorum expected now beside ornamental public fountains

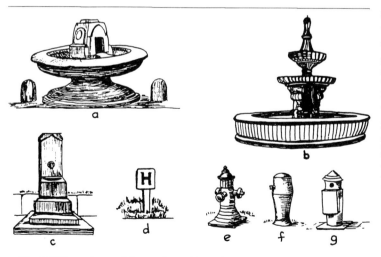

Fig. 3.10 Fountains used for supply. a) Closed, Malta. b) Now-ornamental, Malta. c) Drinking fountain, Czechoslovakia. d) Fire hydrant sign, England. e)-g) Hydrants, France.

Fig. 3.11 Neptune's Fountain, early nineteenth century, Malta (by permission of the National collection of Malta, Museum of Fine Arts, Valletta, Malta). Note the different places from which water is collected, and the distribution of man and beast. Another spout was on the far side.

Fig. 3.12 Roman baths, Malta. Also note irrigation channels on rock.

is notably absent. But the sense of community is equally notably present. There has been loss as well as gain in having water supplied privately to each house! People and animals mixed at the Neptune, to the detriment of hygiene but to some social good. (Note the collection from spout and from open water. A second, and metal, spout is out of view behind the fountain.)

## Washing the person and doing the laundry

Public bathing was standard in Classical times (Public Baths for men). Roman baths are still extant in Malta (Fig. 3.12), in a remote part of the island where it would be long before unfortified luxury could again be built! Public baths were lost in the west, with other civilised arts; returning, as the municipal baths, mainly in the nineteenth century in England (though also before and after that time). They were fashionable and modern in some minor English towns in the

1850s. (In 1850 itself, Mrs Gaskell published stories to support the Manchester Public Baths and wash-houses.) New uses may be found for old (municipal) baths — as on an English motorway, where some are now flower-tubs. Bathing for healing — which the Romans declared they learnt from the Etruscans (in hot and mineral springs) — is described in Chapter 14.

Bathing in the river, for cleanliness (rather than for pleasure: Chapter 13), continued and still continues — decreasing with the coming of baths and piped water into houses and the spread of pollution into rivers. There are few lowland rivers in Europe now where bathing could be encouraged — in Britain the authorities will designate no areas for river bathing.

Turkish baths came from the east, and were quite popular by the late eighteenth century. They start with a hot steaming tub, and are followed by scraping, washing, shampooing and massaging when cool. Saunas are also recommended for health as well as cleanliness. They come from the north. Heating is by water poured on hot stones, cooling is by running out into the snow — which procedure is modified, further south!

In the village of Foxton, Parker (1975) charts the change to indoor washing. In the sixteenth century there were more basins and towels belonging to houses than in the fifteenth century. And at this time there were also fines for washing clothes in the village brook. Fines would not be imposed for doing the only possible thing. Earlier, perhaps, washing in the brook was expected. (There were also fines for washing before 8.00pm, and dumping refuse in the brook.) By the late eighteenth century, rainwater butts were used for washing, drinking-water came from wells, and washing was on one's own premises. (Rainwater had of course always been available — the Romans had pipes that collected water from roofs in Malta, for instance.)

Washing the laundry in the stream has been the norm among many people over many centuries — from Nausicaa to modern Madeirans (Fig. 3.13). Madeira has a pleasant climate as well as poverty, so river-washing is little hardship! Flat washing-stones are typically used, the clothes lying on these and being beaten with smaller stones. Washing-stones were only recently removed from near a ford in the Wash Brook in Knighton (Leicestershire, England). These were five large, flat boulders, now placed on the bank with an Information Board nearby (M. Stokes, personal communication). English pictures of washing-women by streams were common in the eighteenth and early nineteenth centuries (i.e. from as soon as these were considered a proper subject for portrayal by, e.g., J. Bradbrooke and H. Ninham). The women may be on isolated reaches, on mill structures, on weirs and on specially constructed jetties and steps. The main wash in these was not being done on stones in the river but in buckets by the river, though presumably rinsing took place in the river if it was possible to stand by the water.

For use at home, washing-water like other water, could be collected from the river. In settlements the town steps were available — as they could also be for landing from boats (Figs 2.1, 5.2a, 5.6a, 10.13b, etc.).

The paths or roads from the old town centre to the river are often still present, particularly on the Continent. Even villages had these and when a village on a hill had inadequate supplies (e.g. Hoesdorf, Luxembourg; Claverton, England) there

Fig. 3.13 Laundry. a) Madeira now. b) Madeira. c) Dillengen, Luxembourg. d) Blainville, France. e) Alaro, Mallorca. f) Gozo, Maltese Islands (two still in summer use, in the smaller washplace: constant flowing water) (Also see Fig. 9.11f, etc.).

was and still is a path down to the river for larger collections of water. One use of such paths is to reach a wash-place (Fig. 3.14). The wash-place may be just an open path, or steps, or be a fully equipped wash-house, with cover, running water piped through the troughs, and separate troughs for rinsing, with water from the river, or from a tributary leading to the river. Wash-houses of this type are common on the Continent; some (particularly in western France) are still in use, others have been disused for varying periods. The drying and bleaching of river-washed clothes on riverside meadows has been described (in Chapter 2) for the Annual Wash — little washes being done at other times. In England, municipal wash-houses could be built — with pride — with the municipal baths. The Knights' Wash Place in Gozo (Maltese Islands) is still partly in use. Two of the chambers in the smaller house are still used in summer, when the weather is warm, and well-water is needed on the farm. The small stones used for beating can be seen in the picture. The wash-house, however, is fed from a spring, so it could also be classed as a fountain.

Even in the early twentieth century there could be a strong feeling that washing within the house could not get clothes clean. Turngren (1945) describes Swedish farmwives who did

Fig. 3.14 Access to river. a) Sens, France (very old). b) Reisdorf, Luxembourg (old). c) Gozo (new) (and see elsewhere).

a        b        c

two main washes in the year, one summer, one winter. There were little washes between if needed, but the wives prided themselves on having many dozens of all items, so dirty clothes could accumulate. 'Folks who didn't take their clothes to the lake or sea-shore, but were content to wash at home by the well, how could they be considered clean housewives?' The whole household took part. After washing in the lake, the clothes were soaked at home in hot water to remove any remaining soap, rinsed, wrung, hung on bushes to dry, mangled and ironed. It would take more than a generation, even with the coming of hot piped water, to change that attitude! For many of those washing in rivers, pollution also came, to stop the practice. It became obvious that the water was cleaner at home. And where the polluted state of the river was not obvious to the women, the washing-places (as at Rabat, Malta) would be closed by the public health authorities.

## Cleaning the town

And how towns have always needed cleaning! But, particularly in the Industrial Revolution, how inadequately it was often done. For many centuries in many cities refuse of all kinds was thrown from the windows to the street ('Gardez Loo', that unpleasant Edinburgh cry), there to accumulate, raising the piles of dung so that moving through the streets was difficult and dirty. Street cleaning by water-carts (barrels on carts) was frequent — as is cleaning now, by water-lorries, squirting water over the road to wash dirt to the drains. Large, solid waste must always be picked up separately. Some towns used other methods. In 1614, Hobson of Cambridge (he of 'Hobson's Choice', he kept a livery stable and let out his horses in his own order — you chose between this horse, and going without) brought, yet once more, clean water to the centre of Cambridge. He also set water running along the main streets to remove dirt and keep the town sweet and clean. Pepys, also in the seventeenth century, describes a similar system in Salisbury. Nowadays the water-lorry is still with us, and the sweeper, whether manual or lorry.

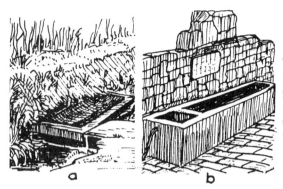

# Watering stock

'Let us graze the cold fields while the morning is fresh, while the grass is white, and the dew most grateful to the flock is on the tender plant. Then when the fourth hour has brought on thirst... command the herds to the wells or to the deep pools to drink water running in wooden troughs [then back to grazing and] give shallow water again, ...at the setting of the sun' (Livy).

Water, as well as grass, has had to be found for stock, ever since there were domestic animals. The quantities needed are considerable — 3 $l$ average daily for cows in temperate climates (plus about 30 $l$ for milkers), and much the same for sheep. Though, unlike for people, the extra water for baths and washing-machines does not have to be found!

All know well that their cars must be given liquid every 300km or so, but tend to forget that the riding and carriage horses which preceded the car also needed liquid — and at far more frequent intervals. And, therefore, water would have been provided. Where cattle, etc., were frequently moved (as in S. Guernsey), the drinking-supplies were even more numerous. Sometimes such supplies could be for both man and beast. In Corsica little 'fountains' of running water (natural course or diverted) are frequent along the rock on mountain roads. The fast-running water would remain clean.

Fig. 3.15 Drinking troughs. a) b) Guernsey. c) d) e) France. f) Menorca. g) Malta.

There can also be two-partite structures (Fig. 3.8), the people taking water not touched by animals. Usually, though, the animal-watering structures are separate from the human. Horse-troughs were necessary in towns (see Chapter 2), and some still remain. On the roads, rivers, ponds and troughs would all serve and the inns would have good supplies. Fig. 3.15 shows a range, differing in grandeur as well as country, from a chateau in France, a Knights' Palace in Malta, and lesser places.

Stock drink from streams (Fig. 2.4) — but need a gentle bank for access. When this is not available, their trampling makes an earthen bank gentle, so ruining towpaths and small flood-protection banks. This is why channelled and drained rivers are likely to be fenced off to keep out stock. Sheep prefer their water standing or slow, hence the Psalmist's 'he leadeth me by the quiet waters' (Y. Bower, personal communication).

Sheep and cattle are still seen in fields. The flocks of pigs feeding in the woods and being taken (by pig-minders, swineherds) to an accustomed place on the river for watering, have almost or quite gone from Europe. The minders were usually boys. Pigs are described as rushing snorting to the stream, bounding to the water, by Ewing (1876).

Ponds were also created for stock and travellers' horses — village horseponds and such like. Until recently British ploughs were animal-drawn, therefore field ponds were needed. In eighteenth-century England, as the land affected by Enclosure Acts increased, so ponds were made in the corners of the new fields to water the animals. Before Enclosure, land was ploughed also. Therefore, as is sometimes forgotten, it also had ponds. These old ponds were scattered along the contour. Before drainage and modern farming, heavy livestock had constant and unrestricted access to ponds in wet (undrained) land. The frequent tales of drownings in farm ponds seem peculiar in present farm conditions. However, in the past cattle-trodden mire and weeds could be over 1m deep at pond edges, so it was almost impossible, once in, to gain a footing or move. It was all too easy to sink and be sucked into the mud.

In appropriate conditions, high on the chalk with no other water source, there were also dewponds. These are shallow ponds, fed by condensation of water from the air.

Farmers pump water from anywhere not prohibited (and, perhaps, from places which are). Little pumps in streams are common sights in rural areas (Fig. 2.6 and Figs above), taking water for stock or crop. This may be ecologically deplorable, as when a remote ox-bow of the Rhône, containing a rare and fragile plant community, is pumped, with the destruction of that community (Fig. 3.7c). Otherwise-disused water bodies can be retained for watering stock, e.g. decayed canals (e.g. Thacker, 1909: North Wilts Canal).

## Waterworks

Mains water comes from somewhere and needs somewhere to be stored for irregular demand, as well as somewhere it can be cleaned — filtered and disinfected

Fig. 3.16 Waterworks. a) Folkestone, England. b) St. Joan, Menorca.

Fig. 3.17 Water towers. a) England (with pumping station). b) The Netherlands. c) Czechoslovakia.

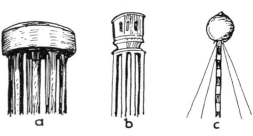

Fig. 3.18 Reservoirs. a) Wales. b) Madeira. c) Mallorca. d) France.

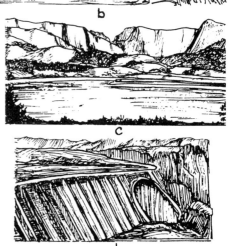

as required. Fig. 3.16 shows an English standard, old-fashioned waterworks, and one from Menorca, less renowned for having disinfected water.

Water reaching houses on hills, and upper stories of tower blocks, may be under pressure — as seen from the Defoe quote above, about London. Now it may be raised by electrical power to water-towers (Fig. 3.17) from which it passes by gravity.

Water may, of course, be supplied in other ways: the city of Reykjavik, Iceland, for instance, has volcanically heated water piped out, separately from the drinking-supply, for hot water and central heating.

# Reservoirs

Increasingly, as demand rises, water is collected in large reservoirs before being moved to waterworks or used for hydropower, etc. (Fig. 3.18). Reservoirs may be flooded valleys, in hills or lowlands, distant or near by the relevant place of demand. Such valleys are ones that can be dammed easily and will fill above the dam. Compared to hill reservoirs, lowland ones are usually in areas of lower rainfall and on land originally more populous and valuable for farming. This means they are a second-best — but now often necessary — choice (e.g. Rutland Water, England; the Eau d'Heure reservoir, Belgium).

Malta has an interesting pattern of water storage. Surface water is collected by frequent dams in the river which create small reservoirs sometimes only 50m apart (see Chapter 2), of which some will fill only with storm run-off. This water is used for irrigation, often being first moved to water-tanks or underground cisterns. While some dams are old, none, unlike many Maltese structures, go back to Roman times. Then the main cultivation was olives, which need but little water and the water table was higher. Spring and abstraction water used partly for drinking-supply may be stored in underground galleries until needed.

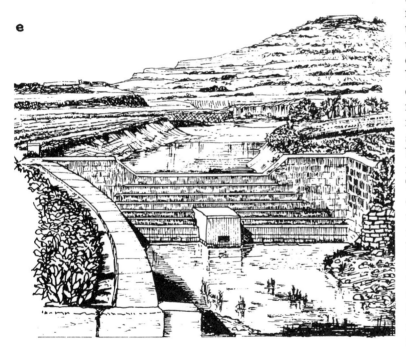

Fig. 3.18 contd. e) Malta (also see Fig. 2.8).

e

# Moving water
*(For other irrigation and drainage, see Chapter 4.)*

Much of our water is moved by underground pipes: which, not being visible above, need not be further considered here.

The Roman Empire made much use of often immense and long aqueducts. The civilisation of Asia Minor consisted of cities watered by aqueducts, and when the

Fig. 3.19 Aqueducts. a) France. b) England. c) Malta (and see Fig. 3.1). d) The Netherlands. e) Mallorca.

Fig. 3.20 Diverting water for supply (also see Chapters 2, 5, 10 and Fig. 3.22). a) Guernsey, small change of level, small earthwork. b) French Alps, larger change, larger earthwork (natural stream to left).

barbarians cut the supply, the civilisation was also cut, there being no effective water supply. Aqueducts brought water into wetter areas too. Rome and Lyons had large aqueducts; Lincoln and Gloucester used clay pipes sealed in concrete, for example. When such aqueducts broke, life could continue — though no doubt less healthily and pleasantly — using main-river and other local water.

From early to modern times open and sometimes closed channels have brought water to cities (Fig. 3.19). The older channels tend to be massive structures, like the aqueduct de la Vanne, France, and the Wignacourt Aqueduct, Malta. In a more modern Maltese aqueduct the water is in a pipe, not an open channel. These aqueducts are expected to last for centuries.

Smaller and more easily constructed open water-channels are also scattered across the land, the examples in Fig. 3.19 being from Mallorca and The Netherlands. Above-ground pipes are also used: less sightly, and of less environmental interest, except where pipes replace streams. In Fig. 6.2 the water table has been lowered and the stream channel is usually dry, but a pipe carries water along the bed.

Whole new rivers can be constructed (see Defoe's c. 30km example above, which is still in existence). And there are now water-transfer schemes, where water is moved from one river to another (with short distances of new channel) from areas of surplus, to areas of inadequate water supply (e.g. the English Tyne-Tees scheme and re-routing the Amur Darya).

Streams may also be diverted for supply. Figure 2.6 shows a stream diverted to supply a farm, and one split with a diverted channel to turn a millwheel. In Fig. 3.20 from the Alps, a channel winds along the base of the little valley on the left. On the right is an embankment with a straight channel beyond leading to a village.

When considering the moving of water, Madeira (Fig. 3.21) deserves a separate mention. There is high rainfall in the mountains, mostly in winter, but the cultivateable coast, where most of the population live, is relatively dry (900mm average annual rainfall in Funchal). The Portuguese, who arrived in the fifteenth century, constructed a wonderful system of open water-channels (*levadas*) to bring water from the mountains to the crops and towns. These may start by catching the local run-off, or by diverting it as explained above, and then run slowly down along the contours, including along precipices. Even if made now, the engineering would be spectacular! The pictures include an Alpine beginning, with a gentle downward slope collecting water well above the natural stream line. A rather lower one shows the *levada* to the right, the natural diverted stream to the left. Two show the channels passing down mountains, one on a precipice. The medium levels where slopes are less are the most likely to have footpaths beside, e.g., Levada de Serra. This eases maintenance. For the channels do need maintenance, regular cleaning by men with rakes, apart from any repairs (channelling lasts several hundred years). The system is run by the Servicio Aqua, who at the base, as well as supplying settlements, divide the water to reach every field, and run water for a suitable time to each field using a complex system of stops.

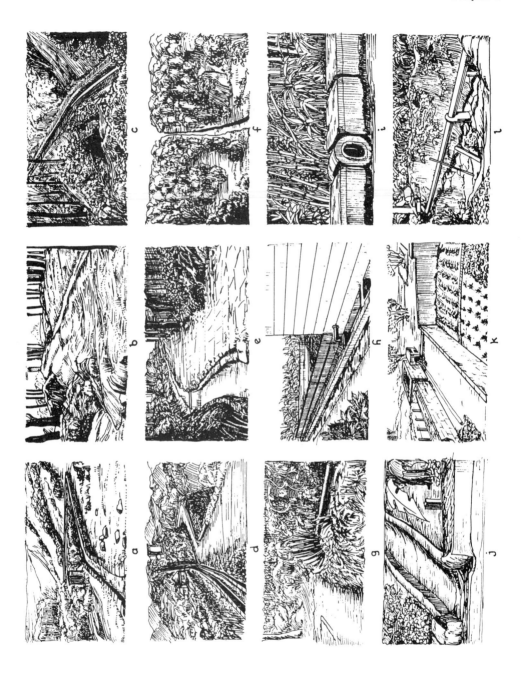

# Irrigation (Southern)

To get good crops — perhaps even three crops a year — in the warm but summer-dry Mediterranean climate needs irrigation, and a great deal of it. In France and Iberia, barrages across rivers in mountain catchments, giving reservoirs, have created a permanent source of water this century, for summer irrigation, allowing much formerly dry pasture land to give good yields. This is large-scale irrigation. Small-scale works have been done for centuries.

In Malta, the driest country considered in this book, irrigation water comes from river reservoirs (see above), direct run-off and from the aquifer below (wells, wind pumps, etc.). It may be collected in water-tanks. From the water sources, water channels run (Fig. 3.22). The oldest on the rock are Roman. Knights' channels are grey stone, now looking old. Pink stone was used in the last 200 years, and the modern ones are concrete (J. Borg, personal communication). They run on the ground, on walls, under gates and on stilts. They transport water long distances or just across the field. Movable stones or bricks allow water out to the fields at the proper places and times, and when out it can be spread around places by moving the earth (the ancient practice referred to in, e.g., Deuteronomy 11.10: 'Thou wateredst it with thy foot'). The channels may now be replaced by pipes: pipes lying on the ground to transport water and pipes with frequent sprinklers laid out across the fields. These need less maintenance.

The earth pattern managed by a mans' foot is shown in Fig. 3.23. This is labour-intensive, and where the earth and the water source can be so arranged that no manual attention is required, this, on large-scale farms, is cheaper. Such patterns are common in, e.g., S.W. Spain.

In Majorca the older irrigation by water-channel is found in only the driest parts but the sprinkler system is laid out much more widely. Disused channels are found, for example, near Mahon, in Menorca, where tourists are more profitable than crops, used channels being in good farmland further away and probably derived from well-houses.

Water-channels may now be connected to public supplies, not just to the farmers' own tanks. In east Malta, many farmers have mid-week jobs and irrigation water is supplied to them on weekends (J. Borg, personal communication).

Sprinkler systems laid in the ground are typically southern. Those spraying from above occur widely, and Fig. 3.24 shows some — note that one is abstracting from a nearby watercourse and spraying there directly, another is independent of an immediate water source.

Where water is inadequate or barely adequate, very complex arrangements can develop about who gets water when (as cited in Morton, 1938).

Fig. 3.21 The water supply system in Madeira. (i) High mountain, a) levada near source; b) levada with water diverted from natural stream to left; c) levada on precipice. (ii) Coming down, d) serving hamlet; e) main levada; f) new channel; g) replaced by pipe; h) removal for field. (iii) For the crops below, i) Servicio Aqua water control; j) channels in banana plantation; k) pattern of controlled irrigation channel, and pipes; l) pipe replacing old channel to cross road.

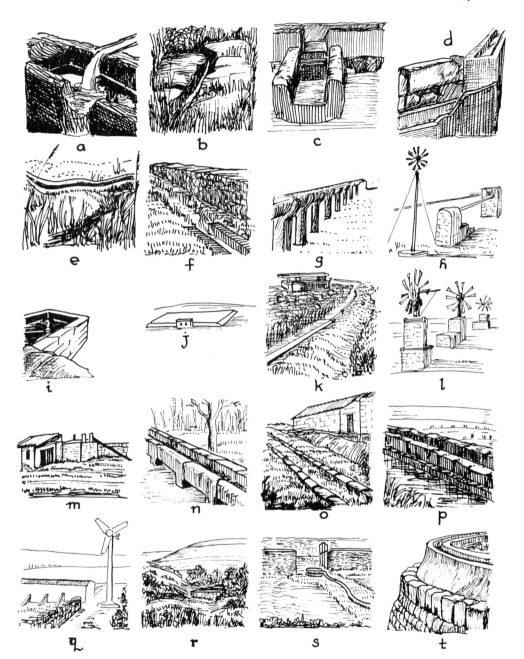

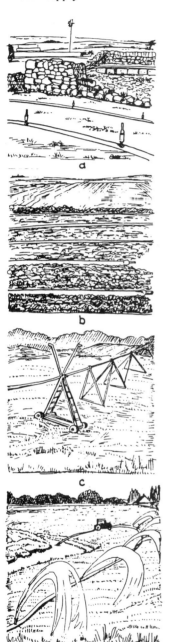

Fig. 3.23 Earth patterns for irrigation. a) manually, Malta. b) mechanically, Spain.

Fig. 3.24 Sprinklers. a) pipes laid at (or below) ground level, Malta. b) pipes laid above ground, Spain. c) large moving sprinkler, Menorca. d) movable pipe, operated by tractor abstracting from drain, The Netherlands. e) Garden sprinkler.

Fig. 3.22 Irrigation channels, tanks etc. a) Traditional N. Europe wooden channel. b)-k) Malta (and see Fig. 3.13, for on rock, 2.8 in stream bed). b) sunk in rock, c) old type, d) intermediate, pink, e) new, high-level, f) new, collecting to tank below: note goes above ground level, g) on stilts across valley, h) wind-pump leading water by pipe to tank, i) farmer's tank, j) covered supply tank, k) pipe instead of channel. l)-n) Mallorca. l) wind pump, m) farm tank, n) disused irrigation channel. o)-t) Menorca. o) disused irrigation channel, p) irrigation channel, q) wind pump and tank, r) isolated tank s) pipes, t) irrigation channel leading from well-house to storage tank.

Fig. 3.25 Moses in the bulrushes, sixteenth century woodcut.

# 4

# To Feed the Nation and Supply Materials

No religion has forbid to draw off streams... and to plunge a flock of bleating sheep in the healthful river. (Virgil)

Now boys, close off the rivers, the meadows have drunk enough. (Virgil)

The drainer is King.

## Introduction

Rivers have always supplied food and raw materials to the lands through which they flow. Crops are taken from the river itself: fish, fowl and plant, etc. The growth of crops on the land beside the stream is influenced by that stream. The river both brings and removes water. Crops grow only within a band of water regime, this band differing with the crop. (Olive needs less water than cotton, cotton needs less than rice.) Outside their optimum water regime, yields decline. Further outside, the crop dies.

Only some of the possible river crops and materials are here described, and the division is arbitrary: some of the matter is included here, some in Chapters 3 and 12. There is a vast literature on commercial fisheries, and an even greater one on drainage and irrigation. Here it is intended only to provide background to the still remaining evidences of old and of modern use.

## Fish
*(Commercial: see Chapter 13 for recreational fishing)*

### Introduction
Fish was formerly the most important food from rivers and remains not-insignificant. Fish are taken from the river itself and in ponds on, or fed from, the rivers (and in lakes, of course, but lakes are not considered in this book). River fisheries vary, from boat-fishing over any part of the river (large rivers only), at one extreme, to netting or catching fish in one particular spot, at the other. Ponds are, technically, man-made pools. It is customary to describe ancient ponds for fish of whatever size, and the large extant ponds of, say, Hungary as 'fishponds' and to use the term 'fish farm' for modern small (and intensive) pond systems, but the nomenclature is arbitrary.

Those manually engaged in fisheries have in the past often had a low social status. Rodgers (1947-8) quotes fishermen complaining that when big weirs were erected for mills, the millers caught the fish and fed them to swine 'which was against the Will of God'. However, fisheries, like other enterprises, were owned and managed — 'I own a chain of fish farms' would today be regarded as evidence of financial standing, and so it always has been. It is useful to note that in 1694 at Raglan Castle, Wales, the Master of the Fishponds, like the Master of the Horse, ate at the same table as the Lord (R.M. Haslam, 1989). All now rate the Master of the Horse high — managing the fishponds, to feed the household, at that time was just as important.

Fig. 4.1 Fishing. a) sixteenth century woodcut. b) sixteenth century tapestry, Bradford (by permission of the Board of Trustees of the Victoria and Albert Museum). c) from Haslam, 1990.

While fishponds are in private (or corporate) hands, it has usually been possible to fish the rivers, at least for coarse fish, either free or cheaply.

## River Fishing

Pictures of fishing are numerous in landscape pictures in and from the fifteenth century. Fish were caught by net (movable, fixed and hand), by paddle, by rod and by hand, by trap and by single and multiple boats (Figs 4.1 and 4.2).

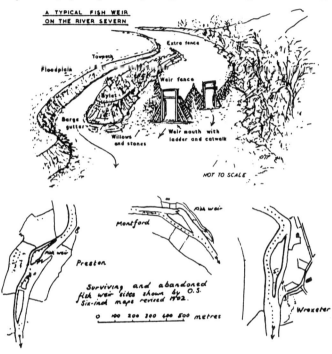

Fig. 4.2 Fish weirs, River Severn, England (from Pannett, 1981).

Weirs are thought to have originated as fishweirs, kiddles, made of stakes, with wattle or oquivalent fencing, which held up the fish more than the water. Fish were then caught either above the weir or while they passed through gaps in the fence (Rodgers, 1947-8; de Buitlear, 1985). Weirs developed — when only for fish — into more complex structures, as in Fig. 4.2 on the Severn (note the barge gutter for boat passage which was, after many disputes, enforced on the weir-owners), or into the stone Irish weirs. Disputes over these were rife, reaching major proportions in, for example, the Irish Battle of the Salmon Weir in 1014 (de Buitlear, 1985).

More common than fixed weirs were the weirs with a 10-20ft (3-6m) movable section in the middle, which was taken out for boats to pass. This was the lock — that which locked the weir. The weir raised the water level, which would be useful for millers, and in many instances mills and fisheries developed together. This is seen in Fig. 4.3, which speaks for itself. Very seldom were milling and fishing incompatible. *Domesday Book* records many of both. The site of fisheries, once established, tended to remain. Sturdy fishweirs may remain, as on the Severn (Pannett, 1981), and the beats of fisheries may remain, as on the Thames (Thacker, 1914): in the late nineteenth century the remaining fisheries near Abingdon were in their seventeenth-century bounds. Sluice-houses could be good places to fish.

Ways of catching fish varied widely. Defoe (1724-7) describes in Totnes (Devon) a dog trained to drive fish into a shove-net (hand net) at a fishweir. Salmon could be speared, with a barbed iron fork attached to a long pole. Gudgeon had special traps. Eels were abundant, and often a separate enterprise: rents, even, could be paid in eels in some places. Eel traps were consequently numerous and

Fig. 4.3 Sixteenth century German woodcut, fishing and mill.

widespread. Darby (1983) records 33,260 eels a year coming from Wisbech in 1086, and eels being used as currency in the twelfth century.

The impression thus given, of fish in a plenty inconceivable now, is correct. Until pollution and drainage spread, and better (eighteenth century) communications allowed over-exploitation, fish populations were no problem: on the Thames in the seventeenth century fish fry were sold at 1d per bushel (1d at that time buying six eggs), and sold by the cartload as food for man and pigs, to use as manure and bait, and to make beads. The complaint was not of declining populations, but that the practice deprived the poor of food. Much local fish was of course eaten locally, but even in the eighteenth century Lincolnshire was sending fish to London in wagons, in butts of water with flaps to give air to the fish, the water being changed each night. The fish were chiefly tench and pike, also perch and eels (Defoe, 1724-7).

This impression of a wide range of table fish is also correct. For instance, trout, bream, carp, crayfish, millers thumb, gudgeon, tench, perch and salmon were cropped from Hertfordshire rivers (Victoria County History, 1902-14). Salmon were over–abundant, in the opinion of apprentices and schoolboys — Hereford apprentices and Blandford schoolboys, among many others, insisted on restricting salmon to no more than twice a week. The change in the British diet is as noticeable as the change in rivers in modern times.

Crayfisheries have shown a slow decline since the Middle Ages. After the First World War there were still a few crayfishers, but crayfisheries had gone: and who hears now of a (commercial) crayfisher? (Y. Bower, personal communication.) (Sweden, though, has commercial crayfishery.)

The Welsh Taff (Mawle, *et al.*, 1986) can be cited for fish devastation. Salmon and sea trout were prolific here before the nineteenth century industrial development, valuable fisheries are referred to from Norman times, and in the sixteenth century the annual catch probably included hundreds of salmon and thousands of sea trout. Fishing was from kiddles (e.g., Fig. 4.2), coracles (small boats) with nets, by hunting on horseback — and by the poachers, dragging with hook, spearing at night by torchlight. Fishing was adequate to at least 1828 and had disappeared by 1860. Four changes occurred:

(1)   The coal mines, heavy industry (iron) and exploding population all discharged untreated waste into the river.
(2)   Weirs had been raised for the factories, without fish passes (so obstructing migratory fish).
(3)   Water was abstracted for industrial and domestic supply. This made the river smaller, and ruined spawning-grounds.
(4)   Too many of the remaining fish were removed. Sufficient numbers for satisfactory breeding populations are needed to maintain fisheries.

Any one of these four causes could have destroyed the fish — and no doubt did so in other places. When the worst of the pollution was removed, stocks improved (e.g., Edwards *et al.*, 1984, on the Ebbw) but not of course to their former level of abundance. The widespread decline of the brown trout — slow decline, so far, not widespread loss — can be attributed to too much human interference in total, and to the above factors: pollution, obstruction, abstraction, exploitation, plus general disturbance (e.g., Crisp, 1989; Giles, 1989; Elliott, 1989a, b).

Fish passes are the principal way the planners and industrialists 'do their duty' by the fish. Naturally this, partly addressing only one of the five causes of decline of fish, does only a little to help. The one concession made to nature in the river stoning of Fig. 13.5d was a fish pass. Passes are now standard fitments, reaching much complexity, e.g., on the Gudenå, Heise (1989) describes eight flights with seven rising pools, and lights and an electric screen to guide the salmonids up the 10m at the hydroelectric station. Since the ponding induced by the station floods the spawning-grounds, the fish remain under threat.

Electric fishing, poisoning and modern spear guns may all be very destructive, since fish of all kinds and sizes, not just those that are saleable, may be killed.

## Fishponds/Fish farms *(Figs 4.4, 4.5 and 4.6)*

Fig. 4.4 Medieval English village fishpond (redrawn from Beresford and St Joseph, 1979).

These were constructed anywhere suitable by castle and village, monastery and country house from ancient times (Fig. 4.4) The Romans had fishponds, and so did Saxon monasteries (e.g. Limbrey, 1983). In 1610, Norden's *Surveyors dialogue*, the Surveyor said: 'I could wish some cost to be bestowed here in making a fishpond, nay it would make two or three, one below the other ...many times also these kinds of ponds may have sufficient fall of water for cornemils, fulling [cloth] or walk mils, syth [cutting] mils and mils of other kindes.' Francis Bacon constructed fishponds (Victoria County History, 1902-14). Walton (1653) describes, from the French, the approved seventeenth-century recommendations: piles at the head of the pond, willows, etc., around it, brushwood bundles for cover, etc.; the importance of inflow from brook or rainwater; the bed substrate for different fish; and the detailed management to obtain the best taste in the fish. In their developed form, fishponds had auxiliary breeding-chambers linked by a maze of channels and sluices, and probably different chambers for different types of fish. So Beresford and St Joseph (1979) describe mediaeval English fishponds, and the description of modern fish farms is similar (for the larger ponds, see below).

However, except in areas of the larger ponds, fishponds gradually became disused. In 1838 Cobbett could write: 'You can see the marks of old fish–ponds in thousands and thousands of places. I have noticed, I dare say, *five hundred* since I left home. A trifling expense would in most cases restore them; but nowadays all is looked for at *shops*; all is to be had by *trafficking*: scarcely anyone thinks of providing his own wants out of *his own land* and other his own domestic means. To buy the thing, *ready made* is the taste of the day.' Cobbett was not the last to complain about the decadent habit of buying ready-made food in shops!

Some old fishponds are still visible (Fig. 4.5), decayed, or changed to other uses such as ornamental. In Much Hadham (England) the present fish farm (Fig. 4.6) with a cress farm in the 1940s, is quite likely on the site of the village fishponds — the earthworks are suitable. The Bishop's (and later the Rectors') fishponds could well have been where there is now an ornamental pond (Figs 9.15 and 13.3).

Fish farms have exploded in the past few decades. They may be in the stream itself, but this is a bad practice as it is too liable to pollution. More usually, water is diverted to them from the stream (Fig. 4.6). The Madeiran fish farm is built also as a thing of beauty: much to be commended. The Danes have complex and sophisticated constructions. Simpler types are found, e.g., in the Black Forest, and deserted in Malta — to cite but those illustrated.

Fish feed on organic matter and produce organic waste. In a fish farm uneaten food is also organic waste. Fish farms/fishponds may need a nutrient input, whether as fertiliser to large Czech ponds, or 'fish food' to trout farms. Pollution can be serious (see Chapter 12), but well-managed systems have but little. Even these, however, can damage a river when that is small or fragile, or when the farms are numerous (as in the Italian Alps), so that the cumulative pollution becomes serious.

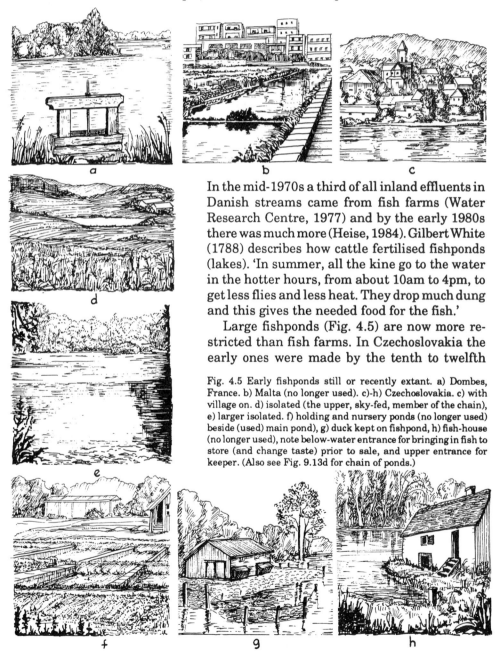

In the mid-1970s a third of all inland effluents in Danish streams came from fish farms (Water Research Centre, 1977) and by the early 1980s there was much more (Heise, 1984). Gilbert White (1788) describes how cattle fertilised fishponds (lakes). 'In summer, all the kine go to the water in the hotter hours, from about 10am to 4pm, to get less flies and less heat. They drop much dung and this gives the needed food for the fish.'

Large fishponds (Fig. 4.5) are now more restricted than fish farms. In Czechoslovakia the early ones were made by the tenth to twelfth

Fig. 4.5 Early fishponds still or recently extant. a) Dombes, France. b) Malta (no longer used). c)-h) Czechoslovakia. c) with village on. d) isolated (the upper, sky-fed, member of the chain), e) larger isolated. f) holding and nursery ponds (no longer used) beside (used) main pond, g) duck kept on fishpond, h) fish-house (no longer used), note below-water entrance for bringing in fish to store (and change taste) prior to sale, and upper entrance for keeper. (Also see Fig. 9.13d for chain of ponds.)

centuries, and most of the rest by the sixteenth; though there are some new ones, many of the old ponds have been reclaimed — those on the best farming-land. They range to *c*. 5km across and are closed with shallow dams. Early cultivation was for carp, bream, pike, perch and catfish (carp travelled well in barrels). Now, it is mostly carp and rainbow trout (Kuklik, 1989). Chains of ponds occur (Fig. 9.13d). The top pond is termed 'sky fed' and is the least likely to be fertilised. There may be breeding-chambers, etc., beside the ponds, but these are likely to be disused. Fig. 4.5 also shows a disused fish-house. Harvested carp smell of mud, and are now kept for two months in holding-ponds. In the fish-house, however, they were kept within, there being a water-door for the fish, an inlet and outlet for water — and a land-door leading to the upstairs where lived the man in charge: surely in an unhealthy and fever-ridden place. There are some 1,200 ponds in the Trebon area, and Trebon itself shows the scale of the enterprise, its access waterway, the Golden Canal (Fig. 9.13) being made for both the ponds and the town built near these ponds (the town was constructed on beech timbers in the wetland), both being fourteenth century.

Fig. 4.6 Modern fish farms. a) Merely a widening of stream, Kent, England. b) Schwarzwald, Germany. c) Jutland, Denmark (non-polluting, almost). d) Much Hadham, England — on cress bed site, maybe on fishpond site (and see Fig. 9.15m). e) Madeira.

Most are on small (natural or diverted) streams; waste and fertiliser pollute the water and when the ponds are drained every few years to harvest the fish, both high scouring discharges and polluted mud go through the streams. Since this is coupled with bank-shading in small streams, it is not surprising that little vegetation is present.

The ponds on the French Dombes plateau are generally smaller and form a simpler system. The early ones date from early monasteries, though new ponds are still being built involving considerable earthworks. They have sluices and are connected by dyke-like channels or low-banked brooks. Their fish is mostly sold to eastern Europe: the locals do not much care — the attitude which led to the abandonment of most old fishponds.

In the late 1940s and early 1950s, Hungarian fishponds were built with land improvement in mind, mainly on the edge of the Hoaobágy, where land is acid and good only for graz-

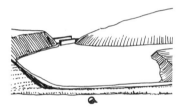

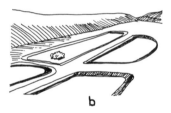

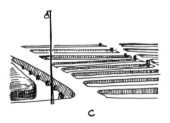

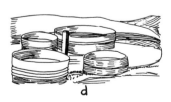

ing. The idea was to cover large areas with water for ten years, use the land after draining for rice paddies and then irrigate. Water was brought from the Tisza for irrigation, only the canals were built to take Russian irrigation barges, which by then were no longer made, and all other makes were too wide for the canal (a triumph for central planning?). Fishing was good in the run-off channels (Y. Bower, personal communication).

# Water fowl

### Swans *(mostly from Ticehurst, 1957)*

English — and indeed continental — mute swans had a special status. They were singled out from other waterfowl and their particular value meant they were retained on rivers, while other large waterfowl declined. Wild swans are territorial, so only a few occur on one river, but most live and have lived for over seven centuries in a semi-domestic state, formerly pinioned and potentially occurring in multitudes.

In England, frequent records — as for other purposes — start in the thirteenth century. By then the swan was a royal bird: meaning that, in theory, all swans at liberty belong to the Crown but, in practice, that almost all swans — except in designated areas — belonged to private owners. De Bracton included in his book on English laws the information that, 'Swans are considered ours if they have the disposition to return to us.' Unlike most other animals, the progeny of swans belonged not to the owner of the mother but to the owners of both parents, that of the father having the first pick, and one cygnet going to the owner of the land on which it hatched (for which the recipient paid a small sum, but could sell it commercially).

Swans were valued as evidence of status, for gifts, for profit (as with any other crop), for food and for, e.g., hearth brushes; swansdown was used as a trimming on sumptuous clothes and gave the name to a cloth made of wool, silk and cotton. Feathers are used for stuffing. Swans were the Christmas dinner of the aristocracy. In 1251 Henry III had over 125 for the Christmas festivities. Some idea of the numbers is shown by a 1625 quote of passing at least 2,000 going up the Avon to Salisbury.

Very complex ordinances developed for the organisation and control on the river of a crop so valuable yet so mobile. Each area had swanmasters to maintain the royal prerogative (usually ignored in practice) to preserve birds and to safeguard the rights of private owners. Swan-rolls date from the fifteenth century, and courts of swan-moot were held regularly. At the end of summer all cygnets and swans were examined and ownership established, and the cygnets marked with the owner's mark (hence cygnet/signet seals). This was the 'upping'. Disputes, including theft, were frequent: disputes both about swans and between swan-keepers and other users of the river, e.g. for opening of hatches, fishing and general disturbance. The right to keep swans was allotted by the swanmaster, in accordance either with Acts of Parliament, or with ancient usage of the common river.

Anyone could keep swans on a private pond. The swanmasters allocated ownership on the common river. Swans could be removed from the river only at the upping. Hence owners needed ponds, swan-pits, swan-houses, in which to keep all the swans they expected to use during the next twelve months. Norwich still has the remains of an eighteenth century swan pit. In Chapter 8 it will be seen that old town moats became used for swans, hence Swan Lanes. These, like other once under-used waters, were convenient for swans.

Swans look beautiful. As a crop they would have added greatly to the community value of the river. And they are very destructive to vegetation, as were the plentiful fish and other wildfowl. It is not surprising that past records of nuisance weed are few! (Also see later chapters for vegetation destruction by transport, mills, etc.)

Even now the Royal Swanherd and the Swanherds of the (London) Dyers and Vintners Companies catch and mark the young swans on the Thames, (the 'swan-upping'). Swans declined in importance from the eighteenth century and they now have little commercial use except for ornament: Stratford-on-Avon and, say, Bruges, would miss their swans. The swan populations recently declined drastically owing to eating lead fishing-weights, increasingly dropped by coarse-fish anglers. Fortunately swans are now returning (see Chapter 12). It is a dreadful example of the common phenomenon, that that which has no commercial value has no rights either. The poisoning would never have been allowed in the first place while swans were jealously guarded.

### Duck and Geese *(Fig. 4.7)*

Fig. 4.7 Water-fowl keeping. a) Czechoslovakia. b) Guernsey (and see Figs. 4.5g, 9.10i, 10.11, woodcuts, etc.).

a                                                b

Swans were for the aristocracy and the wealthy, lay and clerical. Duck and geese were for all, both low and high. They were wild, domestic and in-between (also see Chapter 10, on the Village and Chapter 13, on Recreation). They were kept for food, for bedding — goosefeather beds, eiderdowns, etc. — and for (goose-) quill pens. Quill pens were used from at least the early seventh century, and separate nibs were machine-made in the early nineteenth century. The development of the steel nib, also in the early nineteenth century, led to the replacement of the quill pen during that century (*Encyclopedia Britannica*, 1910-11). Pictures from the fifteenth century show duck, geese — and swans (see Figs 9.10i, 10.11, woodcuts, etc.). Keeping duck and geese on the river now tends to be found in more rural and remote parts: it is a relic of bygone importance. Meat was expensive, and much had to be slaughtered in autumn (because of inadequate winter feed), and preservatives were poor. Fresh fowl and fish were often preferable to expensive or partly rotten meat! Each household may have separate a duck-house for its duck. Fowl can also be kept on village and farm ponds (Fig. 10.11); Fig. 4.5 shows also a modern-type duck farm on a Czech fishpond.

Geese are the more mobile. Why else were there goose-girls? Duck tend to stay put: we do not read of duck-girls. We do, however, have Duck Lanes in villages, leading from the houses to the river. The goose girl would have been near, not always in, the village, looking after the combined flock from the village, or that of the manor. She was thus well placed to figure in fairy stories as a source of information, and a girl whom disguised princes could meet.

In the Foxton stream, Parker (1975) notes a goose-meadow, for the geese in the brook, in early times. By the fifteenth century fines were levied for allowing duck and geese to be in the brook within the village, and by the seventeenth century they were no longer allowed in the brook, pasture or meadow (n.b. pasture is grazed, meadow is cut for hay). This shows both their economic and their nuisance value, in one village with a tiny brook down its centre.

Wild waterfowl were in immense numbers. *Norden's Surveyor* supplies a standard question to be asked about fowls on the property: the Wetland ones he lists are mallard, widgeon, teal, wild geese and bustard, as well as swans. The numbers harvested seem incredible; but as they started to decline, so the birds became more confined to wetlands, such as, in England, the Fenland and Somerset Levels, and special ways of catching them were developed — in addition to shooting. Defoe (1724-7) describes the duck decoys (ponds) in the fens. They are places adapted for the shelter of wildfowl and contain decoy ducks which are taught to allure and entice wild ducks. There are channels leaving the pond, nets being at their tips. The hunter releases his dog into the middle and the duck flee to the nets. The decoy ducks are either taught not to reach the nets, or are there stroked, made much of, and fed. The big ponds need sluices, etc. to manage the water levels. Just one decoy duck produced 3,000 couple of duck a week during the season.

Shooting duck for sport should be gauged on the numbers required to maintain populations: it would have been better for populations if harvesting for food had been likewise.

The stalking-horse (Fig. 4.8) is included to show the original meaning of a phrase still in common use.

Fig. 4.8 Stalking horse (re-drawn from Rodgers 1947-8).

## Grazing by animals

Herbivorous mammals, waterfowl, fish and lower animals all graze river vegetation. Inadequate supplies of food lead to inadequate populations of the animals.

# Beaver

Beaver fur was valuable and in great demand — in Wales in the tenth century a beaver pelt was worth 120d, when marten was 24d, and otter, wolf and fox 8d (Rodgers, 1947-8). Beaver fur is water-repellant and came to be used particularly for hats, as noted in Chaucer; in Europe, it was used down to the mid-nineteenth century, when fashion changed. Beaver was also eaten, its naked tail permitting it to be classed as fish, so it could be eaten in Lent, etc., on Roman Catholic fasting-days. Unlike fish and fowl, though, beaver could not tolerate much harvesting, and soon died out. The last reliable British record was in the twelfth century. Beaver declined on the Continent also, and by the time fashion in hats changed it was becoming restricted to the remotest parts of the New World. Deplorable.

Beavers fell trees to make dams, which in turn dam ponds (in North America, often $10 \times 30$ to $80 \times 100$m). When the wood decays, the dam and pond are lost (after 10-20 years in Canada now). The ponds create water habitat (water plants, ducks, etc.), marshy margins (wetland plants, waders, grazing mammals, etc.). Beavers have been ranked next after man in their effects on rivers. Just think, beaver ponds along British streams, and any one place varying from stream to pond and back!

# Otters *(from Chanin, 1985)*

These were killed for fur, for sport and as a pest, for centuries. King John hunted otters in the thirteenth century. In the sixteenth century, they were officially pests, thought to be harmful to preserved grain, and no doubt also to fishponds, eel traps, etc. Despite this, man's impact was small until the nineteenth century, and not until the twentieth century were there laws to maintain the supply. In England completer protection came in 1978, though by 1975 few died in the hunt. In The Netherlands, in contrast, the near-extinction in the 1940s was (partially and temporarily) reversed by a ban. In The Netherlands, though, the decline was attributable to hunting and trapping.

The British decline is shown in Table 4.1. Other countries, less documented, are similar. Organochlorine pesticides, spread on the land, reached fish and land animals, which were eaten by otters. When the application of dieldrin, etc. was reduced, otter numbers improved in Wales and south-west England, places badly affected by the 1950s decline, and with a low human population. In 1979-80, otters were, in general, most where people were fewest. By this time PCBs, heavy metals and such-like had spread, and these, unlike the organochlorines, are associated with high population density.

There is a third main reason for the otter's decline: loss of habitat. There is general disturbance by anglers and visitors, more specific disturbance and bank damage by boating and by the main culprit, the 'Protectors of the Waters', the legally appointed water authorities. These like nice neat channels, trapezoid-shaped, with no trees to fall or obstruct machines. Otters, however, need cover, places to rest and make their nests and burrows. They want trees overhanging the water with good spreading tree roots (like ash, *Fraxinus excelsior,* and sycamore, *Acer pseudoplatanus.*) If the breeding sites are removed, the otters, necessarily, are lost too.

On the Continent, too, otters become sparse where people increase. Otters in Sweden suffer from heavy metals and fishnets; in France and Spain from general pollution; south Italy is bad, with pollution, bank 'improvement', fishing, hunting and gravel extraction, and so on.

To preserve the otter, the habitat must be preserved — or restored. Fortunately, the low-disturbance river with good waterside trees is beneficial to most other groups also! Otters move over ranges varying from *c.* 10km to *c.* 15km, the shorter ranges being for family groups, the longer for adult males. Nature reserves seldom cover even half this length of river. It is, therefore, the water authorities rather than the conservation trusts in whose hands the fate of the otter primarily lies; not entirely, since the otter is not confined to the river and its banks, and the land around must be adequate — and the otter's food must be safe to eat.

When otters were abundant, they were thought of poorly — from being, legally, pests, to the Bad Otter in Kingsley's *The Water Babies*. Now they are sparse, they are definitely considered A Good Thing.

*Table 4.1*
*Decline of otters, England and Wales*
*(taken from Chanin (1985))*

| | Mean number of otters found per 100 days' hunting | | | |
|---|---|---|---|---|
| | 100+ | 50-100 | 25-50 | 0-25 |
| **England** | | | | |
| Culmstock Otterhounds | | | | |
| 1900-50 | | + | | |
| 1950-57 | + | | | |
| 1957-65 | | + | | |
| 1965-71 | | | + | |
| Dartmoor Otterhounds | | | | |
| 1900-50 | | + | | |
| 1950-57 | | + | | |
| 1957-65 | | | + | |
| 1965-71 | | | | + |
| Courtney Tracey Otterhounds | | | | |
| 1950-60 | | + | | |
| 1960-71 | | | + | |
| Eastern Counties Otterhounds | | | | |
| 1950-60 | | + | | |
| 1960-71 | | | + | |
| **Wales** | | | | |
| Pembroke and Carmarthen Otterhounds | | | | |
| 1950-57 | | + | | |
| 1957-65 | | | + | |
| 1965-71 | | | | + |

# Leech

The medicinal leech, *Hirudo medicinalis*, grows in ponds and ditches. It was widely used for bleeding patients. It declined in Britain by the nineteenth century, when it was most used. The leech is now again used in medicine, for its anti-coagulant properties. It is so rare in Britain that it has to be imported from the Continent — where it has, so far, survived better. There is, however, a British leech-farm.

# Mink

These North American animals are cultivated on mink farms in Europe from which they may escape to the river. In large numbers they are destructive.

# Bees

These are not now thought of as river crop! But are so described in Virgil. Bees are to be put near clear fountains, ponds made green by moss, and shallow rivulets running swiftly through the grass (and where palms or olives overshadow the entrance). Willows should be cast across or large rocks be placed in the water, so bees can stand on them as on many bridges, and open their wings to the summer sun.

The land was wetter then.

## Sheep-washing and -dipping
*(Washing for cleanliness: dipping for medication and disinfecting)*

This is not a crop, but an animal river-use for millennia, and perhaps fits best here. Virgil describes how the foul scab taints the sheep, therefore the chief shepherd bathes the entire flock in the sweet rivers, and the ram with most fleece is plunged in the pool and, being sent away, floats down the favouring stream.

As seen in Chapter 1, sheep washing gave many place names.

Fig. 4.9 Sheep wash (from Girls Own Paper, 1887).

Fig. 4.9 shows sheep-washing in the 1880s. Practice varied. A large-scale arrangement could have a gate downstream of the reach, and two 'pulpits' opposite each other for the sheep washers to stand in. The shepherds had large toothless rakes to push the sheep from one washer to the other, then away. All the sheep of the neighbourhood could gather at one place: about 1,000 were washed per day to clean the wool, about two weeks before shearing. Simpler systems would be slower. Sheep-washing was a favourite subject of, particularly, nineteenth-century land-scape painters.

The foul scab, and other ills, still afflict sheep. Once disinfectants were available, the local pollution became severe — the pollution from dirty fleeces alone was organic, and temporary. The more sophisticated late twentieth-century biocides are yet more poisonous, and are, in Britain, now banned from the river.

## Fresh-water Pearls

These are grown in mussels, and have much declined with pollution and disturbance. As a commercial crop, they declined in Scotland this century.

## Rice

Rice, though not a river crop, requires ample water from rivers — there is slow-moving rather than stagnant, water on the paddies.

The paddies of the Rhône delta are simple (Fig. 4.10), and change between rice and dry-land crops. They are now allowed to dry out, so they are less good for waterfowl. This shows again the declining importance of waterfowl. If the bird crop was valuable, rice yield would be lowered to increase birds. Conservation is irrelevant to owners and managers.

In the Po valley, much of the drainage system is ancient and complex and the pollution from the paddies is worse here (Haslam, 1987, 1990).

Fig. 4.10 Rice paddies, Rhône delta, France

## Medicinal Plants
*(see Table 4.2)*

*Table 4.2*
*Some medicinal plants growing in or by water*

*Acorus calamus* (dried rhizome): for colic, dyspepsia; as a vermifuge, diaphoretic, slight sedative. (Probably introduced to Europe in the eleventh century: to England by 1660.)

*Alnus glutinosa* (bark, leaves): as a tonic and astringent. Once used as gargle and for external inflammation.

*Apium graveolens* (fresh or dried plants, seed): as tonic, appetiser, diuretic; for nervousness, once used for rheumatism, obesity.

*Filipendula ulmaria* (dried flowers, rootstock): for diarrhoea, influenza, peptic ulcers, gastritis, etc.

*Mentha aquatica* (usually fresh herb): for diarrhoea, etc., colds.

*Menyanthes trifoliata* (dried leaves, usually): as gastrointestinal tonic; for liver and skin complaints.

*Nasturtium aquaticum* (leafy stems): as stimulant, diuretic, antipyretic, stomachic; for coughs.

*Nymphaea alba* (usually rhizome): for sore throats, external ulcers.

*Petasites hybridus* (usually dried rhizome): for skin conditions; once as anti-spasmodic.

*Salix alba*: partial source of (pre-synthetic) aspirin (with meadowsweet) (for fever, sore throats, arthritis).

*Scrophularia nodosa* (dried rootstock, flowering tops): as poultice; for skin diseases, once for glandular and tumerous conditions.

*Symphytum officinalis* (fresh or dried rootstock, leaves): for gastric and duodenal ulcers and diarrhoea for pleurisy and bronchitis, for wounds and skin complaints, for neuralgia and rheumatism, once for fractures.

*Valeriana officinalis* (dried rootstock): for nervous disorders, colic, hypertension, insomnia.

*Veronica beccabunga* (fresh or dried plant, leaves): once for liver and gastro-intestinal complaints, externally for ulcers.

The information is inadequate for self-medication, for which see, for example, Stuart (1979), from which most of this information is extracted.

# Watercress

(*Rorippa nasturtium–aquaticum, R. microphyllum* and hybrids = *Nasturtium officinale, N. microphyllum* and hybrids).

This salad plant can be gathered straight from the brook — growing most on lowland limestone or sandstone. A good flow of cool water, as from chalk springs, is needed for the best growth.

For larger crops cress beds are developed. These vary from a widened brook, to many beds with cress of different ages, and all with flowing water (Fig. 4.11). Careful control of water is essential. When the cress is harvested the organic silt is washed out, and care must be taken not to pollute the river with it. Disused cress beds, like old fishponds, are recognisable. Recent — even if now decayed — cress beds may be on former millponds, fishponds, etc.

Fig. 4.11 Watercress beds. a) Hardly cultivated, Guernsey. b) Small-scale, Guernsey. c) Large-scale, no longer used, England.

# Willows, *Salix* spp.

(These include *S. alba,* used for tanning (contains salicylates), *S. alba* v. *coerula,* for cricket bats, *S. alba* v. *vitellina, S. decipiens, S. purpurea* x *viminalis, S* x *lanceolata, S. triandra, S. viminalis,* and various others. There are many cultivars, developed for different uses.)

Definitions vary, but the name 'osier' tends to be used for the tree, 'withy' for the thin branch cut off it — so Fig. 4.12 is a withy bed beside a stream, the branches being harvested from stools at ground level, while willow pollards, cut above grazing-level, are more likely to be called osiers with withies harvested from them.

Basketwork, ladders, fences, hurdles, binding and tying (crops for market, etc.) all required withies, and of course baskets, etc., may still be made from withies. Basketwork is found in Iron Age Glastonbury, England, and, even earlier, in Ancient Egyptian tombs.

The gleaming and golden bundles needed to be put into the stream (or other water) if they needed to be supple (Archer, 1969).

Fig. 4.12 Withy beds, Madeira.

## Alder, *Alnus glutinosa*

Clogs were made from alder, and these were widely worn by those unable to pay for shoes or boots. Clogs were not restricted to the Netherlands!

## Reeds, etc.

*Phragmites communis,* the reed, and other similar plants were used for thatching, fences etc., near wetlands and the reed is still used, now more widely with easier transport. Although reeds can be harvested from some slow-flowing channels, the main source is marshes. Reed Roofs have harsher, straighter lines than those thatched with straw. In Romania, and indeed in Africa, reeds may be used to make the whole house.

## Rushes

The Great Rush (*Scirpus lacustris*), which grows in rivers, particularly clay or part-clay ones, is very good for making chair seats and such-like (Fig. 4.13), and this and other rushes were used for strewing on floors in days gone by. (Rush-bearing Sunday, a Sunday near the festival of the saint a church was dedicated to, was when the rushes on the church floor were renewed: Brewer, 1881). Tussock sedges could be used for seating: these mostly grow beside, rather than in, the river (*C. elata* may be in channels; *C. paniculata*, the largest, is mostly but not entirely in marshes nearby).

Rush lights were much used by the poor and Gilbert White in 1778 describes their making, 'from soft rush [*Juncus effusus* or similar] growing on streamsides and other places. It is best cut in the height of summer, but a little later is possible. The largest and longest rushes are best. They are put into water at once, otherwise they will dry, and the peel not run. The peel is then removed, except for one rib, left to support the pith (two ribs make a watchlight, with a slower and smaller flame). The rushes are then laid on grass to bleach with dew and sun, then dipped in scalding

Fig. 4.13 a) Rush chair seat, Mallorca. b) Broom of Giant Reed (*Arundo donax*) and sedge, Mallorca.

a

b

fat or grease. A rush light will burn for about an hour. 800 hours of light can be obtained for 3/-, on average, and one family told Mr White that 1,200 hours [1.5lb rush] was insufficient for the year.'

Fen Sedge (*Cladium mariscus*) and other wetland plants growing in wetlands and on channel banks were used for litter, thatching, strewing, kindling and many other purposes.

## Flax and Hemp

Both crops were grown widely and are steeped in water for processing (Fig. 4.14). Retting flax was old when Pliny described the process in the first century A.D. Small bundles of ripe, yellowish flax were tied together, hung out to dry in the sun for a few days, then weighted down in warm water until the outer coat became loose. When dried, the flax was pounded on a stone, breaking the outer skin, which was then combed off by being pulled through spikes. Discarded material was used as fuel. The remaining pith was combed, separated and spun. The combing thread was repeatedly soaked and broken, as it improved with rough treatment.

Ireland, particularly in the north, has very good water for flax and there were many factories (some remaining) until the influx of cheap cotton. Malta grew flax in late mediaeval and early Knights' times, and hemp was also soaked in its marshes — the Knights considered the soaking of hemp bred fever and disliked the idea of moving to an island with such an unhealthy occupation. (Actually, although the malarial mosquito does occur in the Maltese marshes, it has never been infected with malaria.) Hemp was used for cords, ropes and sails.

Fig. 4.14 Retting flax, re-drawn from old woodcut.

## Turbary

Digging peat is from peatlands beside rivers, or in larger wetlands. The traditional use for fuel was satisfactory ecologically, not much being taken — except that the Norfolk Broads and some Dutch polders were made by peat cutting in the Middle Ages (they were flooded when the sea level rose). Modern cutting, for garden compost and, in Eire, for hydroelectric station fuel is destroying too much of now scarce peatlands.

## Crops in the River Bed

This sounds unlikely but does occur in the south, being particularly marked in Malta and Corsica. Fig. 4.15 shows the pattern better than words. Lowering the water table through abstraction and drainage has made this more possible

(Chapter 2). Depending on flow, there may or may not be a stream channel somewhere in the river bed.

Fig. 4.15 Growing crops in river beds. a) Malta, river channelled to side. b) Menorca, much-drained.

## Grazing the Banks

The grazing of river banks may be an important source of food (e.g. Fig. 4.16) for sheep. This is on a wide embankment but man-made banks are not requisite. Traditionally banks were grazed and this shape is found in the early pictures of lowland streams. The bank is trodden and firmed by stock. The dredged bank shape, typical of the twentieth century, is sharply different.

Washlands, into which floodwater is released and stored as needed, may also be grazeable.

Fig. 4.16 Grazing banks. a) Rhine near Dusseldorf, Germany. b) Grazed edge to small stream, Dorset, England.

## Bank Stabilisation

Plants from beside the river can be used to maintain the river — and are so, in natural conditions. Riverside species are the most effective and cheapest means of stabilising banks. They become inadequate only when vegetation is removed by disturbance, and this disturbance then continues, eroding the bank soil (e.g. with dense boats, livestock or tourists), at which point piling becomes frequent; or when water authority works have so altered a river that its new course can be kept only with stoning, concrete or steel banks. This is ecologically unsound, and is often also financially unsound, when the unstable river erodes these expensive banks, and they need constant replacing.

In place of stones, in well-engineered rivers, woven mats, bundles, short fences (part underwater), or firmly laid and fixed branches of woody species can be placed on the banks, which then grow, and the banks are stabilised by living, not dead, material (Lachat, 1988).

Woody species which are used in France for different parts of the bank habitat are listed in Table 4.3. Herbaceous vegetation is also used. If planted fresh, a sown mixture of short, low-productive, low-growing grasses (fescue, etc.), preferably with some wild flowers, is recommended on the higher banks. These stabilise well, will require little mowing, and will develop a diverse good flora. At the edge of the water any vegetation is better than none, but a fringe of tall monocotyledons (see Fig. in Appendix) is the most satisfactory. Just above this, in the flood zone, any vegetation other than bushy species that have shallow roots, and so are easily uprooted, is good. Banks left alone will develop suitable vegetation for the habitat — though not, perhaps (or not rapidly enough) for the water authorities who also have other requirements for the maintenance of banks and management of rivers.

*Table 4.3*
*Woody species stabilising banks*
(*From Lachat (1988)*)

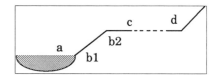

| Species | a | b1 | b2 | c | d |
|---|---|---|---|---|---|
| Acer campestre | | | * | x | x |
| Acer platanoïdes | | | * | | x |
| Acer pseudoplatanus | | * | x | x | x |
| Alnus glutinosa | | * | x | x | |
| Alnus incana | * | x | x | x | x |
| Berberis vulgaris• | | x | x | x | |
| Carpinus betulus | | | | x | x |
| Cornus sanguinea | | x | x | x | x |
| Corylus avellana | | * | x | x | x |
| Crataegus monogyna• | | * | x | x | x |
| Crataegus oxyacantha• | | | x | x | x |
| Euonymus europaea | | x | x | x | |
| Frangula alnus | | * | x | x | * |
| Fraxinus excelsior | | * | x | x | x |
| Hippophaë rhamnoides ssp. *fluviatilis* | * | * | x | x | |
| Ligustrum vulgare | | x | x | x | x |
| Lonicera xylosteum | | x | x | x | x |
| Populus tremula | | * | x | x | * |
| Prunus avium | | * | * | * | x |
| Prunus padus | | | * | x | x |
| Prunus spinosa | | x | x | x | x |
| Quercus robur | | | | x | x |
| Rhamnus cathartica | | | * | x | x |
| Ribes uva-crispa | | | | x | x |
| Rosa arvensis | | | | x | x |
| Rosa canina | | x | x | x | |
| Rubus caesius + sp. | | | * | x | x |
| Salix alba | x | x | x | x | |
| Salix appendiculata | | | * | x | x |
| Salix aurita | | | x | x | x |
| Salix caprea | | | | x | x |
| Salix cinerea | | | | x | x |
| Salix daphnoïdes | x | x | x | x | |
| Salix elaeagnos | x | x | x | x | |
| Salix fragilis | | | * | x | x |
| Salix nigricans | | | x | x | x |
| Salix pentandra | | | | x | x |
| Salix purpurea | x | x | x | x | |
| Salix triandra | x | x | x | x | |
| Salix viminalis | x | x | x | x | |
| Sambuccus nigra | | x | x | x | x |
| Sorbus aria | | | * | x | x |
| Sorbus aucuparia | | | * | x | x |
| Tilia cordata | | | | * | x |
| Ulmus carpinifolia | | | | | x |
| Ulmus scabra | | | x | x | x |
| Viburnum lantana | | * | * | x | x |
| Viburnum opulus | | x | x | x | |

* occurs naturally, but not recommended here for management.
• Intermediate host of important disease.
*Berberis:* host of rust.
*Crataegus:* host of the bacterial fire of Rosaceous fruit trees.

# Materials
## *Gravel and sand*

From wide gravel beds such as those of the Rhône, Rhine and numerous Italian rivers, gravel and sand are extracted in quantity (Fig. 4.17). This is particularly easy further south, since in summer the water contracts, leaving wide areas of dry gravel bed. This removal alters the hydraulic pattern, Chiaudani & Marchetti, 1984, recorded the fact that sand extraction on the Po deepened the river bed by 2-5m in fifteen years, which is serious for the river. And this pollutes. The wash from gravel works is a serious cause of pollution (e.g. Haslam, 1987, 1990). Further north it is forbidden to extract gravel from within the river but where rivers are embanked and have a wide gravel flood plain, as the French Arly, much gravel has been and is being extracted, as it also has been in the Lea Valley, England: where the consequent resulting gravel pits have been developed as a waterpark, good for recreation and for conservation.

Other river quarries and mines are of lesser overall importance. Gold has not been an important European river material for quite some while (not since the Middle Ages in Britain)! (Royal wedding rings are still made of Welsh gold, mined, not taken from a river.) Mud is now dredged regularly from streams over-silted by modern farming techniques. But when accumulation was less it might still be removed to improve fishing or more usefully to the village, when someone else bought the mud (e.g., Parker, 1975).

# Salt

Salt is necessary to man and beast, and there are inland as well as sea sources (former sea deposits). Droitwich in Worcestershire, Nantwich, Middlewich, Winsford and Halford in Cheshire are among the English salt-producers.

Defoe (1724-7) describes how they 'drew the brine and boyled it into fine salt'. That is clearly tiresome, and the discovery of the Cheshire deposits largely replaced extraction from brine.

# Irrigation
*(See Also Chapter 2 on watermeadows, and Chapter 3 on water-channels.)*

## Camargue, the Rhône delta

The Rhône is embanked, and the marsh developing under its influence is no longer flooded by it, which is as well. Though much cleaner than the Rhine, the Rhône is hardly perfect, and there are many fragile and interesting habitats which Rhône water certainly should not reach, as the Lònes upstream and downstream of Lyon.

The Rhône level is above that of the Camargue, and there are channels and pumps (1) carrying irrigation water (for crops: not for the rare habitats!) to the land and (2) at a lower level, carrying drainage water back to the Rhône (Fig. 4.18). Sluices and other gates regulate water effectively within this system.

Fig. 4.17 Gravel
extraction.
a) Appenines,
Italy.
b) Rhine —
extraction beyond
canal.

a

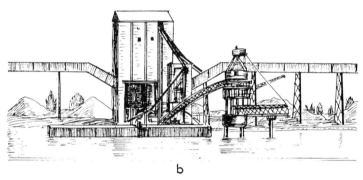

b

## General irrigation

Egypt was irrigating from the Nile by 4,000 B.C., and used the water-wheel by the
third century. Iraq irrigated in 6,000 B.C. The Po valley — very late compared to
the Middle East — had a large canal by 540 B.C. (Potter, 1981). The Etruscans were
efficient engineers and drained both wetland and wet valleys (by much hard work!
(See Fig. 4.19). 15,000 square kilometres of the Po valley are now irrigated
(Chiaudari & Marchetti, 1984).

Irrigation adds needed water. Drainage removes unwanted water. The
correct amount of water for each crop is crucial to yield. Waterlogging reduces soil
aeration and alters the chemical regime (flooding drowns the plants; see Chapter
12).

Watering in temperate Europe has traditionally been by the method described
on the Gelster in Chapter 2. Diversion channels led off along the contour, from
which watering channels ran down at intervals. Diversions would be made
regularly. Fig. 4.20 shows the pattern, a current example from Luxembourg. The
Ostling of Luxembourg has high rainfall but quick run-off, so, unlike other parts
of Luxembourg, it needs irrigation. Wherever needed, this method of watering was
widely found in Europe.

The seventeenth-century watermeadow development has also been described
in Chapter 2. Simpler systems have existed from long before —Virgil comments:
Now boys, close off the rivers, the meadows have been made to drink enough.
Floodmeadows are one of these simpler systems. They take floodwater, with its

Fig. 4.17 contd.
c) Gravel pits by
Rhône, France.
d) Pits by Lea,
England.

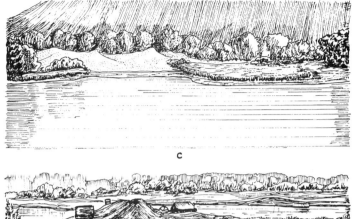

c

d

nutrient-bringing silt, when the floods happen. Because of embanking, few river floods now occur in England (which is as well, since they now bring pollution as well as silt), and because of drainage, few uprising floods occur either (that is water rising in the fields from underground). Czechoslovakia has decayed river-meadows (e.g. on Luznice). Until about 1950 these were managed. Indeed, upstream on the same river they are still managed in Austria. When social changes in Czechoslovakia meant no personal benefit accrued to those having the difficult task of meadow management, the meadows were abandoned — and now form fine semi-natural wetland!

In 1924 Hills wrote enthusiastically of watermeadows: 'therefore when the rest of the world grows dry and dusty, Hampshire valley keeps green and cool, there is movement of water everywhere during the somewhat stagnant period of late summer, and the river meadows have features which other fields lack. Fed by the water, they have thick crops in April, whilst other fields are still bare. Unfortunately, at Mottisfont the old irrigation system is falling into disuse, and many tracts which are still ridged and channelled for the purpose are no longer flooded. But above... there are still many fine expanses. Here the sheep are penned down in April, and when they have nibbled the field bare and brown, water is run in again and hay is cut in June.'

Grassland by the river has always been valuable. The wet, though, was not healthy, particularly in those pre-pesticide days. Ague (malaria) from watermeadows was considered possible in the mid-nineteenth century (Wolseley, 1987).

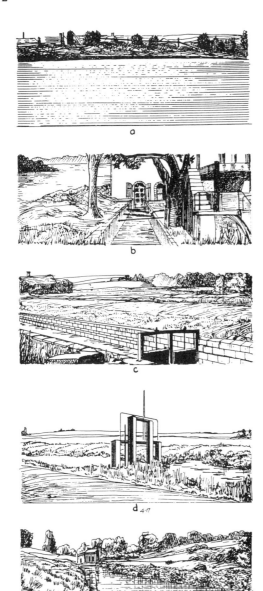

Fig. 4.18 Rhône delta drainage. a) Rhône. b) Pump from Rhône.
c) Irrigation channel, with gate (not necessarily lined). d) Drainage channel, with gate. e) Pump to Rhône.

## Drainage

The previous section, illustrating the moving of water on, and then off land, forms a fitting introduction to drainage, the removal of water.

In Europe the Iron Age people (from *c.* 2,000 B.C. to the Roman Empire) drained land. Dutch fields were divided by ditches. Etruscans reclaimed the Pontine marshes and areas of the Po valley — though there, channels of this date were neglected for rising 2,000 years: in this area mosquitoes flourished and the malaria was too much (Wolseley, 1987).

Settlements sprang up in many wetland areas, summer-grazing of winter-flooded marshes was common, as in Frisia or the Somerset Levels. Evidence of floodwater control of such early date is missing. The Roman Empire provided such control. Their developments in transport and power gave some control over water, and hence drainage: drainage of areas from the Agropontini marshes south of Rome to the Pevensey Levels in England. The climatic decline, and the

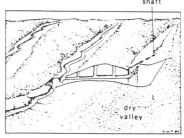

Fig. 4.19 Etruscan drainage (one method) (from Potter, 1981).

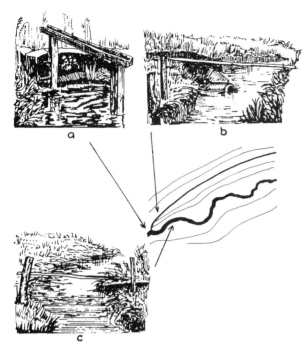

Fig. 4.20 Watering channel, Luxembourg.

breakdown of the Roman Empire led to wide late-Roman deterioration of these wetlands. After which, sporadic wetland drainage and attempts at flood protection (see Chapter 12) increased again in mediaeval times but did not become widespread and efficient until the seventeenth and eighteenth centuries when technology *and* the interest in land improvement combined to drain the land. The steam pump of the nineteenth century, so much more efficient than wind or animal-drawn pumps, gave a further impetus to drainage.

With the wetlands at least in some sense under control, interest in draining moved upwards to the lowlands: the low-lying land by the river which could be flooded (the uplands, a little away, were those lands above flood level — one traditional definition).

The prize essay by Clarke (1854-5) on trunk drainage described the river drainage that had been done, and set the future scene too. Unimpeded outflow to the sea (he says) is needed from rivers to give decent agriculture and decent life to those by the river. The great works on the Ouse, Nene, Welland and others, triumphs of engineering, are needed on other rivers (the Ribble works, for example, being useless). The Severn floods each winter and some summers, other rivers are almost as bad, and strings of floods are cited, including those of 1852, about the wettest year of the century, when a swathe of central England was flooded. Occasional winter floods enrich: longstanding water, kills. Under-drainage (tile drains or equivalent under the soil; see Fig. 4.21) is effective only when water can flow down to the river, i.e. the river level is lower than the tile drains. Active commissioners oversee wetland drainage, not that of wet valleys. Acts of Parliament in 1846 and 1847 permit the mechanism of drainage — changing and repairing ditches, sluices, river banks, river depth, straightening rivers, introducing steam pumps, etc.

Clarke describes the Nene as an example: thirty-nine locks (pound locks; see Chapter 6), eleven staunches (flash locks), dangerous sharp bends, and shoals. This is bad even for the boats: low water is too shallow; high water floods the towpath (and see Chapter 6). Mills are to be altered and improved (a few removed), the river level lowered, locks enlarged, staunches removed, back drains inserted, and the river embanked.

Fig. 4.21 Drainage. a) Under-drainage, Denmark. b)-h) Deepening and straight-ening. b) The Netherlands, c) Belgium, d) e) Eng-land, f) Germany, g) h) Sweden, (i) Stream with fairly natural channel, England, for contrast.

Clarke, unlike so many since, had a sense of balance. He describes measures to improve the Nene and its valley for millers, watermen and farmers and to improve the health of its disease-ridden inhabitants (see Chapter 12). Disputes were inevitable, but all interests were considered — and at this date river damage was still slight, so specific conservation measures were not necessary.

Under-drainage started in Britain in the seventeenth century, but decayed and was replaced by boundary ditches after Enclosure (Baldock, 1984). Subsequent field drainage had two periods of activity, starting in the 1840s and 1940s respectively, the latter under pressure of war. Regrettably the recent drainage continued until the surplus 'butter mountains' and such-like of the EEC became a scandal, and production was deliberately lowered: partly with the laudable inten-tion of preserving endangered wetland, and such habitats as wet grassland. The 1840s drainage was well survivable for the rivers (Fig. 4.9), that of the 1940s has been much more grave (Figs 4.21, 1.11). Some effects of over-drainage are described by de Buitlear (1985) on the Shannon. When floods are prevented and river level lowers, so drains run into it and the flow increases. So does bank erosion, necessitating straightening and bank-lining (e.g. stoning). Bank trees are cut down to permit machine access, storage capacity drops (because the channel is smaller), flow extremes increase, flash floods increase. Salmon fisheries decrease with the loss of deeper pools. Shady trees, nooks in undercut banks and tree roots are lost. Otters, kingfishers, etc., are affected and various plant and animal species disappear. This deplorable story must be balanced against Irish rivers being ecologically some of the best in Europe (Haslam, 1987). It emphasises again what the total loss has been. (N.b.: under-drainage is below-ground drainage; over-drainage is over-much drainage.)

'For who shall make that straight, which He hath made crooked?' (Eccl. 7.13)

Man imposes straightness on the natural variability of streams for transport, mill leats, watering-channels, supply channels for home and industry, the marking of boundaries — and drainage. Drainage now affects the bulk of lowland channels. 'Straight is man-made' is a simple (usually correct) rule-of-thumb when looking at old channels. Roman ones can still be found in Scotland, old tile drains where modern farming is again draining (Limbrey, 1983). Present valleys can be compared: the German nearby valleys of the Lippe and the Ems both have straight channels between fields, but the wetter Lippe has much more straightened larger channels (also see Fig. 4.21). The Germans were among the first to discover that over-straightening of sloping channels may be economically counter-productive (that it is ecologically so, has worried few people anywhere). It leads to over-swift flow and so to stream erosion and downstream flooding: both are expensive. The river habitat becomes deplorable, see Fig. 15.1! Figs 4.21, 4.22 and 4.24 show examples of drained and over-drained rivers, and the structures sometimes needed to maintain them.

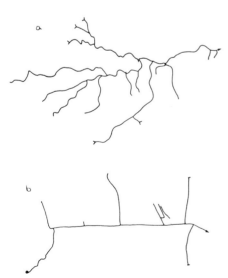

Ditching for farmland (Fig. 4.23) is needed. It is, though, deplorable that such land 'reclamation' is being done on the mountains and moorlands (particularly where, as in Scotland, the wealth and welfare of the nation does not required it). Hitherto these fragile and nutrient-poor habitats have had management on the whole more likely to conserve them. Some differences in land management are traditional. On the hills of the Scots Borders the English side is largely grass, but the Scots side has more arable land: they have much less good farmland elsewhere. In the peatlands, drainage is much more deplorable. High stocking or

Fig. 4.22 Drainage. a) Reasonably natural river, Les Landes-Gironde plain, France. b) Extreme straightening, near Laon, France.

Fig. 4.23 Ditching and brook loss. Ditching to drain, a) Luxembourg. b) Scotland. c) underdrainage, new, Czechoslovakia. d) new mountain ditching and erosion, Scotland. e) former channels being lost, Menorca.

pig units can ruin a fragile river type here (P.A. Wolseley, personal communication).

Naturally people must be fed. But to destroy a valuable natural habitat just because of a subsidy is wicked.

With the recent drainage many old ditches no longer carry water, and are being removed (e.g. Fig. 4.23) or lost through neglect. Old patterns are still traceable in many places.

There is now — at long last — some deliberate ecological improvement of rivers, which partly counteracts the still-continuing destruction.

Stream management and drainage patterns do not just depend on topography and technology. They are also cultural. A village does not say 'We are French, so round here we will have stream patterns different from those in Italy and Germany'! But it might as well do so. Given only a small area, it is easy to say 'This is Denmark', 'That, England' just on the basis of the watercourses. The Danes, unusually, work with right-angle bends and flowing water, the Germans are more ordered than the French, and the Dutch are more ordered than the Belgians. This is one of the first things noticeable on crossing frontiers. And patterns reflect history. Schleswig Holstein is more Danish than German, and the Rhine Vale is German.

Fig. 4.24 Effect of draining (shortened from Kohler *et al.*, 1989).

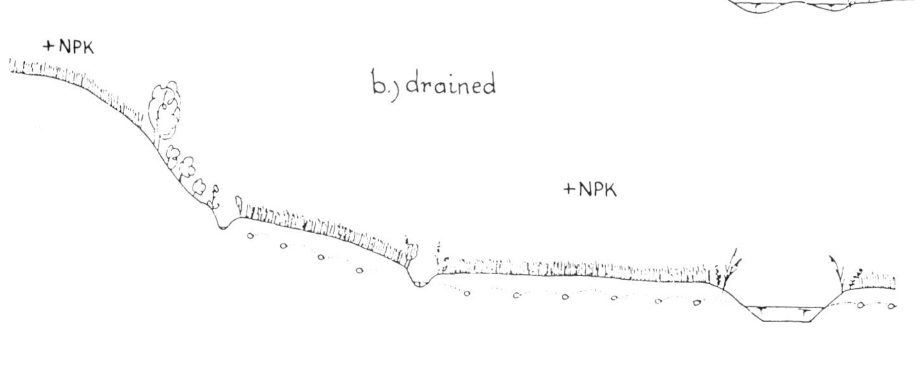

a.) undrained

+NPK

b.) drained

+NPK

# 5

# The Source of Power
## and Site of Industry

A good watermill is an ornament to a manor.

Mills, weirs and locks men do them call
That do annoy that worthy stream,
Against the law they do all stand
But still they drown those simple men.
(1585 appeal to Queen Elizabeth, in Thacker,1914)

THE BENEFIT THAT PAPER BRINGS

The mill itself is sure right rare to see,
The framing is so quaint and finely done,
Built all of wood and hollow trunk of trees,
That make the streams at point deviation.
Now up, now down, now sidewards by a sleight,
Now forward fast, then spouting up on height
As conduits cold, could face so great a heat
That fire should flame where thumping hammers beat.
The hammers thump and make as loud a noise
As fuller doth that beats his woollen cloth
In open shew, then sundry secret toys
Make rotten rags to yield a thickened froth.
Then is it stamped and washed as white as snow
Then flung on frame, and rond hanged to dry I trow
Thus paper straight it is, to write upon
As it was rubbed and smoothed with clicking stone
(T. Churchard, Elizabethan)

*[The present Wookey Hole Paper Mill, one of the two British ones making hand-made paper, and on Victorian machinery, has recently used cotton instead of rags, eliminating the early stages. The cotton is beaten to the 'froth' and the mould is dipped into it, the frame having a fine wire mesh — copper wire, sewn into the paper, makes watermarks — and the sheets are laid, dried and pressed: effectively the same process. Cotton-made paper being more durable is used, e.g. for archive and painting-material.]*

The change in industry over the past few centuries is exemplified in Fig. 5.1.

## Watermills and their development

Since the early centuries A.D., water has been the main element in the creation of (mechanical) power. The watermill, with an undershot wheel with gearing, was present in the first century B.C. (Whyle, 1962). An undershot wheel needs much water but a low head (early ones were horizontal, but vertical ones were brought to England by Romans). The overshot wheel, with the reverse requirements of less water but a higher head (Fig. 2.6) started in the fourth and fifth century A.D. Up to the late tenth century, though, the main use of mills was for grinding corn (Whyle, 1962). *Domesday Book* shows England had 5,624 mills for 3,000 commu-

Fig. 5.1 The development of mills. a) Sixteenth century, redrawn after Bradford Tapestry, England. b) Nineteenth century stream development of water-powered mill on N. England river. c) Twentieth century factory: effluent still entering river.

nities in 1086, and there were probably about 7,000 in the early fourteenth century. The Norse Sagas show their frequency further north, and de Buitlear (1985) comments on those in Ireland — frequent from the sixth century, many connected with monasteries (see Chapter 3).

Other mechanical mills (e.g. tidemills, windmills) remained secondary in importance.

Watermills needed a head of water. The fishweirs offered an opportunity — or new weirs could be made. A mill could use a whole small lowland river, and often did. It interrupted other river uses, and Clarke (1854-5) records the problem and its (eventual) solution: to dig out a new channel by-passing the mill, for the boats, leaving the mill in sole possession of the original channel. Thirdly, water can be diverted off from a river, by leats, leats going to the mill and, of course, back to the river. These are particularly common on (a) large rivers, where placing a weir across the whole was not feasible, and (b) for overshot mills. The overshot mill leat is recognisable by its height above the valley floor. The difference between the side channel cut for the mill and that cut for the boats may be less certain from signs on the ground, but on larger rivers a man-made mill channel is probably the smaller one, and in smaller rivers a boat channel must have been large enough to carry boats. (It could happen that boats used a maintained mill channel, the old stream course on the river base being too small, too obstructed, etc., and the traffic not warranting major engineering works, e.g. Fig. 6.6.) Anyway, by whatever means a head of water is created which turns the wheel and the associated sluices, leats and ponds may be simple or very complex (Figs 5.6-5.8).

The wealth of a community mill depended on corn supply as well as on water supply. The hardship resulting from the manorial requirement for tenants to take their corn to the manorial mill is often remarked upon. Less often is the complementary side given: that the mill was a major investment for the lord, of public as well as private benefit, and it had to be used efficiently in order to get a return on that investment.

Fifteenth century watermills (Fig. 5.2) have vertical uncovered wheels. Covered (enclosed) ones are safer, but open wheels continued, particularly on smaller and more remote mills, for as long as wheels turned. Small mills always

gave a poor livelihood, and large
ones with better water supplies,
working more of the time, were
more wealthy.

The pictures show that the
characteristic difference in
house shape between England,
France and Germany started
at least this early — when the
latter were the French and the
German peoples, rather than
the later countries of France
and Germany. The similarity
between the small German sixteenth century mill and that
now extant, is striking: tile has
but replaced thatch.

In Germany as late as 802
A.D., watermills were allowed
only in town and aristocratic centres. In France and England they
were also in villages and isolated places. These different cultural patterns are still observ-
able. England has numerous ex-
watermills, but more in country
and village than town, in all.
Germany does have isolated ex-
mills, but they are local, e.g.
south of Hannover and in the

Fig. 5.2 Early mills. a)
Wealthy fifteenth-cen-
tury French (by per-
mission of the
Fitzwilliam Museum,
Cambridge). b) Less
wealthy fifteenth cen-
tury French (by per-
mission of the
Fitzwilliam Museum,
Cambridge). c) Six-
teenth century poor
German mill (wood-
cut). d) Extant German
mill, similar to c).

Black Forest (Fig. 5.3). Some towns had numerous mills, e.g. on the Murg (Fig.
9.10). Many have a few (see below). Denmark differs again. Until the nineteenth-
century inwards development, the Danes looked to the sea rather than to the rivers.
They remained with the cornmills, and without the diversified industry found to
the south. Mills were never so crucial to the economy — and, consequently, smoke-
stack industry did not follow water power. Naturally there were scattered industrial mills, e.g. a papermill on the Gudenå in the Middle Ages and nineteenth
century (Heise, 1984). Present old mills are in old centres, such as Ribe (Fig. 9.14),
with the nineteenth-century ones scattered, especially in the inland development
area (Holsted, Brande, Grindsted, etc.; Fig. 5.3).

Mills were built where (1) it was technically possible, (2) the culture and
pattern permitted, and (3) the settlement pattern permitted.

The *Nuremburg Chronicle* picture of 'Ratisbon' (1495) (Fig. 8.2) shows two
mills on the town side of the Isle (see Chapter 8), and a floating mill chained to the
wall. Floating mills were characteristic of large Continental rivers. They are well
seen in a picture of sixteenth-century Cologne (Fig. 8.2). Here they are ordinarily
reached by boat, but towed in by about two dozen men, when required. In

Fig. 5.2
contd.

Frankfurt, in the same century (Fig. 8.2) there are three mills at the downstream end of the inner channel: in the place they can still be seen in German towns (Fig. 9.12). Several wheels can be seen under the bridge in Frankfurt, Fig. 8.2, which was another frequent place for a mill (and where they could be used to raise water for drinking). Strasbourg had a mill using the city tributary stream as it emerged from its now-underground channel in the city.

From the late tenth century, mills diversified: water-driven hammers to full cloth, to process hemp, to work forges. As mills developed, so the English textile industry moved from the largely manually-powered south and east onto the mightier rivers of the north and west. This trend started in the thirteenth century (Whyle, 1962) but was still continuing with the early steam-mills of the nineteenth century.

By 1450 English mills had declined by 20-25%, largely due to the slaughter of the Black Death, and the accompanying manorial breakdown. By then, however, mills were available for: tanning, laundering, sawing; crushing everything from olives to ore; powering the bellows of blast furnaces and the hammers of forges; working grindstones to finish and polish weapons, ore and gems; minting coins; reducing pigments for paint; making pulp for paper — in fact the general tool for the industry of the period (Crossley, 1981; Jones, 1963; Whyle, 1962). (The Black Death led to less manual, so more mechanical, industry.) In 1618 *Norden's Surveyor* enquires into whether, on the manor, there are customary watermills and windmills, for grist, malt, fulling, paper-making, sawing and cutting, iron furnaces or hammers (water moved the wheel which worked the bellows for the fire for smelting and trying metals). Such mills

Fig. 5.3 Mills. a) Isolated German mill S. of Hannover. b) near Wildberg, same. c) Grindsted, Denmark. d) Uppland, Sweden.

would be widely expected, therefore. (Rarer types would not appear separately in the Dialogue.)

The sixteenth century showed a great rise in productivity, in the machine production of goods.

As mills spread which put things in the water — waste from fulling, dying and tanning, for instance — so pollution spread also. Cornmills, putting nothing in the water, are clean. Since wool and hides have to be in contact with water, they dirty it. Where mills were not isolated, but in series, gross pollution could occur, as gross as any coming later — but this remained very localised, as in the Quantocks (Fig. 5.4). Bradford-on-Avon, also in the southwest, was a centre of the cloth trade by the seventeenth century. The river here was large, so had more dilution — but even so pollution must have been considerable. The city's importance faded; it remained beautiful and never became an industrial slum (Chapter 9). Defoe — and others — comment that the Avon water seems particularly qualified for the use of clothiers, that is to say, for dyeing the best colours and for fulling and dressing the cloth. Trowbridge and Bradford seem particularly good for fine Spanish clothes and the nicest cloth mixtures. Witney, near Oxford, was also considered to have a particu-

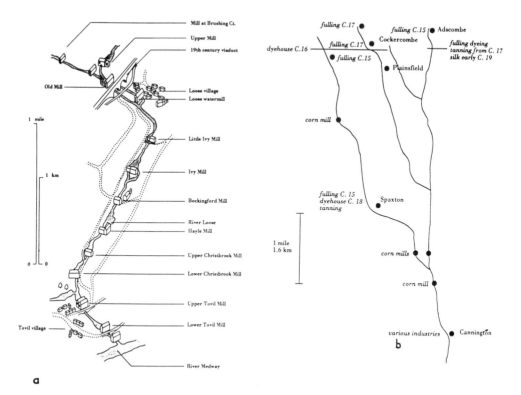

Fig. 5.4 Densley-worked valleys. a) R. Loose, Kent, England (after Reid, 1959). b) Cannington Brook, Quantocks, England (from information kindly supplied by Ms M. Siraut, Victoria County History). Note polluting industries upstream (in the hills).

larly good quality of water for textiles. So was Stroud Water, Gloucestershire. Other heavily worked valleys included the Loose (Fig. 5.4) and Wandle.

Papermills developed at Laverstoke because of the clear chalk water. The diversity of enterprises that could occur in one area was described by Defoe for the Thames by Marlow: foundries converted copper to brass and cast the brass, after which watermill hammers beat it into shape; brassmills made kettles and pens, etc; other mills made thimbles and pressed oil from rape seed and flax seed. Near-by on the Loddon, were cornmills (sending meal to London by barge from Marlow), and a papermill making newspaper. Mills could be very sparse, or densely worked. On the Rhee, about 2-3m wide (Cambridgeshire), Widdowson (1977) records five mills by one small village, in action as late as 1820, i.e. when water power exploitation was at its final height.

Non-corn mills often needed extra space, e.g. fulling mills needed to be able to put cloths in the fields (known as tenter fields), where they were fastened in shape and dried. Prosperous mills would bring workers and this could be the start of settlements and general industrialisation, as in Cornwall; Exe and Culm valleys, Devon; and Sheffield, Yorkshire (Reid, 1959). Sheffield developed the grinding of blades, which started its famous knife and steel industry, and created its wealth — until after the Second World War when these started to decay and new industry was needed.

Mills could change their use over the centuries. The mill site tended to remain, the use varied. Bull Mill, on the Wylye (Watkin, 1982) was a corn mill until the early sixteenth century, then, with the prosperity of the Avon cloth trade, started fulling. It then began weaving also, and was enlarged in the nineteenth century, doing fulling, dyeing, spinning, twisting, weaving and cloth finishing. This ambitious project ended in 1824, after which the mill spun silk instead. With industry becoming more efficient because of steam power, the mill reverted to corn-milling in the late nineteenth century. It closed for business in 1914, and was pulled down in 1920. The site is now a garden centre — with nice ponds. This illustrates the way industry was anchored to water, as long as power came from water. Businesses, particularly if in units on industrial estates, are now easily movable.

Another permanent feature was the mill's involvement with navigation (see Chapter 6) and its liability to flood the land upstream.

The replacement of manual power by water power for metal-working and the development of wrought iron started in the twelfth century in France and Spain, gradually spreading through Europe. Blast furnaces started in the fifteenth century. Central forging services could be provided for several smelting-sites (Crossley, 1981). In Camden's (seventeenth-century) *Britannia*, the Sussex Weald is noted as being 'full of iron mines in sundry places, and there be furnaces on every side for its making and fining. A huge deal of wood is yearly spent. Divers brooks in many places are brought to run in one channel, and sundry meadows are turned into ponds and waters, that they might drive hammer mills.' One such pond (not in the Weald), is shown in Fig. 5.5, together with an old forge. In both the head of water was low, though its quantity was high, and the sites do not appear healthy — for those bug-infested days. Reid (1959) comments that the blowing-houses, stampers and forges, which resembled mills in that they housed gearing and

Fig. 5.5 a) Hammer Pond, Hants., England (very large pond to left, dried mill leat to right). b) Forge on river, Dorset, England.

waterwheels, have left barely a trace apart from the many hammerponds. They needed constant and ample water supply, therefore large and extensive ponds; and much timber. Today many of these waters survive in their grandeur, a fine landscape memorial to a vanished order.

In the later Middle Ages the iron industry remained concentrated in Kent, Sussex, and the Forest of Dean: where wood (charcoal) was plentiful. When timber became more difficult to get than coal, the iron industry moved. Surface coal has always been easy to obtain but it took the invention of an efficient pump to remove water from deep levels to fuel (in both senses!) the Industrial Revolution. The South Wales and northern England coalfields, the coal seams along the north France-south Belgian borders, those of the West of Germany: these were all tapped. The coal was not used just to replace wood fuel but also to increase industry. The steam engine was able to replace the watermill (1772 saw the patent for James Watt's engine). It was more dependable (though initially less powerful). Water was still needed, for steam and processing and the mills were already there, with workers available. So the areas developed in the Industrial Revolution were those with coal and iron to hand, like the South Wales valleys, and those with mills ready for development, like Pennine valleys — for the lighter industries such as textiles. Steam powered, in the early years, was the manufacture of wool, copper paper, snuff, white lead, furniture, spun cotton, woven cloth and much more (e.g. Vince, 1970).

When power changed again, to electric-based rather than coal-based, good motor communications arrived also, allowing industry to become more diversified in both nature and distribution. The siting of industry is now not largely controlled by the placing of power and raw materials. There is always, of course, an overlap of power source when industry changes. Watermills did not become of trivial importance until after the First World War, and indeed still occasionally run (see Chapter 2 and, for Ireland, de Buitlear, 1985). Electricity was available in the late nineteenth century, but it was not until after the Clean Air Acts (1956, Britain) that smoke-stack industry really diminished.

Mill wealth can be seen by the surviving buildings (Figs 5.2, 5.6). Mills could stand alone, without houses, but by the fourteenth century Reid (1959) describes millhouses often being under the same roof as mills. In the early sixteenth century, some millers moved up to yeoman status, and their millhouses could be substantial in size and excellent in design and finish (also see Chapter 2: R. Rib).

Fig. 5.1 summarises mill development. The middle one is characteristic of the lonely mill in the wild Pennines valleys. Eventually, these became a by-word for child labour, but the isolation, originally, was just to find water power. The water power and the steam chimney can both be seen. The mill accrued wealth from water, and more from steam. The modern factory has electric power — but may (as here) still discharge to the river.

There was little change in mills from the fifteenth to the early nineteenth century (see Figs 5.2, 5.6). The head of water and the small wheel of the nineteenth century (Fig. 5.6a) are visible, and the woman is washing with no good access. This is decayed compared to a good fifteenth century mill! Fig. 5.6b is much better: as good as the good ones from four centuries earlier. Fig. 5.6c has a building on a very ancient site. In Fig. 5.6d only the arches through which the mill race has roared for centuries remain. It has been converted to a factory. The arches are (almost) diagnostic: former mill. Fig. 5.6e-g shows varied mills doing well, either on larger streams, or on small ones ponded to give a large head (Caulborne is in the Isle of Wight, with no large rivers: it was therefore worth going to much expense to provide the head of water). Fig. 5.6b and h shows show an interesting pair: the good, early nineteen-teenth-century mill and

Fig. 5.6 Mills. a) Nineteenth century, Dedham Mill, England (J. Constable, by permission of the Board of Trustees of the Victoria and Albert Museum). b) Nineteenth century, England (J. Constable, by permission of the Fitzwilliam Museum, Cambridge.

the later secondary development. 5.6i on the other hand, has not developed. 5.6j is converted to a restaurant. Mildenhall (Fig. 5.6k) has many decayed mills. They reached second-stage development, but no later use was found, whether industrial or domestic, and the town's old industry decayed. Fig. 5.6l shows a mill leat taken off upstream, running along the valley side to give the height to turn an overshot wheel (see also Fig. 2.6). The stream is left decaying in the base. Why is this for a

mill, not as in Fig. 2.2, for irrigating? Because of the large size of the earthworks and the maintenance. Mills are greedy and take a main call on the water. Irrigation channels follow the easy way.

The next series are from Luxembourg (Fig. 5.7) 5.7a on the Sure was wealthy — and needed much engineering to draw off enough water! This did not develop further, unlike 5.7b which had a smaller water flow, but is still a flourishing business. 5.7c, on the Alzette, is typical of Luxembourg architecture. 5.7d is from a small industrial village.

Scotland's northern buildings are grimmer (Fig. 5.7e-g). The owner of 5.7e, as the business prospered, built a new and better house, rather than expanding the old. 5.7f has had secondary — even tertiary — industrial development. The old wheel is seen in the tiny stream: the flourishing business is well over the other side. There is even greater development in 5.7g where the name and leat are all that remain of the old mill — a grand house for the owner, more lately the HQ offices, and factory buildings. But the same old leat runs through, its water now used for processing and effluent disposal, though not for power supply. 5.7h is a characteristic non-developed Welsh mill.

(For Denmark, see above and caption.)

Fig. 5.6 contd. c) Central France, old and new. d) Converted to factory, Cambridge England. e) Caulborne, Isle of Wight, England. f) Essex, England. g) Aberdeen, Scotland — tertiary development. h) Dedham Mill, England. i) Kent, England. j) Cambridge, England. k) Mildenhall, England. l) Somerset, England.

f                                g                                h

i

j

k

l

Two mills from France, one undeveloped, the other developed to the steam stage, are shown in Fig. 5.7i-j.

A Guernsey overshot mill and an undershot mill, both undeveloped, one working, one decayed, are seen in Fig. 2.6. The mill leat in the capital city, however, is worth extra study, it is so characteristic: a decayed watercourse and surround in the midst of a thriving city (Fig. 5.7k; see also Dorchester Fig. 9.1, Chalons-sur-Marne: Fig. 9.5).

German mills are shown in Figs 5.3 and 8.2.

Mills are sparse now in Czechoslovakia, but Fig. 5.7l shows a prosperous undeveloped country mill. Village mills are now perhaps more prominent.

## Hydroelectricity

Water is still used to generate power directly. Hydroelectric stations are the successors of the watermills in function, though they are often sited in different places (Fig. 5.8). The sites of watermills tend to remain in use as industrial estates (usually in towns and large villages, especially in Britain), factories, dwellings or restaurants. Some vanish without trace. But the writer has seen only one used for hydropower production (Guernsey, Chapter 2). The heads of water are still there — if drainers will allow their use — but the amount of electrical power wanted is so great that (barring exceptional circumstances) the hydropower stations are built new. Some smaller ones may be on old mill sites, but most are quite new, set up in high hills with fiercely-running rivers. Hydropower is most important in mountainous countries like New Zealand (forming over half the total supply: Jansen *et al.*, 1979). Norway and Canada. The isolated hill farms of Iceland usually have their own hydroelectric plants, as was frequent in larger places in the Scottish Highlands.

New hydroelectric stations are most often on rivers of high force, where little impounding is needed. Reservoir size increases with greater electricity output, and with lower water force (Skulberg & Lilliehammer, 1984). Very large impoundments are, of course, less satisfactory ecologically (Fig. 3.18). Main rivers, like the Rhine, Rhône and Danube, are also used. The head is not great, but the barrages may be fairly frequent (Fig. 6.17). The pattern is reminiscent of that of the fishweir and barge gutter (Fig. 4.2), with one channel for boats, the other for power or fish. Hydropower generally

Fig. 5.7 Mills. a)-d) Luxembourg. e)-g) Scotland. h) Wales. i) j) France. k) Guernsey. l) Czechoslovakia.

benefits boats as well, as the necessary large engineering works increase channel uniformity: which is, however, ecologically unsatisfactory. (Where not designed for boat transit, though, hydropower stations may hinder boat passage.)

Fig. 5.8 a) Small hydroelectric station, France. b) Cooling towers, France (see Fig. 3.18, impoundments, and Fig. 6.17d, hydroelectric station plus lock).

Lowland countries such as Denmark, have to manage on low heads and high volumes of water, e.g. the Tange station on the Gudenå (Heise, 1984). Reservoirs built after 1945 for other purposes tend to include hydropower stations (e.g. Czechoslovakia: Kuklik, 1984). And new hydropower constructions may also be used as reservoirs, for recreation, etc. The seven power stations on the Po are also storage reservoirs (Chiaudani & Marchetti, 1984). In Luxembourg there are two stations on the Our. The Germans use their cheap night electricity to pump water up and, by day, the Luxembourg electricity generated is fed to the German national grid, as required (M. Molitor, personal communication). France has numerous hydropower stations, e.g. nine large ones on the upper Lot alone (Décamps *et al.*, 1984), five on the Rhône downstream of Lyons, six on the Rhine. Sometimes large amounts of river water are diverted for the hydropower stations: just like mill leats, but on a larger scale. France also has many smaller stations (Fig. 5.8). Power sources are an expression of culture: France has much more nuclear and hydro energy than Britain. Smaller stations could be built on many British rivers; they are built on many French ones.

Hydropower planning forms part of natural-resource planning. Since this is a recent concept, the early hydropower stations were constructed at the site thought best for each. It was later realised that the construction of one site should not unnecessarily hinder the development of others. This concept can lead to the hydropower planning of the entire river — which is completely developed for hydropower when the tail race of one station enters the ponded reach of the next station downstream. Irrigation, flood control, navigation, drainage, industry and other uses of a river must also be planned for (Jansen *et al.*, 1979). But what happens to its conservation? Whole-river planning is necessary, but conservation should be given at least as much weight as any 'use'!

## Electricity generation
### (Other than hydropower)

Electricity generation is the largest single user of water in developed countries. About half the water supplied in Britain (three-quarters of the industrial water) is used for electricity, and a third (being 20% of the total freshwater run-off of the vast country), in the USA. As in the past, water is essential to power generation. Hydropower is one useful source of power, but cooling water is needed for all thermal power generation — coal, oil, gas and nuclear-fuelled works. All generate waste heat. The maximum theoretical efficiency is about 60% but the actual efficiency is only about 30-37%, so there is much heat to be disposed of. The heat not turned into mechanical work in turbines is lost in some other way: by water, mostly. Cooling towers (Fig. 5.8) use less water than does direct heating of the river (Langford, 1983).

Electricity generation leads to the following unsatisfactory ecological consequences:

(1)    Heat: death, distortions and distresses of various kinds, affecting both the present organisms and their posterity, and the food supply (for animals) and predators. In properly constructed stations, effects are small.
(2)    Effluents: added toxins (chlorine, etc.), and waste products from all parts of the works. Effects are necessarily varied.
(3)    Dams, and therefore, lakes: drastic alterations in discharge, in all the physical, and some of the chemical, characters. These affect river life to varying degrees, and interact with the first two factors. (A plant growing at its optimum temperature will be more likely to withstand mild pollution, or inadequate flow, for instance.)

## Mines

Mines normally use water for washing, processing (if done on site) and waste disposal (including the disposal of water pumped out of the mines). Leats are often constructed.

The Romans mined in mid-Wales, bringing water 7 miles (12km) in channels over the hills, for the head needed for winning and washing the gold. The lead mines on the Rheidol and Ystwyth had water brought from even further (Limbrey, 1983). Even earlier, tin was mined in Cornwall, and sold to the Phoenicians. Tin is still mined — a little — in Cornwall. Streams may have been straightened and lined with drystone to increase the flow for these mines, wash ore, or drain marshy ground. There were leats and, probably, overshot wheels for power (Greever, 1981).

In the English northeast, lead mining was probably pre-Roman, silver and iron being developed by the Normans, also, in mediaeval times, with zinc, copper, some barium, tin, nickel, magnesium and others. Julius Caesar referred to the mineral wealth of Britain.

Where minerals or coals outcrop or deeper seams occur, there they will be mined, technology permitting, and there they will have their structures for water use — and their pollution. Some are relatively clean, e.g. river gold (collection causes disturbance, of course). Others are very dirty. The pollution from the Italian gravel works has already been noted. Coal rivers used to be extremely dirty, with much coal dust washed in. Coal, however, though causing turbidity and discolouration, is much less toxic than many modern pollutants (e.g. PCBs, biocides).

## Other industry

Only some early industry needed more than manual power. This is a contrast to today: where is the modern office that functions without electricity? Water might be needed only for man's use, or it might be necessary for processing (Fig. 5.9).

Augsburg in the fifteenth century was a major armoury town — but (see Augsburg, Fig. 8.2) open water was available on a few streets only. Streams could be industrial and much used — see Fig. 2.5, Fig. 5.10 (Black Forest) — and be without as well as with water power. The Black Forest was a seat of clock-makers, glass-blowers and armourers.

Just before the shadow of steam power spread across the land, Defoe (1724-7) describes, in a justly-famous passage, the industry near Halifax, and the use made of water — note the channelling and control implied by the numerous streams, one reaching each house. 'Wherever we pass'd any house we found a little mill or gutter of running water, if the house was above the road, it came from it, and cross'd the way to run to another; if the house was below us, it cross'd as from some other distant house above it, and at every considerable house was a manufactory or work-house, and as they could not do their business without water, the little streams were so parted and guided by gutters or pipes, and by turning and dividing the streams, that none of those houses were without a rill, if I may call it so, running into and through their work houses.' And he describes the cloth hung outside each house. 'It is to be observed [Defoe continues], that these hills are so furnished by nature with springs and mines, that not only on the sides, but even to the very tops, there is scarce a hill but you find, on the highest part of it, a spring and a coal-pit.... Having their fire and water at every dwelling, there is no need to enquire why they dwell thus dispersed upon the highest hills, the convenience of the manufacture requiring it.' He goes on to describe that those of four years upwards are busy, in the masters' manufactury (dyeing, dressing cloth, working looms, and other activities) or at home (carding, spinning, etc.).

Fig. 5.9 Potter at his wheel. Fifteenth century (by permission of Fitzwilliam Museum, Cambridge).

Fig. 5.10 Industrial village, Schwarzwald (note laundry troughs on left) (from Haslam, 1990).

There are few remains of this type of manufacture. The little rills were presumably like those of Fig. 5.2. Industry may have moved — the village in Fig. 5.10 is no longer full of up-to-date manufacture — or it may have developed. Augsburg, the early armoury town, de-

Fig. 5.11 'Industrial Farmland' near Milan, Italy.

veloped much nineteenth century industry, with leats, etc. (Fig. 8.2, 9.10).

The Black Country of the English Midlands was, in its early industrial days, a strung-out web of iron-working villages; heaths and wastes slowly being covered by the cottages of nailers and similar industrial occupations (Hoskins, 1953). Comparable present landscapes would be the 'industrial farmland' near Milan, and the 'industrial *gheest*' of Belgium: industry in rural surroundings (Fig. 5.11).

## The Industrial Revolution

In the late eighteenth century, big mills able to harness large amounts of water power came down from hills to deep valleys (e.g. Heptonstall; Hoskins, 1973). Fast-flow mills attracted newer and *larger* mills: the waterside being for mills, dense working-class housing spread up the hillside. The first factory as we know it was built about 1720, the silkmill at Derby (Hoskins, 1953). It was only when this type of power reached the cotton, wool and iron industries that the face of the country changed. Water power needed no rest — when developed, so that the head of the water was continuous — so mills could be lit and run with shiftwork. Tall, fortress-like structures developed, their pattern limited by the constraints of water power (Hoskins, 1953).

Valley bottoms were developed, with hamlets round the new mills (the hill slopes already being settled). It was reckoned that around Ashton-under-Lyme about 100 cotton mills existed within 10 miles (16km), with new hamlets around them. There was no congestion, as the mills could not be closer than the water power would allow (Hoskins, 1953). On the Welsh Taff, for instance, weirs were reconstructed to provide water power for e.g. tin-plating works (Mawle *et al.*, 1986). Water power itself created no smoke or dirt. Only where industries used the coal directly, like the forges of Sheffield, were towns blackened, and air poisoned (Hoskins, 1953).

That damage was left for steam power. This arrived first in England: the forerunner of equivalent Industrial Revolutions in other European countries. Steam power produced dirty coal smoke. It allowed mills to be side-by-side. Power need not be sought in remote places; it was cheaper on coalfields, or where canals brought coal from coalfields. Water was still — as always — wanted in the manufactories, so the mills congregated near the rivers, on the valley bottoms. Life there was becoming unpleasant, with the smoke and the polluted river, so the masters went to live on the hills, and 'slums' (an 1820 word) developed in the valley bottoms on the land previously wisely avoided because there was bad drainage. Sewerage here was poor or non-existent. These, with factory pollution, overcrowding and bad quality housing (contrast the workers' cottages of the late eighteenth century) led to shocking conditions (after Hoskins, 1953). Once it had steam mills, the Taff valley found coal, iron and all that leads to money (Mawle *et al.*, 1986).

Housing and hygiene gradually improved, and steam power gave place to electric power, air pollution being much helped by the Clean Air Acts (British, 1956). Until the Second World War, though, industry remained mainly based on access to coal and raw materials (the German Ruhr, the Belgian Charlerois region, the English Pennines, etc.). We now consider smog and smoke a deplorable comment on a town. It was previously considered a sign of life, activity and opportunity. Mrs Gaskell, in the nineteenth century, comments approvingly on the pall of smoke hanging over Manchester. As late as 1938 Nevile Shute in 'The Ruined City' could equate the good health of citizens with the prosperity that comes with smoke.

Now, in the late twentieth century, as already noted, power and raw materials no longer determine the site of industry. It still, though, blights the environments to which it comes (wealth increases, but pollution, disturbance, and loss of field and wild land increase also). Who can withstand Progress? Bradford-on-Avon did. It remained beautiful but decayed. How far is civilisation linked to wealth?

New Industrial Estates coming to British villages surprisingly often develop on the old industrial site: the Millfield Estate (Fig. 2.4). They are not related to the river, they just happen to be put by it (compare Figs 2.4 and 2.6). Fig. 5.12 shows dwellings developed from old industrial areas — the Tannery, the Maltings, as in Tanners Quay in St Ives, now a housing complex.

The layers of different river users at Sarrebourg, France (Fig. 5.12) have to be studied to be realised! It is more complex than first appears. In the Vosges,

Fig. 5.12 Housing redeveloped from industry. a) Herts, England (note cogs and milling wheel from mill). b) Sarrebourg, France.

Abreschviller is also complex (Fig. 5.13). Its neigh-bour, Schirmeck, is more like Fig. 5.10, and also in having the stream within, not below, the village. Where there is no recent development the use of centuries is seen. Mill leats high on a hill, with housing built on the leats (for water supply and waste disposal) are seen in Bayon and Vezelise (Fig. 9.1). The water level has fallen now the mills are disused, and the previously-flooded pipes are all too obvious. The developing part of town is away from the leat.

Belgian water-based industrial development is shown in Ingelmunster and Tielt (Fig. 9.4). In the south of France, the canal at St Gilles was an afterthought — the village expanded (like Fay aux Loges: Fig. 5.13b) to use the canal. This is quite unlike Stourport-on-Severn, where the opening of the canal in the late eighteenth century quickly led to the development of this canal-based town.

The Rhine settlements show various patterns. Gernsheim (like e.g., Fig. 6.17f) is Rhine-based. The old walled village has old wharves — and industry. Mainz developed and grew over many centuries. The industry expanded. The original centre and wharf was followed by a richer and rather newer centre downstream; and a yet later centre downstream again. Each centre has its wharves and Water Street leading inland to the Square and Church (Fig. 9.11).

A quite different reason for siting industry near rivers is seen in Madeira! In this mountainous land the only flat areas near roads are where the valleys widen at the coast. These are being devel-oped with the rapid expansion of the industrial base (Fig. 5.13). An old river industry is also shown.

Town and village development is discussed in Chapters 8-10.

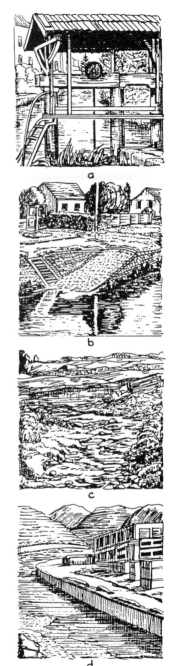

Fig. 5.13 a) Abreschwiller, Vosges, France. b) Fay aux Loges, France. c) Madeira, old industry. d) Madeira, new industry.

# 6

# Transport:
## by Land and Water

That it may please thee to preserve all that travel by land or by **water** (The Litany, *Book of Common Prayer*.)

This river Cam is current through the heart of the shire, with navigation to the sea, and is the life of traffic to this Town and Countrie (Recorder of Cambridge, to James I (Porter, 1969)).

Our island home, her rivers covered in steamboats, her roads with locomotives, her streets with cabs, her skies with balloons (Dickens, 1839).

## Introduction

River valleys are natural lines of communications, used not just by water but by road, rail, electricity pylons and migrating birds. Man uses the river bed for movement, and does so in more than one way:

(1)   *By boat,* by anything from a small coracle via a Viking longship, and towed barge, to a present-day Rhine barge (the Mississippi barges being even larger). The width, depth and type of river determine whether it is used for boats — together with boat size, and the importance of the journey (waiting for a month for water, or carrying the boat and cargo round an obstruction — portage — would not appeal to modern pleasure cruisers, for instance, even though barges may have done it regularly for centuries).
The meanings of the term 'navigation' are described in Chapter 2, section on R. Rib.

(2)   *As a road*, with pedestrians, mounted riders and carts. This can be on the river bed, or on a road developed by a river bed. (In addition, when a road has been constructed, a nearby stream may be attracted to it.) Modern traffic uses those where the road surface is separate, or is the predominant use.

(3)   *On ice.* Frozen waterways can bear skaters, sleighs (including freight sleighs) — and other less-adapted vehicles. Since winters have warmed over the last century (and other forms of communication have become available) journeying by ice has become, in middle European latitudes, an occasional winter recreation, not a main system of travel. Note, please, the loss has been from climatic change as well as from technology.

(4)   *Ways may develop along banks* — where large or significant water-courses need flood protection. Massive earthworks are often constructed. On these,

first paths then roads may speed along the country, above flood level (Fig. 6.1). They are particularly common, of course, in The Netherlands, but also occur in other wetlands and low valleys.

(5)    *For moving water and other liquids.* This can be done either by using the river channel to move water as required (perhaps with short man-made intervention channels, and perhaps with much alteration to the existing channels), or by using the position of the channel as a good site to lay pipes conveying any liquid — or gas (e.g. Fig. 6.2).

The importance of water transport has been lost from the consciousness of the British peoples. The Continent still use it and, therefore, in part remembers. Britain does neither. Her canals are used mostly for pleasure traffic. That they used to carry freight is known by many, that the freight used to pass countrywide by water, is not generally known. Of course the ports of London, Bristol, etc.,

Fig. 6.1 Road on flood protection works, The Netherlands.

Fig. 6.2 Pipes laid in channel. a) water, Mallorca. b) oil, Malta

a

are up from the sea, but they are thought of as inland extensions of the sea, not as parts of the rivers. Some notice old reference to Tudor monarchs and other Great people moving around London by boat; indeed, that Traitors' Gate to the Tower of London was reached by boat. But surely London and the Thames is a special case?

No it is not. As seen in Chapter 1, early river transport in Britain was as common as transport by land. As late as Jane Austen's *Sense and Sensibility*, furniture was, without discussion sent 'by water' from inland Sussex to inland Devon — by river as well as by sea. In Britain, water transport developed outside London primarily for freight. Before the Canal Age, travel was slow, difficult and

b

dangerous by water: difficult, dangerous and expensive by land. The increasing division of movement — people by land, freight by water — was to be expected (except in the vast wetlands of, e.g., the Fenland, where roads remained poor and there was travel by water until the twentieth century). With the advent of canals, better passenger- transport services developed and became widespread, two examples being journeys from Wigan to Liverpool (on alternate days, taking eight hours), and from Ely to Cambridge (six hours: Greenhaugh, 1980). The pleasantness of travel was more considered by the Dutch. They, of course, had early flat waterways (unimpeded by the slopes and numerous barriers of Britain caused by mills, etc.). In the seventeenth century, there were hourly boat services between Delft and Haarlem, half-hourly between Delft and The Hague, many providing special songbooks so that travellers could enjoy the time spent on the journey (Parker, 1977). The Dutch had a well-organised society concerned for the well-being, not just the safety, of its members! It is the lack of this attitude, perhaps more than technology, which led British water transport to fail, outside of, e.g., London.

River transport is ancient. The Egyptian hieroglyphic for going north is a boat. Some of the massive stones for the celebrated stone circle of Stonehenge were, it is commonly believed, brought south from the Welsh mountains by water, perhaps around 2,000 B.C. Alexander the Great was assuredly not the first to move armies by river, but in 325 B.C. he transported, down the Indus, an army of *c*. 120,000 men, including *c*. 15,000 cavalry, together with their supplies (Lane Fox, 1973).

Moving to Europe, the Etruscans made navigable canals in the Po plain by 540 B.C. (Potter, 1981). The Romans developed this technology further, and spread it through their empire. Settlements on navigable rivers grew into centres of trade, e.g. Lyons. The first canalisation of the Moselle in A.D. 58 opened the route from the Saone to the North Sea. The Romans introduced the beam water lifter (Wolseley, 1987). In Britain a waterway was developed (in 120 A.D.) from Waterbeach, in the grainlands of Cambridgeshire, to York. A canal, the Car Dyke, led to the River Witham and Lincoln, where another canal, the Foss Dyke, took the barges to the Trent, giving access to York and the north. This waterway determined the unusual town pattern of modern-day Lincoln (see Chapter 9): yet another example where the past can be read in the present.

Mediaeval times brought improvements after the post-Roman decay. In the twelfth century the Archbishop of Trier could travel to Frankfurt with a convoy of forty ships. In the thirteenth century, the army of St Louis could travel down the Rhône. Paris had the Guild of the Merchants of the Water, who controlled the river traffic (and, naturally, charged prices considered too high by those who had to pay).

Royalty — whose lives were guarded and comfortable — went by boat across Europe, e.g. Maria, the prospective Queen of Hungary, in the sixteenth century. A fifteenth-century king of Hungary (Sigismund or Zsigmond) fought against the Turks from his ceremonial barge in an unexpected battle (Y. Bower, personal communication). The boats of the Doges of Venice were splendid. The Continent retained river travel for the Great, Britain lost it, except by London. The Continent kept some freight travel on water in the Railway and Motor Ages — indeed is still increasing it. British waterborne commerce decayed.

# River-bed travel

When landscape pictures start, they show shallow (summer?) streams being used as roads, particularly in the Low Countries and England (e.g. Fig. 6.3). This seems likely to have been a usual means of transport. A telling comment on the state of the roads! They do not exemplify nature conservation either! All too plainly vegetation is almost eliminated in a stream whose natural attributes would permit high-quality vegetation. These streams are around 3-8m wide, suitable for carts, and not large enough to have over-deep water

Fig. 6.3 Stream used as road (J. Siberechts 1627-1703, by permission of the National Gallery). Detail.

Smaller streams make part of what, in English, are termed water lanes (not to be confused with Water Streets: Chapters 8 and 9). Here the roadway — earlier, the track — is wide enough for wheeled traffic. The stream is narrower, except in flood, and now flows at one side of the road (Fig. 6.4). For such streams in villages, see Figs 2.2, 9.13, etc. Most water lanes are old, but Fig. 6.4d shows a new one — in Malta, the only country studied here where new water lanes are being developed (with some doubts about flood safety!). Otherwise the water is being removed over the decades, either into little stream beds at the sides, or by general drainage.

In the south, smaller rivers often dried all summer and even in winter did not necessarily fill all the channel, and a different pattern developed. Fig. 6.5 shows a series of present riverscapes, demonstrating the stages from a riverside path to a main road beside a river. These are a developmental series in space. However, they surely represent past history, showing how *Wied* roads came into being — from path to track, lane and finally road. Many of Malta's old and non-military roads are *Wied*-developed ones (*Wieds* had public rights of way, unlike the farmland beside). Similar paths are seen within other southern rivers, e.g. the walled ones of Majorca. And in N.E. Spain summer-dry rivers may be used as roads — with a footpath, as on British fords, for pedestrians in wet weather (Fig. 6.4).

Communications are necessary; and the best and simplest way, in the conditions of the place and the period, will always win.

## Navigation

Most river travel has, of course, been by boat. River and man-made factors both affect navigability. River forces (hydraulic forces) mean that rivers tend to form meandering channels, eroding on the insides and accumulating on the outsides (e.g., as shoals). Rivers carry sediment from the land, which they deposit as the flow is checked (e.g., again, as shoals). These hindrances can be minor or major. The blocking of the outflow of the Great Ouse (see below) led to a new course — and a change of important ports. The silting of the channel to Bruges was even more serious. The city trade decayed, despite a second channel. Flows may also be too fast for navigation, as in mountain torrents. Though it is surprising, where no alternative transport existed, in what rough water, with awkward portages, boats did pass. A reminder can be seen in the better historical Western films: transport really did occur in those places, both in plains and in mountains.

The following example should be noted for its own interest and for the general point that commercial navigation was widespread on streams which most people would pass by without a thought of the possibility. Fig. 6.6 shows a navigable stream and wharf! Yet barges (small ones, obviously) came up here till the turn of the century. The wharf area is now rather decayed. Still more decayed is the stream, which has lost water. Even to the 1960s it was 30-60cm deep in summer. Dredging in 1970 reduced it to what it is now. The mill, of course, no longer functions. The pond upstream to give the head (now ornamental) is still there.

The millers, when their wheels turned, would let down more water. They could also let down water without powering the mill. These flashes of water on ordinary rivers had to be paid for by the bargemaster (this was reasonable, as the miller lost water for his grinding). Wide lowland rivers, mountain rivers with rapids, and small brooks — all would know boat transport. When necessary, the boats got through. (See Table 6.1.)

Sea-going boats came to be different from river ones. Early, the difference was more between small boats for local or small-river transport, and those for distance.

### Improving boat passage

Man can ease the passage of boats; can make the river navigable. Shoals — of ordinary sizes — could be dug out. This could be easy, or a difficult feat of engineering. When the Great Ouse near Huntingdon needed complete dredging, the water was cut off, the bed dried and a vast array of workmen armed with spades and wheelbarrows hastily removed the soil. Straightening shortened the way and helped boat passage. The people in control of weirs, mostly the millers, both

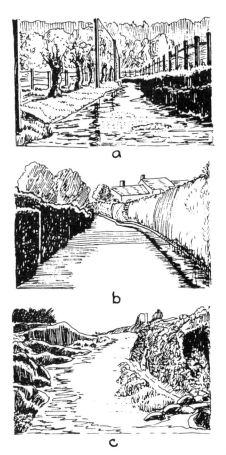

Fig. 6.4 Water lanes. a) Much Hadham, England. b) Guernsey. c) Near Rabat, Malta. d) New, near Mellieha, Malta. e) Mallorca, walled rivers. g) Costa Brava, Spain.

*Table 6.1*

*River-boats in pictures*

*(As shown in those easily available to the writer)*

**Twelfth-century (few examples)**

Mostly small (two to eighteen people), coracle or gig-type, high-ended, mostly oared, some with sail, some poled.

**Fifteenth-century.**

Varied. Boats often high-ended, merchant ships wide and rounded. Oared coracles, gigs, punts, poled punts, rafts. Sailing-ships of differing sizes (up to sizes larger than the other types).

**Sixteenth-century**

Varied. Rhine sailing-ships (which are also oared), include larger ones. Covered barges; and towing by gangs of men (prominent, though presumably not new). And as above.

**Seventeenth-century**

Similar. Proportion of barges and variety of sail, *as depicted,* increases. Poled boats/rafts with stores, and **for** local travel, still common. Water-taxis numerous in London.

**Eighteenth-century**

Similar. Horse-towed barges appear, and trains of barges. Sailing-ships decrease. Suggestion of, in general, fewer and larger boats.

**Nineteenth-century**

The more dangerous and labour-intensive practises decrease — e.g., rafts, gang-towing. Commercial boats larger. Recreation boats more obviously different. Steamboats appear. Freight and passenger traffic decrease in Britain by end of century.

**Twentieth-century**

Barges larger and fewer on the Continent (and see Table 6.2). Petrol-driven boats appear. Pleasure cruisers appear and dominate suitable waterways. Punting and rowing decrease and are mainly recreational. Passenger traffic mainly recreational.

e

f

g

hindered and helped navigation. They hindered it because the weir had to be passed. A weir — or its movable section — locks the river, that is, locks the water in above the weir. But boats had to pass through them. These structures are now known as flash-locks, as water was let down in flashes by a miller, and in the flash a boat could ride down, be pulled up or — even some way downstream — could be floated off a shoal on which it had grounded. Flashes could be organised from several mills, to arrive together, when grounding became serious (e.g. Thacker, 1914, on the Thames). This was expensive but efficient. (Interestingly, even to the late nineteenth century on the Thames, a herd of cows could be used for the same purpose. As they stood close in the stream, water could be held up behind them. When they were hustled out of the water, the resulting flash of water moved many a barge: Thacker, 1914.) The cost of the water was, naturally, a cause of resentment, and the miller could refuse to supply the flash, whether this was, as the watermen liked to say, out of ill-temper, or whether it was because millers had their own business to run, and contracts to fulfil, and had to do their milling some time, as the millers would say.

Floods also could stop barges — for up to thirteen weeks on the Nene (Clarke, 1854-5.) Horses could swim when towpaths were flooded too deep, but this was slow and limited.

The problems lessened when the pound-lock spread (it was introduced to England in the sixteenth century, but was not in common use until the eighteenth). This had two gates, impounding the water above and between them. Only the water between them was lost on upstream passage, and none on downstream passage. The loss of water from boat passage therefore became minimal. The alternative was to have channels cut around the mill, as described in Chapter 5 (Clarke, 1954-5). Lesser rivers never gained either pound-locks or diversions, e.g. the English Lark and Little Ouse, which carried commercial traffic into the twentieth century. Natural and man-made forces, particularly millers, fishermen, and livestock and riparian owners, led to rapid channel decay at all times. Passage was an adventure against the elements and men. As late as the seventeenth century, Thacker (1914) quotes an epitaph of a by no means unusual occurrence.

> Near Boveney Church a dangerous stop is found
> On which five passengers were lately drowned.  (1632)

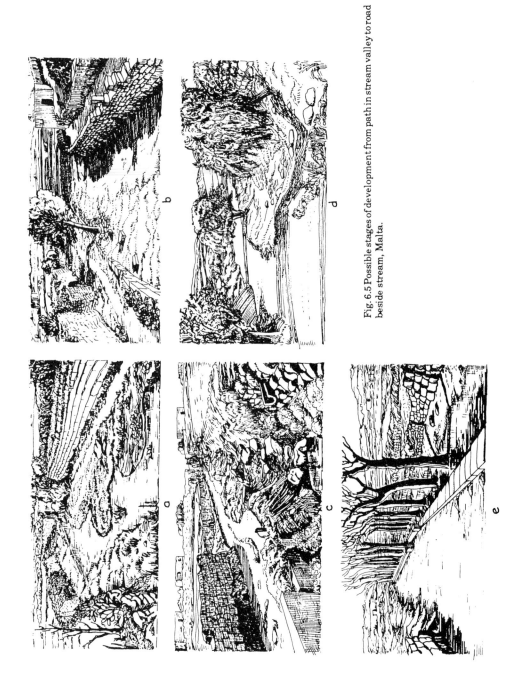

Fig. 6.5 Possible stages of development from path in stream valley to road beside stream, Malta.

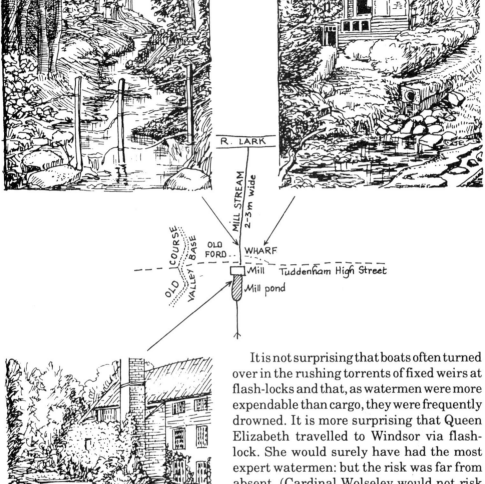

Fig. 6.6 Old barge access via Millstream, Tuddenham, England.

It is not surprising that boats often turned over in the rushing torrents of fixed weirs at flash-locks and that, as watermen were more expendable than cargo, they were frequently drowned. It is more surprising that Queen Elizabeth travelled to Windsor via flash-lock. She would surely have had the most expert watermen: but the risk was far from absent. (Cardinal Wolseley would not risk going under London Bridge. He walked round!) At flash-locks boats often plunged under water, as horses, men or engines pulled them up. Portcullis-like doors could be lifted, or vertical boards removed from the central section (Clarke, 1854-5).

Locks are needed to traverse slopes. Frequent locks enable water to be kept ponded and deep for upstream passage. Whole flights of locks could be constructed for steep slopes (as on the Kennet and Avon Canal at Devizes). Intermittent locks occur now on navigable rivers, the Moselle, Danube, Rhône, etc.

Careful control over water level and removal of shoals were needed to ensure sufficient depth of water continuously. Even in the nineteenth century on the

a

Fig. 6.7 Canal versus river transport a) late eighteenth century. Re-drawn from a print of the Duke of Bridgewater (English canal pioneer) standing by one of his canals. (Note river straightened.) b) Towing on a fen waterway, about 1830. Note damage done by tow-rope to vegetation, therefore perhaps also to bank, from low rope (by permission of the Cambridgeshire Collection, Cambridge Public Library).

Thames, Thacker (1909, 1914) records barges waiting at a flash-lock for a fortnight in ordinary summers, a month in dry summers. How much more on lesser rivers to which less attention was paid!

Next comes the question of towing. It is portrayed in sixteenth-century pictures, but more boats then and in the previous century, were self-propelled (by sail, oar, quant—that is, punt-pole) than towed. Towing needs a suitable way on the bank, and what is suitable differs greatly between man- and horse-towed barges. Towing by man (Fig. 1.8; Fig. 6.7a) took a gang of men, towing by a mast, walking well away from the river. This has its obvious disadvantages: waste of man-power, use of much space, likely hindrances to passage, etc. It has the advantage of flexibility and intelligence (people are better than beasts at dealing with new obstacles: therefore towing by beast has to be near-free of obstacles). Incidentally, it is frequently commented that the roads of the Middle Ages could not have been as bad as is reported, since the bridges were good, and the roads must have corresponded. Fig. 6.7a shows that—at least here — there was no such correspondence! Towpaths and horse-towing in Britain were mainly eighteenth century, on the rivers made 'navigable' and the specially made canals. Even so, man-towing survived well into the nineteenth century (Thacker, 1914). New and solid (technically 'made') towpaths were constructed on these new canals. On rivers where banks with paths were built instead for flood protection, as on the Great Ouse (e.g. Wilson, 1965), the

Fig. 6.8 String of barges on the Rhine, (compare present Rhine villages, e.g. Figs. 6.17f and 12.6, for fortifications and wharfs. The village on the left is a trading one).

passage of towhorses was immensely destructive; up to *c.* 1m of the banks was lost a year. The watermen saw no reason to pay for a flood-protection bank that had nothing to do with them; the drainers saw no reason why their expensive banks should be destroyed. Disputes were the norm, not the exception, among river users!

With horses, as can be seen from Figs 6.7a,b, 8.2, towing is on a flat surface (except at locks), with an easy pull. It takes less space — though more weight is put on that space, so more strength is needed on the path. Single horses could pull what teams of men used to pull — though the heaviest barges on the Thames needed six to twelve horses to pull upstream (Thacker, 1914). Towing on a path could also be from the boat itself, not the mast above. The rope, being lower, was more destructive to the bank (Wilson, 1965). Again there was a conflict, this time between the watermen wanting easy towing and those responsible for bank upkeep. Because of difficulties with riparian owners, the path often switched from side to side. Barges might carry the horses across, as on the Great Ouse (Wilson, 1965), or ferries might be provided, as on the Thames (Thacker, 1909, 1914). Barges, particularly those in gangs, might have one boat of the gang carrying just the spare horses (Wilson, 1965). Compare this with Fig. 6.9, the Rhine barge of today, carrying its car! In towns the towpath would normally be on the side opposite the main town — there were more wharfs and docks to get in the way on the main town side (e.g. Fig. 8.2, Frankfurt). This can still often be seen in towns: the path, now for recreation, is on the side away from the town

Fig. 6.9 Rhine barge, 1980s, (note car carried).

centre (e.g. Godmanchester). In the country there might be fences on the path separating property, with 'jumps' (2-3ft, *c.* 60-90cm high), for the tow-horses. Constable's 'The Leaping Horse' shows one such jump on a towpath. Other obstacles might be added. Colleges of Cambridge, through whose property the Cam ran, objected to the watermen's presence anywhere: they were an unseemly example, for the undergraduates. So they were forbidden to land. Instead a causeway was built in the river, along which the towhorse could walk, which, when the river became deeper, put yet another unreasonable burden on the watermen.

While all these improvements were going on for towing, the invention that was to abolish towing, and the fixed connection between bank and boats, was spreading. The steamboat was devised. The first paddle-steamer on the Saone was in 1783, but steam tugs did not reach the Great Ouse until nearly a century later. Now, of course, most are petrol-driven, like road traffic, and the towpaths have lost their function. That they are still firm and abundant (where not re-developed), speaks highly of the skill with which they were constructed.

Firming the banks, to resist both erosion and meandering has also been part of making rivers 'navigable'. In fact Fig. 6.10 represents the ideal commercial waterway — a straight, smooth passage, with obstacles and hindrances removed. This was slow to be achieved. Almost every stretch of bank or stream had someone responsible for it, and there were continual complaints about obstructions in streams (which were sometimes even granted as concessions by the King: Thacker, 1914) and unrepaired banks. Ancient customs applied, and sat uneasily with constant calls for better management.

Fig. 6.10 Navigation river (from Haslam, 1990).

Easier and easier passage has been not just desired, but required, by boats over recent centuries. From the Vikings to the late twentieth century, there has been a general trend from numerous small boats passing on waterways of many sizes and types to fewer and larger boats, passing on specially-constructed or specially-modified waterways giving smooth passage, restricted only by large (and safe) locks. Formerly navigable rivers may be as little as 2m wide, hardly suitable for Rhine barges of up to 1,350 tonnes! Nature conservation has benefited more than it has lost. The large rivers are worse, but the small are free from this type of disturbance, and any aquatic life in the man-made canals is a bonus!

**Recent boat traffic**
The eighteenth century was the British Canal Age, lasting just into the nineteenth century. The Continent with greater interest, continued to make, improve and widen canals (as well as the rivers), so keeping pace with commercial demand.

Waterborne transport decreased a little with the 'better' eighteenth-century roads, but decreased very much more — and in Britain was ended as a commercial force — with the coming of the railways. After very few decades, freight found found the railways better prepared. (Similarly, in the later twentieth century, freight in Britain moved largely to the roads: these, not the railways provided the service that industry required.) The Continent managed better. A network of economically viable and commercially useful waterways (Fig. 6.11) exists. France in the 1980s had over 3,000 miles of canal, and over 4,600 miles of navigable river (Wolseley, 1987). Rhine traffic, in tonnes, rose from 20 millions to 190 millions from 1900 to 1970 (Table 6.2). In 1970, about half the goods carried were building-materials, about 90% bulk cargo (Jansen *et al.*, 1979), i.e. small and more valuable goods are moved by other means. Trade is sea-orientated, therefore downstream-orientated. And downstream is where the drivers are bigger and can carry larger boats (the nearly complete trans-Europe Rhine-Main-Danube Canal sidesteps this difficulty: Jansen *et al.*, 1979). Capacity is determined by the bottlenecks: in the past by mills, shallows, etc., now by curves, bridges, shallows, terminals and canal junctions. None would be impediments to the smaller boats of the past! Locks are sophisticated, and often seats of hydropower also. When there are none of any, then navigation is determined by depth, width and flow (Jansen *et al.*, 1979).

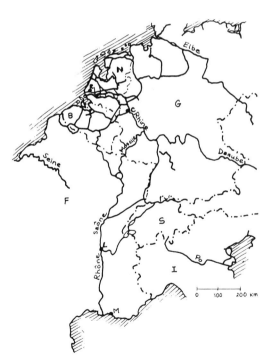

Fig. 6.11 Commercial waterways of Europe (from Wolseley in Haslam, 1987).

*Table 6.2*

*Traffic on the Rhine*

*(From Jansen et al. (1979))*

| Date | Millions of Tonnes | |
|------|------|------|
| 1900 | 20 | |
| 1910 | 40 | |
| 1920 | 28 | (post-war slump) |
| 1930 | 70 | |
| 1940 | 60 | (war) |
| 1950 | 60 | (post-war) |
| 1960 | 130 | |
| 1970 | 190 | |

The rest of this chapter singles out a few of the aspects of water transport in more detail.

# City of Venice

*(Fig. 6.12; largely from Howard, 1980)*

Venice: the city of canals. Various towns claim the title of Venice of the north, but none with justice. Venice alone has roughly as many canals as roads.

Fig. 6.12 Venice,
Italy.

Venice was built on islands in lagoons, and the canals are the remains of those lagoons. The city was constructed on conifer piling with (at least in the Middle Ages and again now) bundles of reed (*Phragmites*) between, to catch silt, etc. In the fourteenth century the city was a compact land mass. The island settlements had grown with land reclamation and come together, leaving just canals between — though the 'pieces' fitted together poorly at the joins. Even bridges are often at an angle, and streets not aligned. At this stage the city became fossilised. Modern development, industrial etc., is on the land beside, not within the city (fortunately for conservation!). Canals were filled in gradually — some even before the fourteenth century (and including one by Napoleon).

Earlier, tides were encouraged, to remove waste, debris and sewage. Now the city is protected from tides, so waste must be otherwise disposed of, and the canals must be dredged. The old water supply was from the roofs and from fountains in the squares, as usual. There are streets and alleys and footpaths along one side of many canals. The canals carried high social status: palazzos could front a canal and have a back entrance to the road.

Venice has the oldest naval dockyard in modern Europe, all properly behind a fortified access on a canal. Boatyards took the place of coachbuilders in other cities. Each market had both water access for goods, and a street for the citizens to walk to and fro. The general rule may apply even in Venice, of water for freight, roads for people! Food, fuel and trading-goods (e.g., for the vegetable market) come by boat at the present time.

The present Venetian canals are as much subject to traffic congestion and legislation as are the roads in other cities. Good waterbus services are available (with bus stops as on land) and so are taxi-boats; many citizens have their own boats, and painted gondolas are available for tourists. Add this to the commercial traffic, and the usual traffic jams and delays result.

Chioggia, to the south, is smaller and less wealthy. It still has large fish markets, and 'parking' space for residential boats. Markets again connect to both canal and road.

Other cities, like Amsterdam, Bruges, and even Birmingham, which may term themselves northern Venices, may certainly have much water — the Birmingham area has a greater length of canals than Venice. They, however, have more roads, and the life of the cities is road-based, not canal-based — as also in Amsterdam.

## The Low Countries
### *In the Fifteenth Century (Vaughan, 1970)*

The town of Bruges was expertly adapted to river-borne trade. It was a ring-canal town (see Fig. 9.4; and Fig. 8.2: Middleburg) with an outer canal for defence and plenty of canals all over for access — the number of bridges was estimated at 525. This shows the wealth of both canals and business! There were undrained marshes within as well as without the ring: not a healthy place to live in. (Now, of course, all is drained, and the town extends far outside the original ring.) At this time, in the 1400s, Bruges was more commercially active than Venice. No higher claim could be made! As seen in other ring-canal towns like Middleburg, Ribe and Strasbourg, the main canal (with a fortified entrance) leads up into the middle of the city. Bruges was in communication with all Christian countries, and at times over 700 ships sailed from Bruges each day. Minor waterways brought trade from inland, as, for instance, flax from Tielt. The Waterhalle took the ships to the sea. There were large sluicegates, acting like pound-lock gates. When the tide rose, ships sailed into the Bruges harbour. At high tide the sluice was locked. When the tide was falling, the gates were opened again, and the ships travelled out: it is said, on the same tide that brought them in. 700 ships, a rapid turnover, and the control of the tide, is extremely impressive. (Some Dutch towns, like Haarlingen, still have tidal sluices.)

Looking next at movement for war rather than for trade, when Philip the Good wished to move his army east, his officials' report shows a high degree of expertise, both in the rivers and in the organisation needed for their use in massive transporting. His officials gave him two possibilities. He could go by Italy; the main army would then assemble at and near Chalons-en-Saone. Boats would be bought to take the infantry down the Rhône and, since they could not return against the current, the boats would be sold at Aigues-Mortes, if possible at a profit (a nice touch!). Ducal carts, and artillery not fitting on the boats, must be abandoned. (Another part of the army would go by land with the Duke). If the Duke opted to travel via Germany, however, all the army was to assemble at Regensburg, on a tributary of the Danube. The bridges over the Rhine by which each detachment would cross, were specified. From Regensburg the army might go by river, taking at least a month; or by land, taking at least two months; or be divided, perhaps taking six weeks. Up to 300 boats would be needed for the whole army, each boat taking 24-30 horses, 100 men, 2 carts in pieces, and provisions and baggage for the men. It is not surprising to find five to six months needed to assemble 300 boats of such size. If five to six months was too long, 100 boats would carry part of the army (the six-week option).

# Great Ouse
*(Fig. 6.13; Darby, 1968, 1983; Faulkner, 1977; Greenhaugh, 1970;*
*Summers, 1973; Wilson, 1965)*

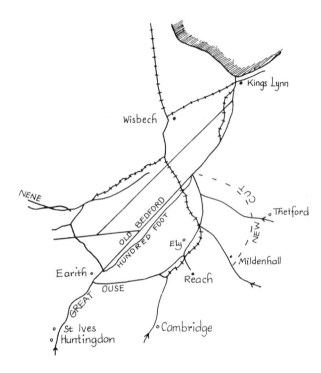

Fig. 6.13 Great Ouse (England) river plan, diagrammatic, (simplified from Darby, 1983). Hatched lines, old extinct waterways and coast line, plain lines present waterways, drained and straightened since the move of the outfall from Wisbech to Kings Lynn, except dashed line, the recent fen edge New Cut.

The Romans built the Car Dyke along the edge of the fen for transporting grain north. In post-Roman times, their waterway system decayed. Viking harbours occur along the Great Ouse, dating from the ninth century. Border posts — on the river — followed the establishment of the Danelaw in 886, (part of) the river being a military highway. The Vikings penetrated even into small and tiny brooks (e.g. Widdowson, 1977). Their docks were also used for shipbuilding and as refuges in war and from floods.

The old course of the river led through Wisbech to an outfall in the Wash. As for all great rivers, Government constantly pressed for navigability, while locally there was an equally constant heightening of weirs for mills and fisheries — which hindered the passage of boats. Sea-going boats came up river especially to the Great Fairs, held annually — at Reach, Cambridge, St Ives and elsewhere. Reach was a decayed Roman port, becoming the principal port for Cambridge at least by the twelfth century. It was given a charter by King John in the thirteenth century. Reach is now much decayed again — to put it mildly! At the height of its prosperity it had seven churches. The fair received boats from all the east-facing Continental trading-ports, both sea and river. Boats came from the Hanseatic ports, the Elbe and the Rhine, from Bruges and Rouen and further afield. Cambridge's Stourbridge Fair in the fifteenth century sold timber from the Baltic, silks from Italy, and iron from Spain (Darby, 1968). Now Reach is a fen village, away from anywhere (i.e. no main roads or railways), though with larger open spaces than one would expect for its size.

The end of the thirteenth century saw the first significant change. Silting of the Wisbech estuary diverted the river to Kings Lynn. This and the engineering works it made necessary much improved the access to the main towns like Cambridge on the Cam and Thetford on the Little Ouse. Luxury and necessary goods came up by river, though the Ouse was blocked by mills above St Ives, where portages were necessary. The continual disputes between the various river users can be imagined.

In the fourteenth century, the Ely rolls show constant water transport, bringing cloth, wax, tallow and lead, etc., from (Kings) Lynn and Boston, and for transacting everyday business. Stone came from near Peterborough (Darby, 1968).

Denver sluice was erected in 1650-2. This blocked access upstream to all but the smallest sea-going vessels, and most goods had to be transhipped to (what developed into) the Fen Lighters, barges derived from the Viking longboats. The sluice was part of the scheme to drain the fens, but the hindrance to boat trade — and such important trade it had been, too — was great.

Staunches, that is, structures with two channels (either a weir and a single gate, or two single gates, each flash- not pound-locks), became common in the seventeenth and eighteenth centuries.

The drainers provided a towpath, but some time passed before agreement was reached on payment (see above). The unfortunate watermen suffered again — every other man's hand seemed against them, on site, whatever Central Government might say! The eighteenth-century towpaths were good from the start, though owing to difficulties with riparian owners, they varied from side to side of the river. Sails and quanting could aid passage. Masts had to be high and sails big to catch the wind above the banks and trees.

In the eighteenth century, the constant difficulty of trans-shipment at Denver sluice was telling, in the decline of foreign trade. The sluice itself broke in 1715. Boat size, though, was increasing as the main river passage became smoother (though far from perfect, staunches were a great improvement on mill locks). In 1649, 40-ton boats came to Cambridge (which had a large river) 10-chaldron (12.7 ton) ones to Thetford and Mildenhall (which had smaller rivers). In the early eighteenth century the river was worse; 40-ton boats had to stop before Cambridge. After the rebuilding of Denver Sluice in 1749, though, 130-ton lighters were possible.

Down the centuries there were constant complaints about obstructions, whether mills, sandbanks, or the 'hards' (gravel places used as fords). Hards held up the water between them, so aiding navigation, but were difficult to cross; the Ely ones, for example, were over 260 yards (about 200m) long. Deepening the river was a constant call. The speed of silting-up increased when the nineteenth-century sewage explosion reached the rivers.

In the eighteenth century, regular passenger-boat services were established connecting Ely, Cambridge, Kings Lynn, Huntingdon, etc. The rivers were very busy — anglers near Bedford complained that constant barge traffic ruined the fishing; indeed in 1710 there were 3,000 barges in the spring quarter alone, downstream of Huntingdon, and a similar number (11,725 for the year) in the lower river in 1713.

1832, another significant date, saw the start of the last great reconstruction of the river for navigation: the last, as within two decades railways were attracting trade from the river. In 1849 the horse-drawn packet boat was replaced by a steamer. Extensive fleets of lighter boats continued until the late nineteenth century. The total incoming supplies to the towns increased — but an increasing proportion came by land. Now, in the late twentieth century, the lower river is again busy, in numbers busier than ever before. But this is leisure traffic. Apart from maintenance boats, commercial or industrial barges are sparse in the extreme.

## The Middle Loire and Seine
### *(Fig. 6.14)*

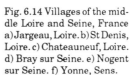

These rivers are two of the great French waterways, navigable down history. The difference is that the middle Seine is still a busy commercial highway which can hardly be said of the Loire. The pictures show why. Although the Seine traffic has decreased from villages like Bray (which now have unused space by the river in their centres) the Seine is busy. New industries, not just old ones, are sited on it — and are on it to use the river. There is use and redevelopment — the newer industry has

Fig. 6.14 Villages of the middle Loire and Seine, France a) Jargeau, Loire. b) St Denis, Loire. c) Chateauneuf, Loire. d) Bray sur Seine. e) Nogent sur Seine. f) Yonne, Sens.

moved away from the centre and old wharf. It wants more space, so it has gone to the edge of town.)

Contrast this with the Loire villages. Here there is decay. Why? It is not because boats pass by and no longer stop. On the contrary, the river itself is here not suitable for large barges. The answer is to be found by looking at the wharfs and houses or the map. The Loire is hill-rising, with storm flows and overall fiercer flow than the Seine. Levels are liable to rise. Navigation is more difficult and rail and road became more attractive for moving goods.

## The Essex Stour
*(Fig. 6.15)*

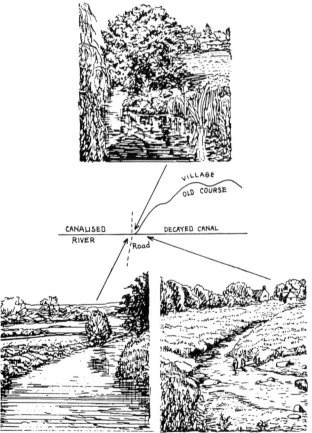

Fig. 6.15 Stour Canal (Essex, England).

This, like the part of the Loire illustrated above, is a different type of decaying navigation. Commercial traffic, though, was not much until after the 1705 Navigation Act. The Loire was always a main highway, and this shows even in the decayed villages (which unlike, say, Orléans, were not ports of any consequence).

At the head of the Stour canal, Sudbury is an eighteenth-century main canal port; small, but important. The waterway and towpath are still good and continue good some way downstream, except that the towpath is lost to farmland. By Fig. 6.15, though, just below a weir, the canal is lost.

At the village of Nayland the old course (that is, the river) runs by the village: it was a river village, but was cut off by the canal (cf. villages losing their livelihood to by–passing railways or major roads in later times). The new course looks most peculiar. It is near-straight, so man-made, and it is small. Clearly it has been altered: and from what was the canal. The canal is still lost at Higham, but is found again at Stratford St Mary, near the base. This village is partly on the river, partly not. Dedham Mill (Fig. 5.6) has already been illustrated: the canal construction is still evident above the mill lock. Part of the canalised river and associated structures is left, part has gone.

## The Thames by London
### *(Fig. 6.16)*

This has continued to be a normal and fashionable waterway unlike other British rivers. Indeed a jetfoil river-bus service has recently begun, running from Chelsea harbour to Greenwich at 15-minute intervals: as in the ancient past, travel by river is much quicker than any other cross-London transport.

London was the major English port from Roman times. 'London' was two cities: London proper, the merchant centre, downstream; and Westminster, the seat of government (as it became). Thames-linked Royal seats included Nonesuch, The Tower, Whitehall, Hampton Court and Windsor Castle.

River processions occurred on state occasions (also see Chapter 13). King John and the barons went to Runnymede by barge to sign Magna Carta in 1215 (Rodgers, 1947-8). Royalty came to the Tower by barge to inaugurate their reigns. Henry VII's Queen, Elizabeth of York, came to her coronation; Anne Boleyn (Henry VIII's second wife) had a particularly fine procession. Hall, the Chronicler, described it as: 'Just before the Mayor's barge was a boat full of ordnance, with a great dragon, moving and casting wild fire, with other monsters and men about also casting fire, and making hideous noises.' This — not surprisingly — cleared the way for the Mayor's barge. Following the Mayor were his fellowship, the Haberdashers, the Mercers, the Grocers and so in order all the City Guilds, and finally the Mayor's and Sheriff's officers. All the barges were richly decorated with silk and carpets and banners and streamers, and indeed with musicians, making great melody.

The water traffic, from water-taxis through local boats to ships, is seen in Fig. 6.16.

Fig. 6.16 The Thames at Richmond, D. Symoens, 1816 (by permission of the Fitzwilliam Museum, Cambridge). Detail.

Thames bank was built up with wharves, landing-stages and ferry steps —
with grassy banks only on the outside. In Mediaeval times boats traded into the
Fleet where, in spite of much pollution from tanners and waste, fish could still be
caught. The damage, though, led to the loss of the river, the Fleet now being small
and underground. (Fish were caught in quantity in the Thames.)

## Large rivers
### *(Fig. 6.17)*

Large rivers differ from small. The Rhône in Fig. 6.17 (a) is the Canal de Flute, a
completely channelised watercourse. It could equally well be an equivalent part of
the Rhine! The channels are in pairs, the canal and the very-channelised Rhône
itself. Hydropower dams and locks occur; and lesser French locks and a little jetty
are also shown. Upstream of Lyon the two channels, here some distance apart, are
the Miribel and the Jonage. The weir in Fig. 6.17d is the oldest control on the Rhône,
and now powers hydroelectricity. There was a ferry upstream. (The river is too large
for a ford downstream: the expected pattern in smaller rivers.) The Ferry Inn (as
was) on the south, and the landing-place on the north, are still there. Now crossing
is by bridge.

The Rhine is a larger, more populous and more industrialised river (and is in
consequence much more polluted). German industry and the barge traffic are
shown in Figs 6.17, 6.9. Fig. 6.8 shows old villages. Their walls are still high, and
at the waterside. The Rhine has been much channelled since. One village has an
indented harbour, so was probably a trading village. Present villages, have old
brick and now-grassed wharfing, and new leisure jetties. Their old walls — and new
ones — are low, to mark rather than fortify or refuse access. Old access may be
converted to leisure areas. (Figs 6.17, 12.6.)

## Wharves

It is no use having good boats carrying good cargo unless there is somewhere for
them to land. Consequently wharf and river-for-navigation development go hand
in hand. Early patterns, consisting of just beaches, are seen in Fig. 8.1 (this pattern
occurs 'early', the date varying with the culture — from pre-Roman to the North
American West: with variations on the inland pattern). The Romans had good
harbours for their main towns, starting with that on the Tiber. There are massive
Roman waterfront constructions at London, and many other riverside towns must
have had the same (Limbrey, 1983). Decay followed, of course. Twelfth-century
access is shown in Fig. 1.5; see Chapters 8, 9, 10, etc. for later access. In the fifteenth
century, galleys were typically still fastened to the city walls, or drawn up to an
unmodified — but now eroding — bank. Some, though, did have projecting jetties
(allowing more boats in one place and/or giving shelter). The amount of stoning of
the wharf reflects the flow: faster flow means potentially more erosion, so more
stoning is needed. The picture of Ratisbon (Fig. 8.2) has a more complex pattern,

but less stoning. Watergates may be present.

Sixteenth-century Antwerp had better wharfing. Frankfurt (Fig. 8.2) has wharves both sides of the river, a towpath and an actual harbour on the old city side. Cologne is developing its harbour (see Chapter 8 for island, Double Channel, and harbour development). Middleburg (Fig. 8.2) has the central harbour as described above for Bruges, but it has a later, also fortified, one at the side, for the larger sea-going ships. London has a good example. Defoe in 1724-7 wrote that the Pool of London, the main harbour area, extended from Limehouse upstream to the Custom House. He said it contained more and greater ships than Amsterdam, counting 2,000 of sea-going sail and excluding barges, lighters, pleasure boats, yachts and the navy. He counted (from the Hermitage Bridge to Blackwall) three wet docks for laying up, twenty-two dry docks for repairs and thirty-three building-yards for merchant ships, not counting the wherrybuilders and above-bridge barge-builders. Docks well inset into the land developed later.

While this was going on in trading-cities, lesser places were of course continuing with their earthen banks or even beaches (see Figs 1.8, 8.1, 6.6). As always, diversity in space shows, to a considerable extent, the pattern of development in time.

Once a certain stage is reached, little more happens. The Harbour Masters' look-outs in sixteenth-century Frankfurt and twentieth-century Strasbourg (Figs 8.2, 9.9) are

Fig. 6.17 Large rivers. a) Rhône, Canal de Flute. b) Lock on Rhône. c) Small jetty on Rhône. d) Miribel and Jonage division, upstream of Lyon; i upstream, ii downstream, with hydroelectric station, (upstream, ex-ferry with, on south, the ex-Ferry Inn, not shown.). e) Rhine, Mannheim. f) Rhine, village.

a

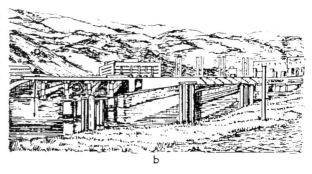

b

c

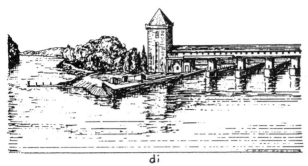

d i

d ii

e

f

remarkably similar. The difference is that the place, on the tip of land leading to the harbour, is, in modern Strasbourg, much further from the centre, the total wharf and dock area being so much larger.

The seventeenth-century Amstel, as seen in Fig. 6.18 is busy, indeed very busy, and poor for aquatic life. The bridge ahead could be used against water-borne invasion (see Fig. 9.9 for a fully fortified example). The Amstel is here above ground level, the drainage channel is below it, and the windmill (wind pump) for removing the water is shown. The farmland is hardly above ground level, even in summer: not good for crop yields. Flood-protection works are good, since houses — the Dutch being sensible — are built on this low level as well as on the canal. Seventeenth-century Pisa has unloading-steps, not special walls, in Fig. 6.19. Walled villages, with outside access — and barge trains — are shown on the Rhine in Fig. 6.8.

In the eighteenth century, Defoe describes much of Britain's river-borne trade. Kings Lynn is a great port, supplying eastern England, especially with wine and coals. (It received the goods to be transshipped through Denver Sluice (see above)). The passage to Lincolnshire he notes as dangerous and uneasy.)

Taunton has a fine new channel, bringing it coals and heavy goods including iron,

Fig. 6.18 The Amstel near Amsterdam, (J. van Ruisdael, 1628-82, by permission of the Fitzwilliam Museum, Cambridge). Detail.

lead, oil, wine, hemp, flax, pitch, tar, groceries, dye, stuffs. A comprehensive list! On the Trent, ships of good burden could go the about 40 miles (65km) to Gainsborough; there were no stops to Nottingham, though beyond that there were locks.

Nineteenth-century docks are large, complex, able to handle many large boats — not much different from the twentieth-century ones on, e.g., the Rhine, (Fig. 6.20). The large docks, as in Ludwigshafen, Rotterdam and Hamburg, may be increasingly busy. Others have been passed by time, like London, which is no longer a sea-port of any extent. Two factors caused the loss. Firstly, there are no longer active upstream ports to give a river trade (as opposed to a downstream sea-going trade). Secondly, container ships need much land space for the storage of those con-

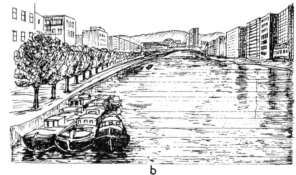

tainers. This was not available in London. Hence the London docklands are being redeveloped for housing, recreation —and, very pleasingly as continuing the tradition of transport, air travel (Fig. 6.21).

Sea-going trade is moving to the coast (e.g., also, Bristol trade to Avonmouth), and river-borne trade flourishes where it can reach a trans-shipment point and where interest remained in it during the early railway decades. Interest is perhaps the operative word. It is easy to let an enterprise decay through continuing to operate as in the past: it is more difficult to change to meet future needs.

Much has been said of railways replacing waterways. However, initially—and indeed even recently on

Fig. 6.19 Seventeenth century Pisa, unloading at steps.

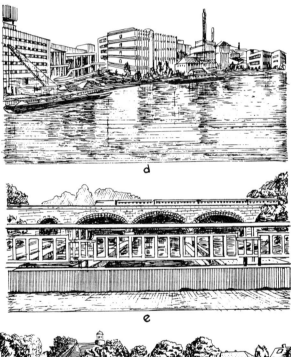

the Continent — the two were thought of in combination. Fig. 6.20 shows the water and rail communications joined together, here with the rail disused; Fig. 9.9 shows (part of) a complex dock system linking to a current complex rail system.

Fig. 6.20 Wharfs and docks. a) Small, rural, Rhône near Condrieu, France. b) Small, urban, Brussels, Belgium. c) Remains of old, Antwerp, Belgium. d) Large, Mannheim, Rhein. e) Large, Praha, Czechoslovakia. f) (former) water and rail junction, R. Amstel, The Netherlands.

Fig. 6.21 City Air-
port, on old docks,
London,  Eng-
land.

The two can also be independent. Both the Rhine and the Rhône characteristically have railways — and roads — along both sides of the river (bridges were more
expensive than laying rails).

While docks can be major, commercial barges can still, as in the past, operate
with negligible wharf, as in this Fig. 6.20b part of Brussels. Absence of docks does
not mean absence of trade, merely absence of abundant trade (even bulk cargo can
manage with tiny wharf space, e.g., the gravel-works jetty of Fig. 6.20a).

# 7
# Crossing the River

## Introduction

Rivers, though uniting those travelling along them, divide those living on either side. Fig. 9.4c shows apparently two parts of a town — both similar — united by a bridge. In reality, Dinant and Bouvignes (which is in fact centred off the river) were actually at war in the Middle Ages.

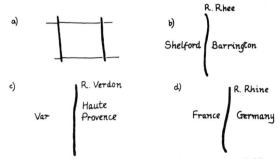

Fig. 7.1 Streams as boundaries. a) ditches separating fields. b) stream separating parishes. c) river separating provinces. d) river separating countries.

Waterways form convenient frontiers: between countries, e.g. parts of the Rhine (France-Germany), Vils (Germany-Denmark) and Maas (Netherlands-Belgium); between provinces or counties, e.g. Stadtskanaal (Netherlands), Waveney (England), Adour (France) or just between farms or even fields (Fig. 7.1). Crossing the river has always been a preoccupation. Where streams are small enough they can be walked over, but even small channels can swell with flood and flow swiftly enough to prevent walking and make crossing difficult. In really rapid rivers, it may be impossible to walk in water only 30cm deep. Swimming, and forming human chains, however possible, are inconvenient for travel and carriage. Therefore special crossing-points are chosen: chosen as being possible technically and convenient socially. The more difficult the river, the fewer the crossings. Hence crossings become, at all levels of the scale, the Gathering of Ways (Figs 2.4, 7.2). Table 7.1 lists some English place names connected with crossings. Crossings must have hard landings both sides that are not quickly turned to mud by the passage of feet. As well as size, culture, money and technology determine whether there will be a ford, ferry or bridge (or indeed a tunnel, but those, together with underground pipes, are not considered here). When any form of crossing looks odd, it is wise to look for a reason: there is usually a good one. In Canada, for instance, with deep snow-melt floods in spring, (if roads are on ground

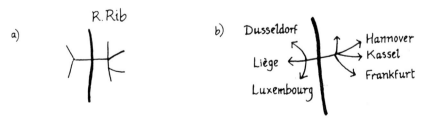

Fig. 7.2 The gathering of ways. a) crossing of small river (R. Rib at Larches, see Fig. 2.4) minor roads and footpaths. b) crossing of R. Rhein at Köln (only some roads marked). Diagrammatic.

*Table 7.1*
*English place names connected with crossings*
(Some examples from Ekwall (1960))

*brycg:*
OE 'bridge', e.g. Bridge (Kent), Breighton (Yorks.), Handbridge (Cheshire). Also 'causeway', e.g. Bridgend (Lincs.), Ricebridge (Durham: probably 'brushwood causeway').
*faer:*
OE 'passage', probably 'difficult passage', e.g. Denver (Norfolk, of Danes), Laver (Essex, at a place a Roman road was lost for 2 miles, perhaps in marsh).
*ferja:*
ON, ferrye: ME, 'ferry', e.g. Ferriby (Lincs.), Ferry bridge (Yorks.).
*ford:*
OE 'ford'. Probably the second most frequent topographical term. Some have become major towns, e.g. Bradford, Hereford, Guildford, Oxford. Most were crossings of only local significance, e.g. Fordham (Cambs.).
Many compound names describe the ford, e.g.:

| | |
|---|---|
| 'broad', e.g. Bradford (Avon, etc.) | 'hidden', e.g. Durnford (Suffolk) |
| 'deep', e.g. Defford (Worcs.) | 'foul', e.g. Fulford (Devon, etc.) |
| 'long', e.g. Longford (Beds. etc.) | 'red', e.g. Radford (Devon, etc.) |
| 'rough', e.g. Rufford (Lincs., Notts.) | 'shallow', e.g. Scalford (Leics.) |
| 'bright', e.g. Shereford (Norfolk) | 'double', e.g. Twyford (Bucks. etc.) |

Other names describe the ground, e.g.:

| | |
|---|---|
| 'gravel', e.g. Gutford (Beds.) | 'sand', e.g. Sampford (Devon, etc.) |
| 'mud', e.g. Mudford (Somerset) | 'stone', e.g. Stafford (Dorset) |

Parts added by man are in e.g.:

| | |
|---|---|
| 'planks', e.g. Bretford (Warwicks.) | 'posts', e.g. Stapleford (Cambs. etc.) |
| 'tree-trunk', e.g. Bamford (Derby) | 'flagstone', e.g. Flawforth (Notts.) |

Goods carried over are shown in, e.g.:

| | |
|---|---|
| 'barley', e.g. Barford (Beds. etc.) | 'hay', e.g. Heyford (Oxon) |
| 'charcoal', e.g. Coleford (Glos.) (probably) | 'chalk', e.g. Chalford (Glos.) (probably) |

There are many other elements, including personal names, animals and topographical features.
*gelad:*
OE 'difficult river crossing', e.g. Evenlode (Oxon).
*gewaed:*
OE 'ford' (out of use early) e.g. Wadebridge (Cornwall), Iwade (Kent: 'yewtree'), Lenwade (Norfolk: 'lane').
*vath:*
ON 'ford', e.g. Wath (Yorks.), Waithe (Lincs.). The commonest first element describes the ford, e.g. 'long', Langwathby (Cumbria), 'stone', Stenwith (Lincs.).

---

level) bridges are higher above ground than for similar-sized streams in Britain. Canal bridges may be high because masted sailing-ships passed beneath, or because they cross a valley (Fig. 6.7a). A ford eminently suitable for carts must be shallowed or bridged for cars, whose clearance is so much lower.

Legends abound about crossings. The Boy of Egremont was dragged down by his dog when jumping the wharf (Yorkshire) at its narrowest. A young man, travelling on 'Pegs' night' near Clitheroe, Lancashire, was warned against crossing stepping-stones, as no sacrifice had been made that year. He crossed and was drowned. A little bridge in Suffolk is unlucky for newly-weds because St Edmund, hiding under it (in 870 A.D.) was seen by such a couple and betrayed to the Danes (Rodgers, 1947-8). There are private as well as public crossings. It was normal for riparian owners, villagers, etc., to have small boats, to cross or move along rivers. Fords and bridges may also be within properties.

# In Classical times

Classical authors describe the ingenuity of armies crossing rivers — showing also the shortage of public crossings. Alexander the Great crossed the Oxus and Danube on rafts of stuffed hides — these are still used round the Oxus. The Romans continued the practice, having squads of 'bladder-bearers' (Lane Fox, 1973). Livy describes several ways: stuffing the skins used as tent-covers with dry grass, and stitching them up as floats; inflating the hides of the stock grazing around and tying them with the ropes used for the baggage animals, stringing them across, putting wood and earth on top to make a bridge. Caesar used basket boats of bamboo, thorn and leather, an idea copied later by the (future) Duke of Wellington taking his army across an Indian river (Bryant, 1971). Livy and Caesar both describe pontoon bridges. Caesar crossed the Rhine by a wooden bridge which took ten days to build. He commented on this as being unduly long, but the Rhine was such a difficult river. Only ten days! The bridge was destroyed when the army returned. Caesar refused the fleet of boats offered by the locals partly for fear of treachery, partly as being beneath his dignity.

Roman fords were common and sometimes paved. The Romans also built causeways and bridges — Worcester Bridge may have been partly Roman as late as 1781. These and other engineering works altered channels and channel migration; the Romans gave some control and stability to rivers. The Anglo-Saxons continued using them, but less, allowing decay from lack of repair in England (Limbrey, 1983). Further south they may be still present. The writer's brother became annoyed at the traffic jam caused by an over-narrow bridge in Italy, and thought it could surely have been built wider. He was then held up beside its inscription: 'Roman'. He then considered it was only to be expected that modern traffic would clog up a Roman bridge.

# Fords and ferries

### Ferrymen who carry
Early, a ford was a going, a way, not necessarily a passage by foot. The term was applied to places much too deep to wade, where there must have been a ferry. Ferry then meant 'crossing with help', e.g., in the thirteenth-century Njals Saga a beggarwoman was ferried across by armed men on horseback.

Ferry service was a lowly occupation (so worthy of mention in Sagas only in unusual circumstances). The *Niebelungenlied*, about 1200 A.D., describes a knight required to render ferry service. As this was unfitting, he and his staff did not accept payment — he had, though, the ability to transport an army of 1,000(?) in his boats, no other boat being anywhere near. When he was killed, his death was revenged since he (so unusually) was a noble. This tale says a lot about the rarity of crossings, and the skill and status of ferrymen. Monks could also offer ferry service, presumably without degradation.

Fig. 7.3 St Christopher the Ferryman. Sixteenth century German woodcut (note, unusually, the plants are drawn inaccurately — in a regularly used Way the reed-like leaves by the ferryman's pole would not be thick, tall and straight — contrast *Nuremburg Chronicle* Figs. 1.6, 8.2.

St Christopher, so the legend goes, was a ferryman (Fig. 7.3), helping pilgrims across a river. In one night of storm a little child asked to be taken across. At each step the child on his shoulder became heavier — St Christopher had carried the Redeemer of the World and the burdens of the world. St Christopher is, of course, the patron saint of ferries, as St Bartholomew is for bridges and causeways.

## Fords

Fords are many (Fig. 7.4): the simple ford, with too little traffic to destroy the stream's own bed; the ford with a made bed, in busier parts concreted, and often with a bridge for foot passengers; the ford with stepping-stones — for pedestrians, not for cars. Stepping-stones hold up flow, so may cause difficulties. The position of old fords is often still plain, if they were properly made and have not been redeveloped. The German Tauber has a series of bridges leading to villages. By each is an old ford. These shallow places have much vegetation, the deep stretches

Fig. 7.4 Fords. a) b) Stepping stones. c) Horseman fording. d) e) With footbridge, also see Fig. 2.4. f) Replaced by bridge (and see elsewhere).

a

b

c

d

between have little (Fig. 11.11). Fords by mills have already been noted (Fig. 2.4; Chapter 2). Here water was shallow when the mill-water was ponding, and traffic could cross.

**Ferrying by boat**
Ferries in the modern sense (boats) and ex-ferries, are shown in Fig. 7.5. For a boat-ferry, the bed must be deep enough — or shallow enough, as the case may be — for ferries to land, and to land when the water level is at different heights. Rivers may be tidal well inland (e.g. the Thames at London). Levels of mountain-rising great rivers, like the Severn, vary greatly (or, be-

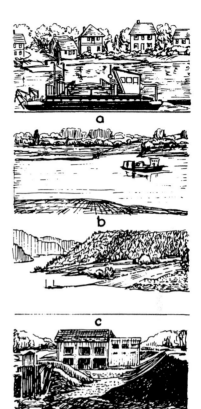

Fig. 7.5 Ferries. a) Rhine ferry. b) Dutch ferry with access points, Ijssel. c) Recent ex-ferry, Rhine. d) Old ex-ferry, Ain, France (also see elsewhere).

fore regulation, used to vary greatly) with the upstream rainfall or, on the Continent, snow-melt. When rivers

e

f

are active, with a wandering pool pattern, the ferry point may need changing. Most European rivers have been so confined, especially over the last few centuries, that the ferry points have remained — and can often still be seen (and in Fig. 7.5 the difference between old and new ferry points — new, to cross the channellised Rhine for maintenance, for instance — is also easy to see). Many were early, most were for travellers. However, many on, e.g., the Thames were made when the towpaths were built in the eighteenth and early nineteenth centuries (Thacker, 1909), and built in short lengths on each side of the river. The ferries were to transport towhorses across. (On the Great Ouse the barges took them across; Chapter 6.)

Now, a tale to end the section. The Eynsham ferryman (near Oxford) paid 6/8d to the vicar yearly, which he brought in a basin of water. The vicar distributed the water to the people around, to remind them of the custom (that the ferry owed service to the church). In Rogation week, the vicar and parishioners crossed to the Oxfordshire side of the river and laid hold of twigs and reeds, to assert

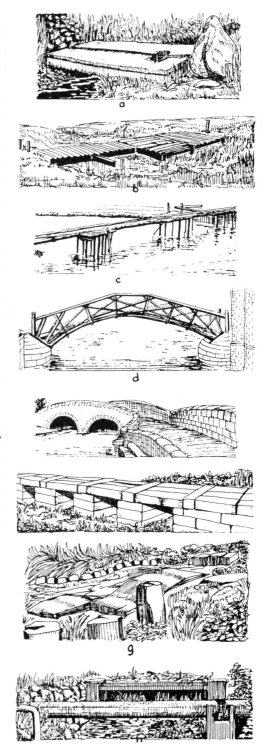

Fig. 7.6 Bridges (and see Figs. 2.4, 2.8 and elsewhere). a) Malta. b) Denmark. c) S. France. d) Cambridge, England. e)-g) Packhorse bridges, e) Dunster, England, f) Malta, g) remains of bridge *and* ford, Malta. h) Pipe crossing also, Scotland. i) With chapel, St Ives, England. j)-k) Drawbridges, Dutch. Note similarity of k) and g2). l) Madeira. m) n) Mallorca. o)-r) Malta. s) Wales. t) u) Madeira. v) Menorca. w) x) y) England. z) Scotland. a2) Switzerland. b2) c2) Rhine. d2)-f2) C. France. d2) re-built cheaply, e2) decayed, f2) note two generations, each attracting building. g2) Spain. h2) Early nineteenth century, England (the River Kennet, near Newbury, J. Linnell, 1815. By permission of the Fitzwilliam Museum, Cambridge). Detail.

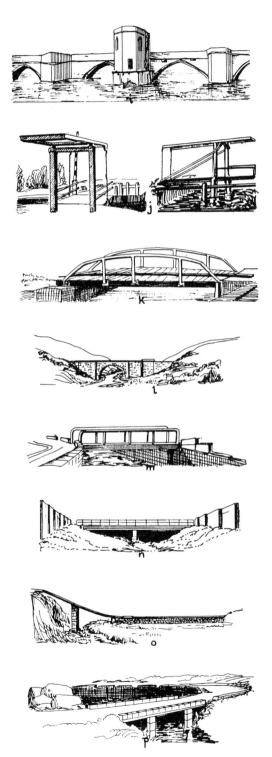

that all the river in fact belonged to their parish (a river is usually a divide). This had recently stopped at the turn of the century (Thacker, 1909). It serves as a reminder that behind bald statements of suitable and ancient ferry sites lie centuries of ancient and particular customs, and disputes between all those who vaguely think they have a possible claim on the river.

## Bridges
### (Fig. 7.6)

### Where and why?

A ford can be impassable when its stream floods only a little. Ferrymen who carry occur in only some cultures (no one now in Europe would expect to find and fee one!). Boat ferries are inconvenient with much traffic and are not immune to closure during storms. Bridges are the usual alternative. They may be built on an existing crossing-site or elsewhere. The Romans built for military, not domestic, considerations. (Even now, in Pollensa, Mallorca, the Roman bridge is outside the (later) settlement (Fig. 9.17a). Later bridges were built for peaceful travellers and traders more often than for armies. The pattern and vicissitudes of building are shown in the story of Arundel Bridge in Chapter 1. Bridges would attract traffic for a long way around, being preferable to uncertain or dangerous ferries, hence the Gathering of Ways and, later, a few bridges superseding many fords or ferries. Only in the twentieth century have bridges proliferated. The immense traffic and accompanying immense wealth and technology have

Fig. 7.6 contd.

allowed this.

Bridge use was also cultural. The sturdy Highlandmen splashed through streams when the quiet English expected much more ease. Hence, after the 1745 uprising:

If you had seen these roads [including bridges]
  before they were made [made solid]
You would lift up your hands, and bless General
  Wade.

Defoe (1724-7) who enjoyed bridges, commented that 'no part of England can show such noble, lofty, large and long stone bridges as that between Trent and Tweed [the north], and almost all are stone; while in the south, wooden bridges are abundant' (see Fig. 1.8). He found an interesting site at Glasgow. On his first visit he passed over on the ground by the bridge (bridge tolls were expensive!) the water being hardly over the horse's hooves. And he wondered why the magnificent eight-arch bridge, with three very large and high central arches, had been built so big. As noted above, there is a reason for such things: on his return, water had filled all the arches and the lower part of the town, causing the inhabitants the greatest consternation imaginable.

The stone bridge over the Nene near Castor had been built, replacing a ferry. Defoe considered it very fine, and was much applauding Lord Fitzwilliam's generous action, knowing how difficult the ferry was, especially in even a little flood. But his applause was much abated when he found the toll was extortionate (at 2/6d).

If a bridge and its associated works has any contact with the river bed and flood plain, the river is contracted. This means scour, hence typically ponding upstream and scouring-out and rapid flow downstream (as, in excess, with Old London Bridge: Fig. 7.7). In a flood this is enhanced and the

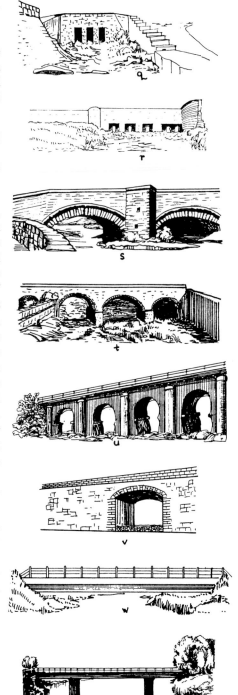

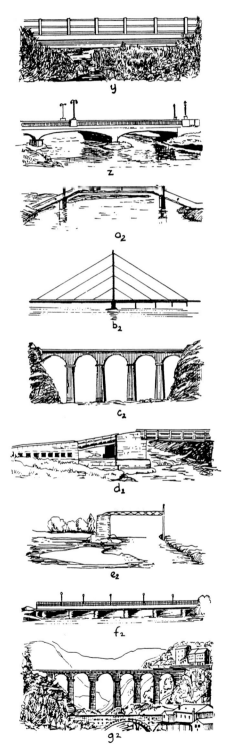

engineering has to take this into account. A long bridge eases problems, but a shorter one is cheaper. It was not until twentieth-century wealth arrived that long bridges could be built in abundance, saving the thought that is needed to solve the hydraulic problems of shorter bridges. Short arches (or bridges) need care. Will logs, ice and miscellaneous objects come down with enough force to damage the bridge? Material scoured near a bridge will be deposited downstream. A river changes its banks if flowing naturally: this must be allowed for in the design. If it is acceptable for floodwater to drown a bridge from time to time, the bridge may be built more cheaply, but will hold up storm flows more, with consequent trouble (Jansen *et al.*, 1979).

Cables and pipes may cross rivers, either by bridges (which is easier for maintenance) or separately (shorter routes).

A handrail is an improvement. Pack-horse bridges, able to take laden pack-animals in single file, are ancient, varied and pleasing to the eye. Bridges can be made of hurdles and in other simple ways. Over the centuries wooden bridges were replaced by stone ones (later concrete or metal). Stone bridges can, as noted above, be Roman. The change may also happen at very variable later dates: 1176 St Ives (see Beresford and St Joseph, 1979); 1754 the main Cambridge Bridge; 1841 a lesser Cambridge bridge. Wooden bridges, in a variety of sizes, ages and purposes, are now used mainly for ornament. Major wooden bridges are usually beautiful. Only the simplest plank bridges are merely functional. Bridges vary greatly: single-arch; multi-arch; suspension; stream-in-a-pipe; solid, usually older structures; and the more flying lines of usually new ones; dams (e.g., Fig. 2.8: Malta) and also the right-angle Maltese bridges (Figs 2.8, 7.6p), where the road had

Fig. 7.6 contd.

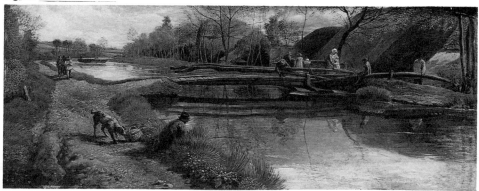

to expand to give turning-space for motor traffic; high bridges taking high-level roads; and the more ordinary low ones; bridges made of various types of stone, concrete, wood and other materials. The pictures are more graphic than words.

Pieces of 'dead bridges' are frequent (e.g., Figs. 2.4, 7.6e2).

The *Nuremburg Chronicle* gives a good array of fifteenth-century bridges (Fig. 8.2), wood and stone, fortified and plain, simple and grand — grand for the main city bridge, plainer for side ones and smaller settlements. Bridges, like houses, reflected the status of their place and builder. Note the greater fortification of the Continental ones. England was a much more settled country, and fortifications to a great extent (see, however, Chapter 12) disappeared earlier than on the Continent; old fortified bridges are still extant in, e.g., France: Fig. 9.9, and Germany).

### Other uses of bridges

Bridges may be single-purpose, solely to allow passage across without any other uses built into their design (e.g., they are not high to allow boats to pass). Or there may be a second or combined use. Fishweirs might be developed into bridges. If so, the control part may remain movable. Bridges of this type were, of course, superseded. But a central movable part is also found in drawbridges, drawn up for boat passage. These may be small and frequent, as on minor Dutch waterways with access to only one or a few houses, or more majestic as in Tower Bridge, London (on the Thames). Bridges may bear chapels. Few do now. One of these is at St Ives (1414). It became a dwelling at the Reformation, and is now again a chapel, in which Roman Catholic Mass is said weekly.

Houses were also put on bridges, the most famous example being Old London Bridge (Fig. 7.7). This was finished in 1209 with at first just one chapel in which the builder was buried. Later, houses were built (nearly 3,000 people were killed here in a fire in 1429). Its wide bridge pillars made passage through extremely dangerous, ponding above being 5ft (*c.* 1.5m), giving a great force of water. The

Fig. 7.7 Old London Bridge.

houses were removed in 1755 (and the bridge demolished in 1833: Rodgers, 1947-8). The Pulteney Bridge at Bath was so covered by houses it was not noticeable as a bridge to those passing. An extant example is Lincoln Bridge (Fig. 9.15b). Fords by mills often bear bridges later, and so may be placed by the old mill weirs. (This is not a secondary use of the bridge).

In towns, bridges were often by wharfs, to the manifest convenience of both. See, for example, Fig. 8.2, *Nuremburg Chronicle* and Cambridge, where the wharfing (post-fifteenth-century) was by the Main Bridge and the upper (upstream) bridge (where punts are now hired). Mills could also be associated, likewise for convenience.

An earlier type of drawbridge was to draw the bridge up for defence, not passage. Drawbridges were sited over streams — and over moats — to castles and towns. Novels suggest they were restricted to castles: but, as Fig. 9.13 shows, they were equally common in towns, and indeed castles and towns are not clear separate things. When a fort housed more than guards, it developed outbuildings, which could become a town. (Others, built late as major castles, e.g. those of Edward I in Wales, had all services within the walls, and a town could grow around, but not be part of, the fort.)

Beauty must not be ignored as a function of a bridge. 'A thing of beauty is a joy for ever' as Keats wrote, and the quality of life is much enhanced by beauty. Wordsworth wrote in 1802 on the building of Westminster Bridge over the Thames:

> Earth has not anything to show more fair
> Dull would he be of soul that would pass by
> A sight so touching in its majesty...
> Ships, towers, domes, theatres and temples lie...
> All bright and glittering in the smokeless air
>                     [just pre-Industrial Revolution!]...
> The river glideth at his own sweet will....

A note from the writer's other speciality may, perhaps, be added. Bridges are points of legal access overlooking the whole width of rivers. The writer's vegetational work on rivers has been done mostly from (or near) bridges: which have been of great use to the project!

And finally

There are also other ways of crossing watercourses. Pole-vaulting was well-known in Flanders, where waterways were many, bridges few. To save the time going to bridges, agile men take great poles and cross the water with one leap. This ancient custom (recorded at least in the thirteenth century) has become a modern sport (Chapter 13).

# 8

# How River Towns Grow

## Introduction

Settlements, like individuals, have a beginning, growth and decay. The growth of settlements, unlike the growth of individuals, may be stopped at any point, without destruction occurring (though of course settlements, like individuals, may be destroyed at any point). Growth may start in places where further growth depends on factors not present at the start (e.g., deep iron mines), and decaying towns may be revitalised. New developments and old patterns co-exist down the ages. Some of the factors influencing town development are to do with their rivers, but not all. Others are to do with social patterns: kingdoms, principalities and other types of nation must have seats of government, and resources and trade routes. Old river capitals have different priorities from old river trading-centres. Other variations are due to social dynamism, which fluctuates. Bruges, Belgium, decayed when silting blocked the harbour and adequate alternatives were not forthcoming. It revived in the twentieth century: it is not greater than other cities at the time of writing, but great among cities. This came with the revitalisation of the Belgian Fleming culture, for long dormant. (It is the Walloon Belgian towns which in their turn are now decaying.) Other places grow or regrow with changing access to communications or materials. The two, though interacting, are separate: and both are easier to predict with hindsight than with foresight.

The ravages of war, the turns of diplomacy, the influence of domestic politics: all may be crucial, but may also merely cause delay or slight diversion. A recent example is Nuremberg (Fig. 8.5), redeveloped with little change of pattern after much damage in the Second World War. Examples of movement include the loss of merchants from Antwerp after the sixteenth-century Spanish Fury. Bruges, Ghent and Namur likewise gave place to expanding Amsterdam and Rotterdam.

Each settlement has its own history, and apparently its own particular development. In Durham, for example, the Bishops built the mediaeval bridges and developed the mills, and in the fourteenth century extended the walls to include the market place (e.g., Beresford & St Joseph, 1979). The query immediately arises: what would have happened without the Bishops? Wellingborough was divided, by choice, between two manors in the early modern period. Surely this is reflected in a two-partite development? Grave was a (Dutch) trading-town, Rastatt, a (German) capital town, Huy a (Belgian) manufacturing one. It all seems haphazard. No general pattern — surely?

Yet if a town has consistently existed, and at least partly developed, over a number of centuries it follows, at least in Europe, a fixed and determinate outline pattern. If Durham had not had bishops, someone else would have done something similar. Rastatt and Huy differ in emphasis, not in pattern. The ancient town of Rome went through the same stages — at a very different date — as the newer ones of Frankfurt and Cologne (Fig. 8.5). There is a fixed and unchanging pattern, which has but few exceptions. There is an individual pattern, due to a town's building-materials, social culture and dynamism, its great men, etc. These can give a different superficial look to towns which, in basics, show the same pattern. (It is the same basic pattern, not the same *detailed* pattern; see Fig. 8.5.) This book, of course, concentrates on the river, introducing other topics just to explain patterns of river use.

Town development can be seen to be in a state of balance, of tension, between the inexorable, determinate patterns of growth, common to all, and the individual thrust, described in Chapters 9 and 10.

## Early development

Human settlements require water. As soon as people settle they pick sites with running water, if possible (otherwise underground water of easy access or, rarely, with reluctant acceptance of humping the water some distance. And see Chapter 3). At this stage big rivers are unwanted; they are too fierce, liable to kill and flood and change their course. So the settlement is built on a tributary. The main river is ignored for a considerable length of time.

Development proceeds at different rates in different places. Fig. 8.1 illustrates early European patterns. The Romans built away from the river, on the tributary, with a straight road to the river. The next stage has the Old Tower (e.g., Fig. 2.1) guarding the crossing, with the small village on the tributary, close to the river. Boats come here enough to create a small beach. 8.1c shows the next stages, the developments of a beach; a wharf; the old fort, replaced by a newer one; general fortification increasing; the old church replaced by the newer one, and so on.

The *Nuremburg Chronicle* (Fig. 8.2) shows the next stage, and the developments in use of, and reliance on, the main river. Fig. 8.3 shows these and later developments in plan form.

There is a small settlement on a tributary of the large river. If there is trade, and if there is a crossing over the large river, either a ford or a bridge, the town can begin to develop. By contrast, the Romans ignore the crossing-place completely and fortify inland anything up to a mile (c. 1.5 km) away from the river, wherever the main roads parallel to and going across, the river come together. Around the Roman town an emporium can develop. This at some stage will come down to the river and touch it at one point. The wharf is very small, guarded by a stone tower. The town lies at an angle to the wharf and is roughly square, usually fortified with a palisade possibly brick, possibly earth with wood on top. Inside it is a market place (necessarily as the town must trade to be a town), small church and some sort of civic centre. Workshops are along the tributary and some 'allotments' also tend to be near water.

Fig. 8.1 Early stages in settlement development. a) Roman. b) Dark Ages. c) Early Mediaeval. Compare with Figs. 8.2, 8.3.

During the early Christian era monasteries settle around the periphery — there must be some years of political stability. The monasteries and nunneries are named after saints. When times change it becomes necessary to incorporate the religious foundations inside the town defences. A new wall is made, running outside the old one; the wharf is extended downstream and refortified. New town gates are named after the saint whose monastery is nearby — St Mary, St Peter. St Giles is the patron saint of lepers, who lived outside the town; hence the St Giles' Gates in

Fig. 8.2 Early German woodcuts of cities (*Nuremburg Chronicle* 1493, courtesy of the Master and Fellows of St Catharine's College, Cambridge, and the Syndics of the University Library, Cambridge. Titles of cities not all reliable). Compare with Figs. 8.1 and 8.3. Note position of river and tributaries, modifications and fortifications on both, position of shipping, harbours and the development of the double channel — City Island, churches within and monasteries without the walls, mills, floating, on bridges and otherwise, etc. a)-e) *Nuremburg Chronicle* a) Rome (see Fig. 8.5b), b) Patavia, c) Ratisbon, d) Ulm (see Fig. 9.10), e) Florence (defended — and channelled — river: as also in Eastern England, Fig. 8.5c, Norwich). More development on the opposite bank than where the main defence is just of the city, as in b)-d)). f) Frankfurt, sixteenth century (more development and towpath, on other side. Harbour master's lookout — compare Strasbourg, Fig. 9.9 — and Island). g) Cologne (part), sixteenth century (Island, used for grazing, boatbuilding etc. mills and their towing, etc.). h) Kempten sixteenth century. i) Augsburg (part) sixteenth century (dry moat, sewer down centre of some streets). j) Middleburg, seventeenth century ring-canal town. Note main 'stub' canal to centre, larger later harbour to side, and fortifications.

so many towns. (In Viking times 'Gate' meant 'street', so beware of all the gates in York, they do not mean what they say.)

The Water Street may be introduced here (Dutch *Water Straat*, German *Wasserstrasse*, hence a useful term to describe all). It leads from the river. Figure 8.4 shows a typical one — now leading from a bridge, with a bridgemaster; more anciently from a wharf, no doubt with a ferry- or harbourmaster. The Water Street was the main town access, leading to the Square with the Church at the opposite side — showing the incoming traveller the beauty of the town and the importance it put on the worship of God. When new near-river centres are developed (see below), Water Streets are part of them. (In small places like Megève (Fig. 2.1), the square may touch the river, with no Water Street.) Many towns stay in this phase, e.g., Aberteifi, Cardigan (Fig. 8.5), Dolgellau and, better still, Welshpool where the market place is still on a thirteenth-century site. This phase extends somewhere around the thirteenth to fifteenth centuries in modern European towns depending on other factors.

At this point, somewhere, the pattern changes from the mediaeval one: the central market place has been too small for a long time; there has been a market place outside the walls (it is possible that, as in Cambridge, the main large markets

happening once or twice a year were always held on a site outside the walls). Now, however, this (second) market place is inside the town's new fortifications. It will be nearer to the main river than the original mediaeval one and the complex of Church + Town Hall + Market will move onto it. This complex dates at least from the Greek *agora* with, as in Assos, temple and assembly rooms at opposite sides of the square.

At the same time the wharf complex grows too, downstream usually, though there are exceptions. It seems that this is when digging slits for harbours becomes popular. An odd feature in some towns now, particularly on the Continent, is what appears to be a double channel out from the town centre. First comes a much-

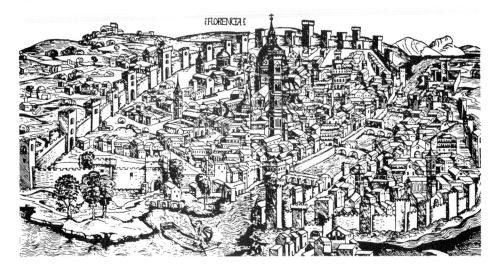

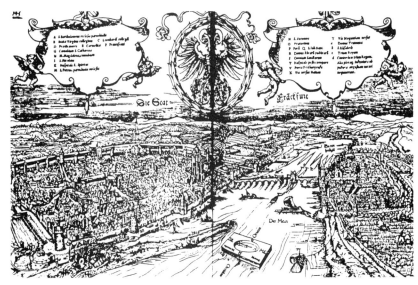

Fig. 8.2 contd. Frankfurt.

Fig. 8.2 contd. Cologne (Köln)

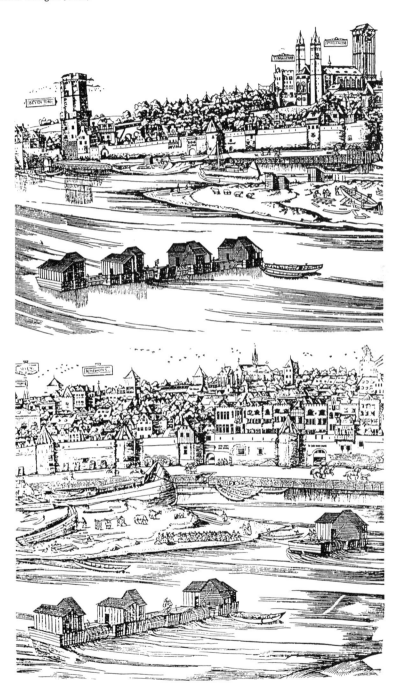

Fig. 8.2 contd. Kempten

channelised channel. This has the old access to town centre (by way of the Water Street), and the downstream end of the channel is likely to have mills. Then we come to a second channel. This is less channelised and has clearly less signs of old use (though it may have pleasure cruisers, picnic areas, etc.). A Double Channel, of course, presupposes the existence of an island. Fig. 8.2f: Frankfurt, shows this isle — and if there were a bridge at this point, there would be a Double Channel. Middleburg (Fig. 8.2i) shows it also. Here the ring-canal has been excavated to form a harbour (on the left side), and the bridges already show the Double Channel. In Cologne (Fig. 8.2g) the slit is a separated island — Middleburg is a wedge; in Frankfurt the island is joined to the mainland by mills. These show the development. Remains, to various degrees, occur widely — as a 'breakwater' only, at Orleans; as a rather large centre to the lock/weir system in Newark, England; and still properly developed as at Warendorf (Fig. 9.12). Islands near river towns or villages — such as various ones on the Rhine (where islands are also due to the rechannelling) are always candidates for being ex-wharfs.

The wharf area is fortified with a tower or a bastion or something, but it is definitely not inside the main fortifications (see Figs and for a smaller type, Fig. 2.1 — Megève). The tributary or (by now) tributaries on which the town still stands are now fortified by watergates (see Figs 8.2, and 9.15c). At this point, if the town is continuing to be successful, it gets a new cathedral and (possibly) a new set of walls. If there is no ford, it will already have a bridge. Now it may build another, again usually downstream from the first, but this is not a hard-and-fast rule. Local circumstances, roads, other villages, will decide where. This is the time when universities are founded and charters obtained for towns.

If there is a separate castle it will be, as it were, elsewhere, the site being determined by historical or topographical features. Often it is simply put on top of the Roman fort: waste not, want not.

This typical town is now a more or less irregular shape, with a longish waterfront (often the longest side of the town). It is heavily fortified with big walls and lots of towers; it has a lovely Cathedral, an opulent Guild Centre and an imposing Town Hall. The water-intensive craft shops are still down the tributary. A nice example of mediaeval pollution is recorded in Cologne: Tanner Street, later renamed Blue Beck Street. Similar occupations congregate: Silver Street, Mill Street, Copper Street — every town has at least one of these. Foundry work seems to be done outside: there is more than one Smith Field around the place, incorporated into the town somewhat later. The Haymarket is another outside feature, together with the Swanmarket and sundry cattlemarkets. These are also swallowed up in the fortifications as the town grows. As described in Chapter 4 swans were important at least from the twelfth century and, under the kind of control exercised in England, could be removed from the river only once a year: hence the

Fig. 8.2 contd. Augsberg.

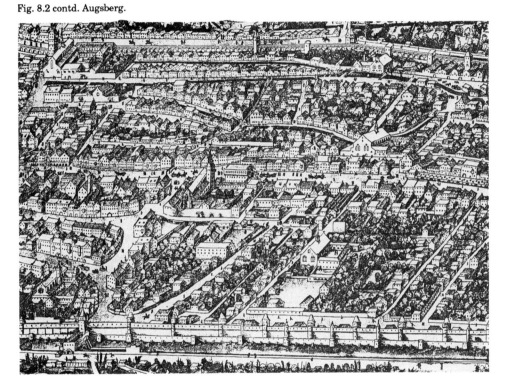

Fig. 8.2 contd. Middleburg.

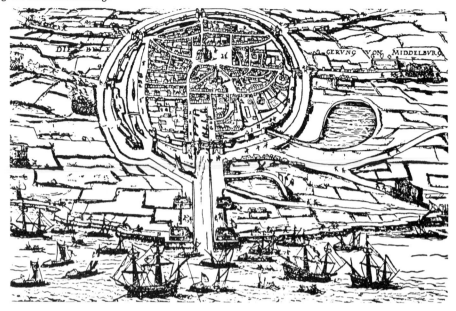

use of ex-moats for swans — and indeed their value was such that, even without that control, the spare waters of the wealthy (whether of guilds or of nobles) would be wanted for swans. The Swan Lane is a very characteristic town-street name (see Figs for its position along the moat).

The next stage is the spread of the 'stellate' fortification, definitely late fourteen and fifteen hundreds, right into the early seventeenth century here and there. With this, the town adds another bridge or two, more spread of wharf (again by necessity because it is the increase of trade that causes the growth of the town and by now much of this trade goes down the waterways). Mills are often slung under the bridges at this stage and some of the small tributaries begin to go underground. The new gates are called by their position, North, South, etc., there being enough travellers to need directions.

By no means all towns go through this particular phase; some seem to go into a decline for the next hundred years or more and miss out on this stage altogether.

The seventeenth century introduces town-planning, especially in places like Sweden, but also in England, some parts of Germany and elsewhere, if Early Development has hit the town. Small but geometrically laid-out streets in a grid pattern characterise this phase (e.g. Valletta, Malta: Fig. 8.5g). If there are still town gates, they will be called by the name of the town that the road they stand on goes to. For the first time in centuries people now consider they are going from the town as well as to it. The town spreads outside the walls and many walls are down by the end of the seventeenth century.

In parts of (richer) Europe extensive private building starts on the outskirts of the town. The Big House is a feature of the eighteenth century everywhere. There is a slight stagnation in the town at this point, though some places go in for Theatres and Opera Houses and various municipal buildings of varying monstrosity. What

Fig. 8.3 City development, plans (typical eras for Europe). a) Early Mediaeval. b) Middle Mediaeval. c) Late Mediaeval. d) Late 1500s to about 1700, depending on area. e) Cologne (actual).

By b) the basic 'furniture' consists of guard towers, castle, harbour, monasteries, garrison, mill, tannery, church, market, ice cellar, smithy (silversmith). The harbour-church-market place-tithe (=town) hall complex behaves as one unit. Walls are usually named after the bastion or church nearby. The stone tower is sometimes, not always, associated with the harbour. The crossing can be ford, ferry or bridge, with little or nothing on the far bank. The market place was for the town. Trading fairs were held outside the walls (perhaps being later incorporated, e.g. as the poultry market).

Building grows, town walls are pushed out, often leaving the original harbour defences intact. The tithe barn becomes a town hall, the market place church a cathedral. The nunnery and monastery have new churches, other religious foundations develop outside the wall. A ditch is added to the fortifications. One wall is likely to be called Swan's Wall, often associated with a goose or swan market, with later Swan Lane (swans on any spare water, Chapter 4). There may be a gate here. There is no obvious waterfront development — harbour is doing well — and there may be a citadel or other fort on the river.

Next, some towns are re-fortified in the stellate form. The harbour often moves downstream, and the old one may have been eroded into enough for the City Island to form (see Fig. 8.2). If the harbour moves, the market place moves with it, often with a new town hall. Increased industry may cause pollution — in Köln, Tanner Beck becomes Blue Beck. The market place may even move away from the river, when there may be a 'hay market' by the harbour. The original keep will probably be re-built as a dwelling-castle. There is usually a moat, if space and terrain allow. Gates and walls are named after compass points.

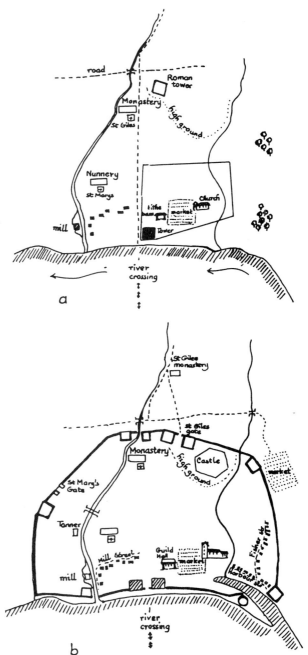

Fig. 8.3 contd.

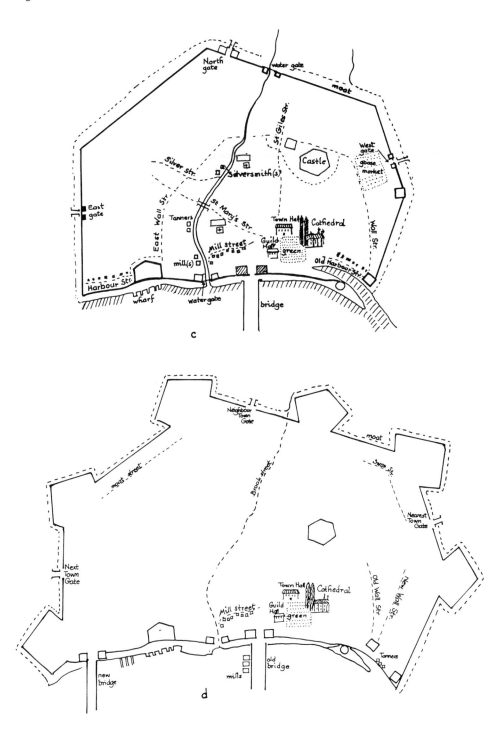

c

d

In the seventeenth century *villages* expanded, developing their own, and hardly-fortified harbours. Much fishing is still done locally, but declining towards the end of the century. By then in Germany the watermills on small streams have declined. City gates are often named after the town the road leads to.

In the eighteenth century, there is an industrial waterfront, warehouses with living accommodation above. The mill moves to the main river, and tributaries may be covered over as sewers. Building increases outside the city walls (where these were left), castles are re-built and re-furbished, and parks created round palaces. The moat may be turned into an ornamental lake. Fishing and fish-harbours decline. Streets on the periphery are often named after the town they go to.

The nineteenth century has a definite town plan, perhaps with a fan of boulevards. Much peripheral building may obscure remaining fortifications. Ornamental lakes replace moats — if not done so earlier. The railway appears quite often following the line of a straightened river or a tributary. The new town hall may be built anywhere. The waterfront moves outwards both up and downstream and on both banks (where space and bridges allow). New bridges are common. Street names often commemorate kings, writers, battles, etc. Cultural buildings (opera, theatre) appear, mostly within the old town.

In the twentieth century new ground is acquired beside the river (channelling, drainage), often used as parkland, and leisure use of water is now distinct from commercial. Leisure buildings (sport, parks, etc.) increase, and so do tower blocks and industry on the peripheries.

Fig. 8.3 contd.

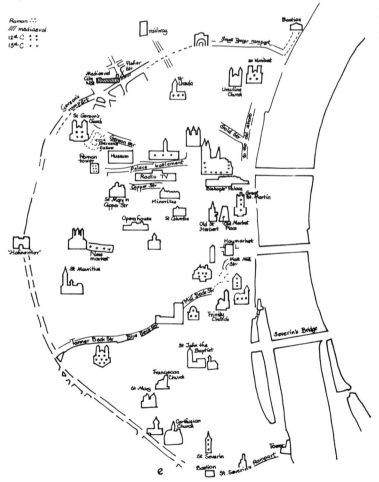

private building goes on tends to be either industrial and mean or cultural and magnificent. The grid system of streets is still favoured. If the town wants to have water above ground, it makes extensive canal networks; if the town does not like water, it starts putting streams underground.

In towns that are going to develop, the emphasis then shifts from the water to the railways. Town-planning has invented the semi-circular and the radiating boulevard and the town centre is extensively rebuilt.

Industry moves away from the riverside and congregates around the railways. The nineteenth century goes in for extensive reshaping of the town; the Market Place + Church + Civic Centre complex may well move again, possibly without the church, but often with a neo-classical basilica or some such newly built church. All small waterways, except ornamental ones, are now moved underground. There is extensive 'posh' development along the waterfront, or it may become exclusively slum (see Chapter 9). Dozens of bridges are built around the end of the century. With the arrival of the builder/property developer there is a great rift between the architecture of 'good' and 'lousy' housing — the tenement rears its ugly head, just as in Augustan Rome. It is in this phase that, typically, the town may make its first foray across the river. The development is usually recreational — parks, sports centres, etc. Augustan Rome did

Fig. 8.4 Water Street, Doetinchem, The Netherlands. Note street direct from river to market place and church — and bridge-master's office. Wharves beside, not shown.

Frankfurt.

▨ Cathedral    ▦ City Hall

o o o  12th C. rampart
× × ×  13th C boundary
× o ×  16th C boundary

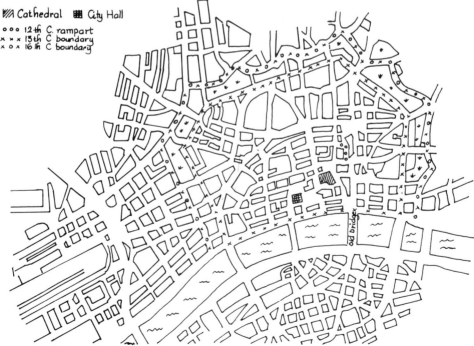

the same.

The twentieth century does nobody any good. In Germany, at least the new development is kept away from the old town, but England, France and Belgium (to a certain extent The Netherlands as well) pour concrete over the old town. The suburb is the characteristic invention otherwise. Waterfronts are often completely neglected, or else purely recreational. It is only in the late twentieth century that any interest appears in urban rivers and the little tributaries which originally determined the site of the town have gone without trace or memory (except, perhaps, in the records of the sewage companies which have incorporated them in the sewer network. A sewer was originally a natural drainage channel (see Chapter 4)).

This is the basic European town plan (Fig. 8.5). There are variations. There is the ring-canal town, like Middleburg (Fig. 8.2), where the outer fortifications are a moat (see the description of Bruges: Chapter 6). Strasbourg started on a tributary of the Ill, and then developed a ring-canal (Fig. 9.9). Such towns have a central harbour, early, then develop outer harbours as the need arises — not the

Fig. 8.5 City plans. Compare Figs 8.2, 8.3. a) Frankfurt, to show typical modern European development. b) Rome, to show the same developmental phases at an earlier date. c) Norwich, to show a 'defended-river' type town. d) Nuremburg, to show a town with severe twentieth century war damage re-created on the old plan: as common on the continent. e) Coventry, England, to show a town with severe war damage of the same date, rebuilt quite differently. f) Cardigan, Aberteify, Wales, to show a town frozen in the mediaeval phase (lack of resources). g) Valletta, Malta, to show a planned seventeenth century town, quite different to e.g.Frankfurt, and frozen in this phase (lack of space).

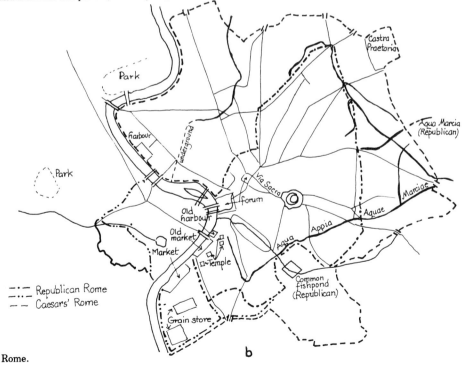

Rome.

Fig. 8.5 contd. Norwich.

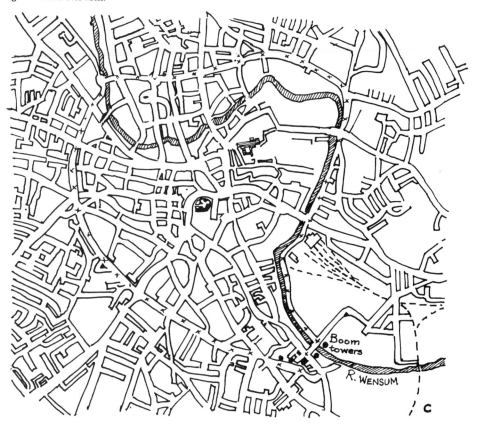

Most recent city wall × × ×
on both banks of river

Fig. 8.5 contd. Nuremburg.

d

Rebuilt from mediaeval centre ...
Rebuilt from late mediaeval centre × × ×
City wall ▭▭▭▭

Fig. 8.5 contd. Coventry.

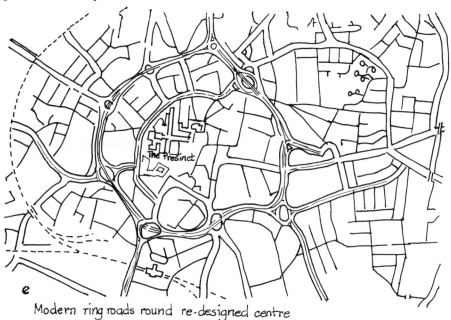

Modern ring roads round re-designed centre

simple along-river development of the normal town (e.g. Fig. 8.2g: Cologne), but a
major new siting. In Strasbourg, the docks moved nearer to the Rhône and the
present large docks developed on that site, the ring-canal now being without trade.

There is also the city developed from numerous small villages. Bonn,
with some forty villages, is a good example. It is likely that each village was
developed on a tributary and they coalesced into an Old Town.

Thirdly, there are the rare towns which have developed on both sides of
the (main) river early. There may be two early settlements (e.g., Cambridge,
Danish and Saxon; York, a Roman fort on the north east, a Roman civilian
settlement on the other bank: Beresford & St Joseph, 1979). This gives an impetus
to joint development (once the risk of joint warfare — see Dinant — is over). In
Britain, Edward the Elder in the early tenth century was fortifying both sides of
sites on rivers (e.g. Buckingham on the Ouse, Stamford on the Welland, south of
Nottingham on the Trent: *Anglo Saxon Chronicle*). This was perhaps started by
Alfred the Great, to repel Vikings (see Chapter 12). The present ex-fortified river
towns are east-facing ones in England (e.g. Norwich, York) and seem to be devised
on the same plan: to repel Vikings. Italy has the same pattern (Fig. 8.2) — double
bank settlement because of double fortification.

Then there are the towns with massive re-development on a scale that masks the old (basic) plan. This is not only from the ravages of war. Cambridge, for instance, lost a quarter of its old town in the fifteenth century when the land became (University) Colleges and their gardens. Wharfage was lost at the same time. On the Continent, war damage is more often made good: the old towns being restored (e.g., Nüremburg, Warsaw). Britain is more likely to redevelop and lose her heritage (e.g., Coventry: Fig. 8.5).

Fig. 8.5 contd.

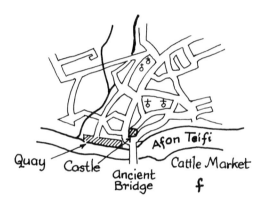

Quay    Castle    Ancient    Cattle Market
Ancient
Bridge    **f**

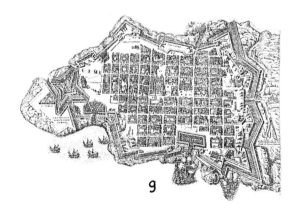

**g**

# 9

# The Placing and Purpose of Settlements

## Introduction

Rivers are the key to European development; the Rhône aided Roman civilisation, and the Rhine and Danube complete the trio. The thrust of European settlement was east to west, with settlements on communication routes. On larger rivers, upstream places like Augsburg (Danube) and Bamberg (Danube tributary) became centres of trade, craft and government, and middle-river places like Koblenz, Würms and Strasbourg became German strongholds. Towns were the enduring legacy of Rome, though, as a principle, Roman sites were chosen for strategic reasons, and only remained settled in mediaeval and later times if they were also good for trade. Most of Europe was settled before the thirteenth century.

## Interpretation
### *(Fig. 9.1)*

Recognition of river use is important, whether in town or village. Great Wishford, above the flood plain of the English Wylye, has no stream flowing down from it. That cannot be; people settle where they can drink — and, sure enough, a decaying bridge shows the former presence of a stream. Lippborg, on a tributary of the German Lippe, is one grade more complex. The main valley was wet and flooded, so without a settlement: living away from the valley was much more suitable. The immediate tributary bears the old mill. This was still too liable to flood. So the old village street is not centred on this tributary, but is at right angles to it. Looking in the stream wall, it can be seen that water enters from here through a pipe. The tiny tributary which ran down the village centre, which was the supply stream (and which was too small for much fierce flood), is now underground.

Water-based industry is characteristic, and has been shown in Fig. 2.4. It is not always where expected! In the inland English market town of Dorchester is an old canal and a pathway with associated buildings; here barges came up the River Frome. Dorchester is a county capital, but when mills became more important in the later Middle Ages, blocking the river, it lost out on trade, though some remained.

The next series of Figures show building-patterns for river use, non-use, rebuilding after use, and decay. Bayon contrasts the new housing, which just happens to be set near the river, and the old mill stream, with housing built to use the river — including discharging waste into it! This part has an air of decay. (The wealthy lived on the hill-top, which perhaps was healthier.)

# The Low Countries
*(Figs 9.2-9.5)*

## Introduction

The Low Countries were special: facing both inland (France and Germany), and

seawards, (the Thames, Great Ouse and the rest of Eastern England). Part or all of the Low Countries has always had social dynamism: perhaps on the Toynbee hypothesis (e.g. 1955) that this is created by stress. Even in the absence of enemies, the Low Countries, as their name implies, have always been under threat from the sea.

The points of development were set in the Middle Ages. Bruges, Ghent, Antwerp and Dordrecht were all good positions for trade and communications (there was early drainage in Holland, particularly, but the special wealth was from trade, not farming). Two types of town emerged, those orientated to the Zuider Zee; and those orientated to the Rijn and Maas estuaries, early Middle Ages trading-towns, just above the tidal zone, like Waalwijk, Tiel and Dordrecht (Dordrecht being, like Rotterdam now, a trans-shipment centre). Rhine towns were important for the Baltic trade.

With New World trade, towns on the mouths of small rivers, like Amsterdam and Rotterdam, expanded. For internal communications canals were needed. The Amsterdam-Tiel Canal (see below) became important. All parts became connected to the Rhine — and to the sea. Rotterdam in and from the nineteenth century became the 'emporium of the world'. The centres grew, developing their own communities. Dutch Gheest, in the south, was sandy, infertile land (until modern farming), cheap for manufacturers; hence the nineteenth-century manufacturing development of Tilburg, Eindhoven and Helmond, and hence also the canals to link with the

main network. Small towns on the Ijssel are set back from the water, e.g., Wijke, Olst, Epse and Deventer. Zutphen does front the water — but this only later. The old town is on a tributary (now a canal). Towns near the major centres of colonial trade, like Amsterdam, developed inland (water-connected) towns for processing colonial goods, e.g. Zarstreek, Langstraat. Aalsmeer (Fig. 9.2) has found a new rôle

with a marina, sited in the old commercial port. This pattern will be seen again: the port now unfit for commercial trade, for one reason or another, which has become a marina, or otherwise turned to tourism. It is better than decay, but there is never the same atmosphere as when a place thrives in its own right (e.g. modern Bruges).

The mid-nineteenth-century picture of Makken (Fig. 9.3) is worth study. The river — embanked well above the drained farmland — is the main traffic route; the traffic there is plainly heavy and long-distance: that on the road, typically local. Wind pumps bring water up to the river. Housing is on the high level, with canal access and, as it is above river level, flooding is improbable. A minor point of interest is that in the drainage dykes the plants are correctly drawn — tall monocotyledons are tall without grazing, short with it!

## Towns
Looking at these in more detail, the first Figure shows a typical plan of a Waal (Rhine) town, with the centre — sensibly — on the highest ground available. Arnhem is large and very prosperous, Tiel intermediate and rather decayed, especially for water trade: contrast the

Fig. 9.1 Recognition of river use. a) Great Wishford, England. b) Lippborg, Germany. (Positions altered to show all parts: main tributary is a long way from river (above flood plain), minor tributary and old village is upstream — not downstream — of mill.) c) Dorchester, England. d) Salzhemendorf, Germany. e) Stockbridge, England (little recent use, this view). f) Bad Salzuflen, Germany. g) Rodenburg, Germany. h) Bayon, France. i) Annecy, France.

Fig. 9.2 Aalsmeer marina.

Fig. 9.3 Makken, The Netherlands, mid-nineteenth century (by permission of the Fitzwilliam Museum, Cambridge). Detail.

wide under-used wharf with the busy docks of Arnhem. Arnhem has, downstream of the old town, the present large industrial area. This is often the position, as there tends to be more trade downstream (Chapter 6). This is an advantage, of course, to a more pollution-conscious generation. The river curves round the higher ground of the old centre, the church being at the top (a large public building here has the secondary advantage of being a refuge in flood). Aalten, on an Ijssel tributary (Grevink), has the same pattern. From the river, the road goes up the hill to the church. Here, though, the industry is upstream of the old centre. Tiel has a ferry, but the busy river makes crossing difficult. Tiel profited by the canal to Amsterdam, but the Figure demonstrates that this town developed on the river: the canal has nothing to do with settlement. The Maas valley is a string of small ports. Culijk is more of a city than Grave, though it is much decayed from its former activity. Both have a few barges, Grave the more pleasure craft. Such a contrast in atmosphere to bustling Rotterdam!

Tiel is a river town and contrasts with nineteenth-century Helmond, which is a canal town. The canal is vital to the town's communications, the river irrelevant.

Bruges in the fifteenth century was described in Chapter 6: before silting spoiled the canal access. It is now revitalised, with road transport: the quieter parts are those on the old ring- and similar canals. The Figure is for contrasting with Fig. 8.2: Middleburg; it is the later version of the same town plan.

Namur is on a major river confluence (Sambre and Moselle), an excellent position for the trading-town it became. As is typical of trading-towns, the wealthy housing fronts the river: developed on from the time when merchants lived 'over the shop' or, in this case, by and over the trading-place. The wharf space, now

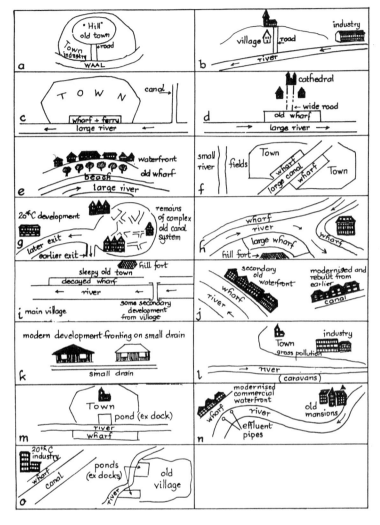

Fig. 9.4 The Low Countries. a) Waal town. b) Aalten. c) Tiel. d) Culijk. e) Grave. f) Helmond. g) Bruges. h) Namur. i) Dinant (top) Bouvignes (bottom). j) Zutphen. k) Olst. l) Diest. m) Tielt. n) Jodoigne. o) Lochem.

unnecessarily large, is still there. A few barges do still trade. As expected, such a formerly-busy junction was guarded by a fort on the hill above.

It often happens that a town has, upstream, a smaller (and, when developing, poorer) version of itself. Here this is Dinant, and, only recently (see Chapter 6), Bouvignes. Dinant had a protecting hill-fort. It is clearly sleepy (except for tourists), and was so in the nineteenth century (when the writer's forebears were surely not the only people to leave for Brussels or other pastures new). Namur is still a minor commercial centre. Dinant does not rate that. The river-fronting housing, though, shows the early trading importance. With the bridge, Dinant and the riverside edge of Bouvignes look like two parts of one town. Knowledge of development—or expert knowledge of the local history — shows this was not possible. The similarity is late, bridge-based.

Zutphen, by the Ijssel was also a trading-town, whose importance can be gauged by the size of the wharfage. This, however, though decayed in river trade, is decayed in no other sense. Merchant wealth on the Ijssel was considerable. It is a late development, the old centre being on the tributary. Redevelopment in the centre is, carefully, still canal-based — in appearance, if not in fact. Tradition is preserved. The Dutch are rooted in their waterways, to a greater extent than other nations (e.g., the Figure showing bungalows facing a drain: the nearest thing available to old houses on canals).

Diest is on a tributary of the Demer. Upstream the tributary is ornamental, and the water clear. It curves round the town: a good defensive pattern. Belgian water-purification leaves a lot to be desired, and in the industrial area downstream of the centre, pollution is gross. This is a town set in the early phase, which never developed to having busy use of the main river — in contrast to Zutphen, an otherwise similar sort of town. The main Demer protects another side of the town.

Tielt is also an old-established town, famous for softening flax in its river water (for the textile industry in Ghent). The town, like for example Aalten, is on a slight hill, with a tributary of the Schelde flowing beside. 'Flowing' is hardly the right word. Water movement, in flat Flanders, is sluggish (which makes pollution dispersal difficult). 'Sluggish' is no word for the town, which, like so much of Flemish Belgium, is vibrant with new industry and wealth. The old is still there to be found: the dock, now a pond intended to be ornamental, the wharf and the canalised waterway all much polluted. One way of life decayed: another, not water-based, appeared.

## Villages

Jodoigne is a peaceful, small town in comparison; the old commercial area near the river with good wharf space is clear. The old centre is up the hill. The river has been redeveloped and walled, and signs of navigation have gone — but signs of (mostly former!) effluent discharge are far from gone. The old industrial area was upstream of the commercial (downstream of the Centre). Industry above barges was a sensible pattern, industry being liable to block passage.

Lochem has old docks on the Berkel in the village (the ancient centre being on the hill above). These are decayed and semi-ornamental. Business has left. There is no activity on the river outside the village either, though the old towpath is still there. The river and village have been by-passed by the Twenthe Kanaal (like Nayland, Chapter 6). And on the canal there is wealthy business, factories with water-borne freight. There is continuity of business but change of site (cf. Hoyoux, Chapter 2).

South Maasland (Fig. 9.5) is new development, arranged so the Julianakanaal is available for freight, and a motor-way for traffic. Between the two lie new (but over-similar) settlements, e.g., Born and Buchten, with roads connecting the two routes, and each other. For business, efficient waterways are still in the forefront of Dutch planning.

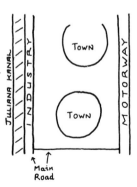

Fig. 9.5 South Maasland, plan.

# France
*(Figs 9.6-9.9)*

## From the Vosges to Alençon *(Fig. 9.6)*

The Meuse-Moselle area developed early, with cheap water transport from the centres. The late-twentieth-century lack of vitality is in marked contrast to, say, Flemish Belgium. Luneville, an ex-royal residence, and Blaineville are good examples (see also Bayon, above). Both are on the Meurthe. The Blaineville waterfront was formerly impressive and is now decayed — note the river entrance to what was a grand hotel. Luneville reached the stage of three channels to the river. In Haroué, both the old chateau, and the new housing estate benefit from views of the river. The former is by the crossing (site of the Old Tower?).

Chalons-sur-Marne is a communications centre. It is built on a tributary to the Marne, as expected, and on quite a large tributary too, also as expected. Upstream of the square, the square being the main commercial stop, is the old industry: the same unmistakeable pattern. The tributary now goes underground through the square, past the present cathedral. Somewhere here were the wharfs. The stream is not clean above the square and it emerges dirtier: there is too much pollution. It is, though, long since the tributary was the hub of trade. The water-trade is now on the Canal de la Marne, to the side.

Vitry-le-François is a lesser communications town, upstream of Chalons (River Ornain), now on the junction of the Canal de la Marne and the Marne au Rhin Canal. Modern industry is on the canal, separated from the town: developed for the canal (cf. the Lea and Essex Stour, England: Figs 2.4 and 6.15).

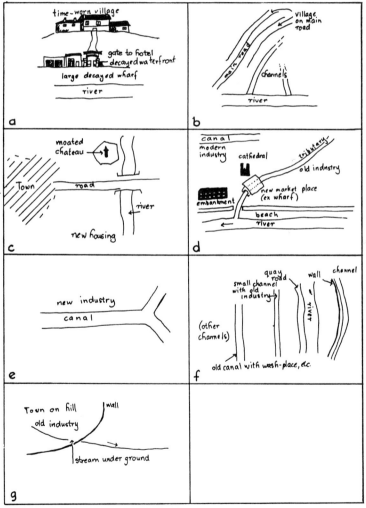

Fig. 9.6 North Central France. a) Blainville. b) Luneville. c) Haroué. d) Chalons sur Marne. e) Vitry le François. f) Montargis. g) Pithiviers.

Vitry is further upstream, i.e. further from Paris, and is overshadowed by Chalons.

Moving west, the next series of towns have waterfronts on the main rivers — not on a tributary beside, like Chalons. The Seine is the Paris river, formerly with excellent trading, still with good commerce (see Fig. 6.14). Capitals attract goods. There is still riverside industry and (some) freight carriage.

West again are the fortress market towns like Alençon. Pithiviers, on the Essone, is a local centre on a minor river. It is built on a defensive hill, and the position of the old walls is still visible. The river flows through the town with some former industry and it emerges out of the old town from underground, as is depicted in the *Nuremburg Chronicle* (Fig. 8.2). A bend in the river provides extra defence. This was a market town (not a major trade town attracting goods from afar like Chalons).

Between these, geographically and in pattern, is Montargis, on the Loing, and on the 1604 Canal de Briare. As at Pithiviers, there are lades with old industry. As at Chalons, there is a main river, a canal channel and a defensive outer channel. Montargis combines communications, industry and (still visible) fortifications. There is also a nice wash-place remaining, with the old access into the town.

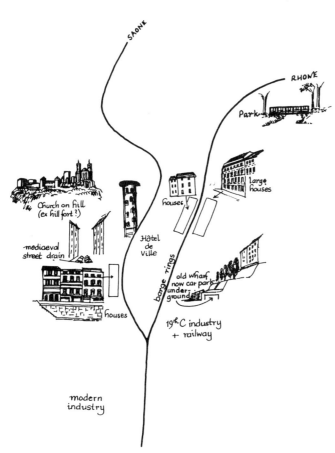

Fig. 9.7 Lyon, France.

## Lyon *(Fig. 9.7)*

Lyon, on the confluence of the Saone and the Rhône, with communications to Switzerland (and hence the east), to the north and to the Mediterranean, has been a great city since Roman times. It had much traffic — including main Mediterranean traffic before the railway link — but was primarily a capital rather than a trading-centre. It has had flourishing minor industry for long: earlier, silk, etc.; now factories, etc., well downstream of the main centre. The old city is by the Saone, which had a hill behind available for defence and as a refuge from flood. The oldest present buildings are Renaissance. The old sewer is the old tributary and still runs along the old centre, parallel to the river. It is now ornamental. On the hill there used to be a Roman camp, later presumably a hill-fort. Now, on this site, guarding the city from a different peril, is a nineteenth-century church erected in gratitude for the ending of an epidemic. In addition to the guards on the hill above, there was, naturally, also the Old Tower by the river.

The city grew. The characteristic good French houses became bigger as the years went by, and so the Saone frontage of the old city has bigger houses than the centre; house size increases progressively to the east of the Saone, the west of the Rhône and the east of the Rhône. There was superb frontage development. Wharfs were not large (the barge rings are still there, and note the new use of wharfs as underground car parks). The main docks were built downstream, at the confluence — well away, now, from the town centre. Railways here joined the docks (like Strasbourg: Fig. 9.9 and Fig. 6.20). Upstream an old meander cut off in the late nineteenth century formed the basis of a pleasure garden. Ornamental — and other — water use is also seen in the various fountains, as expected in this very cultured French city.

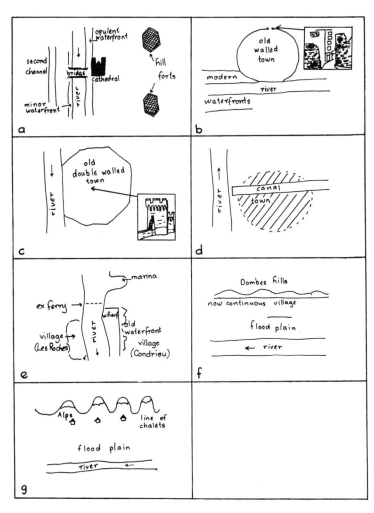

Fig. 9.8 South-central France. a) Vienne. b) Arles. c) Avignon. d) Beaucaire. e) Les Roches and Condrieu. f) Rhône floodplain. g) Dolon flood plain.

## Lower Rhône settlements
*(Fig 9.8)*

Vienne is downstream on the Rhône with nice waterfront development, and hillforts above. Its use

of the river has
decayed. All the
expected fea-
tures are there
— old bridge,
access, quays
(on the far side),
but it contrasts
sharply with
the river-active
Bray or Nogent
(Fig. 6.13)!

Towns
contrasted in
structure or
function are of-
ten illuminat-
ing. Arles is the
town nearest
the mouth of the
River Rhône,
Avignon is an
equally major
town a little
upstream. Avi-
gnon was devel-
oped for the Sec-
ond Popes in the
fourteenth cen-
tury. This was
before large
cannon balls
became com-

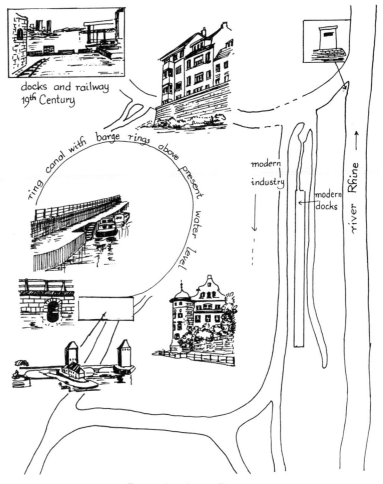

Fig. 9.9 Strasbourg, France.

mon and the mediaeval fortifications are picturesque. Arles needed defence much
later and has massive stoneworks. Both towns had Rhône trade. Arles is now a
centre for canals as well and has pleasure craft as well as a little commercial traffic.
It is far the more river-active of the two, with a much larger quay area.

Tarascon and Beaucaire lie almost opposite each other, between Arles and
Avignon, and are now joined by a bridge. The Rhône here is much channelised and
embanked, and former town connections have gone. Both towns are centred off the
river. Tarascon is quiet. Beaucaire is bustling, more of a trading type, with a canal.

Two smaller places upstream are Condrieu and Les Roches, also now connected by a bridge. Les Roches has, and had, little interest in the river, compared
to the trading-town of Condrieu (see the wharfs). Trade has now passed Condrieu
by — and, keeping the river connection, it has developed a marina just upstream
(not on the old quays).

**The Middle Rhône flood plain** *(Fig. 9.8)*
The Rhône flood plain has, upstream of Lyon, continuous settlement along the northern edge — developed from old villages away from the main flood area. With the present drainage and flood protection there is now a new village in the plain itself. (Old settlements in recently drained wetlands are usually on islands, e.g. Ely and Upware in the English Fenland.) On a lesser scale, with houses instead of village, the same occurs in the Dolon flood plain.

**Strasbourg** *(Fig. 9.9)*
Strasbourg forms a convenient bridge to Germany, as it has developed under both influences. The city is on the Bruche, which is on the Ill, a tributary of, and connecting to, the Rhine. Later, a ring-canal was constructed and eventually two canals were added: the Marne au Rhin and the Rhône au Rhin. The ring-architecture is mainly German: the later, mainly French. Strasbourg's strategic importance is obvious — even to those with no knowledge of France-Germany history. Town fortifications were extensive, and can be seen on the entrance to the ring-canal and elsewhere. As ships got bigger, the canal became too small for the main trade. (There is now a pound-lock on the ring-canal. Barge rings are still present on the canal wall, but the water level has been much lowered. Tourist barges pass frequently.) Underground streams come in to the canal, in the same pattern as in fifteenth-century Germany (Fig. 8.2). The fish wharf was just outside the ring, removed from the wealthy merchants on the ring. The harbour moved outside the city entrance and subsequently nearer to the Rhine. There is a network of channels and rail connections for trans-shipment (Fig. 6.22). There used to be a canal connection to the ring-canal (the Ill-Rhin), but it was filled in during the nineteenth century when it was no longer needed.

# Germany
## (Figs 9.10, 9.11)

### Introduction
The excellent German habit of preserving the past means that many features, seen in part or in ruin in other countries, can be interpreted by reference to their complete representation here.

### Trading-towns
Donauworth, near the Lech-Donau confluence was a wealthy trading-town with a good waterfrontage — a German version of Namur. With the loss of the upper Donau trade, Donauworth converted to business and is thriving (though less wealthy, comparatively speaking). Landsberg was less stately (with less wealthy housing) to start with — but was also a trading-town (on the Lech) and, when trade passed it by, it declined, like Dinant and unlike Namur. It now has many hotels. Smaller river-ports need not necessarily decline: Tielt, Zutphen, Bedford, Nogent-sur-Seine show otherwise — to name but a few. Landsberg and sixteenth-century Füssen — further up the Lech — are remarkably similar. The town pattern is the

Fig. 9.10 German towns and villages, 1. a) Donauworth. b) Landsberg. c) Bamberg. d) Forcheim. e) Augsburg. f) Ulm. g) Gernsbach. h) Ellingen. i) Blaubeuren. j) Fussen, sixteenth century woodcut.

a

b

c

same; the houses are only a little more ragged in Füssen; the position of the town wall (fortification) in Landsberg is clear from the Füssen picture, the weir is the same, with the same 'barge gutter'. The Füssen wharf is by the weir and bridge. Navigation is all too clearly difficult, and it is hardly surprising that river trade was dropped as soon as possible. The present Lech confirms this view — it would require very major engineering to make navigation easy. Landsberg's stream — the tributary on which the town was built — is, once more, underground, as in the *Nuremburg Chronicle* pictures (Fig. 8.2). There is also a hill-fort to guard crossing, trade and town.

### Craft towns

Bamberg and Forcheim are another pair of mother-and-daughter towns, this time craft towns, but Bamberg, the downstream one, is also trading. Bamberg, on the confluence of the Regnitz and Main (leading to the Rhine and North Sea) was more concerned with craft and export than with trading — so is not so river-fronted architecturally. It continued to develop, way beyond Donauworth. Its fifteenth-century aspect was fairly standard (its hills being, as usual, exaggerated in the *Nuremburg Chronicle*). Forcheim is upstream, beside the Regnitz, formerly also with craft and water-based industry. Its manufactures used to go downstream to Bamberg.

The population of Augsburg, by the Lech, was massacred in 1125. In 1458 Aeneas Silvius described it as the dirtiest city in the world, though Diets were held there. It has been a major craft centre, for armoury among others, and the firm of Fuggers (who sustained the empire of Charles V) were of Augsburg. In the sixteenth century (Fig. 8.5) some streets had open channels and were lined with small shops. Augsburg had then no mills. But later it became heavily industrialised

d

e

f

with various lades.

Ulm is also a craft town (Figs 9.10f, and 8.2), this time on the Donau. Comparing the old and new, the town is of course much bigger and the walls have been replaced, but it is still, in a sense, a walled city by the river. The present underground stream is on the left of the new Fig. A tower present in the fif-

teenth century is still present now! The bridge is to the right. The hill height — though exaggerated in the old picture — is sufficient for the stream to drive mills. In the lower town the stream is now underground, but it is industrial above and is suitable for industry. Neither picture shows much wharf and waterfrontage: craft export requires much less than trading (not needing the storage time, or space for goods). This is important. It shows that towns with little surviving wharfage could yet have been river-based earlier. The fifteenth-century rafts (going downstream only — just for export) and boats had fully adequate wharfs and passage in the past. The boats are mostly on the unfortified further bank, but then there is a bridge and light goods could have been removed quickly in the event of a raid. Günzburg, downstream, is laid out like Ulm, but smaller, with an old centre on the hill and a good ex-commercial waterfront.

## Aristocratic towns

Rastatt was aristocratic in a big way, a court, a capital. The bridge leads straight towards the Palace, and there is little waterfront. Goods must be received, but the town's business is government rather than trade or craft. Upstream of Rastatt, still on the Murg, is the mill town of Gernsbach, with grand engineering. The old large

Fig. 9.11 German towns and villages, 2. a) Nienburg. b) Rastatt. c) Treutlingen (right) and Pappenheim (left). d) Munsterschwarzach, left above; Munsterstadt, right above; Munsterschwarzenau, below. e) Rhein Town, Mainz-type. f) Wildberg. g) Nuthelm. h) Tubingen. i) Middle Ages reconstruction of Tubingen.

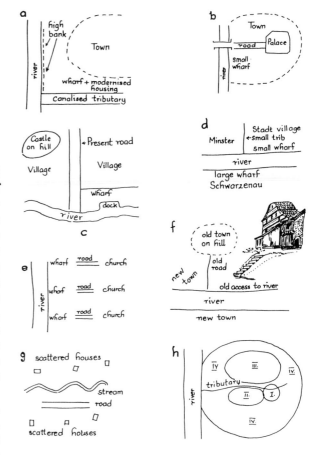

weirs (cf. Landsberg and Füssen) direct the river off sideways, and the mill-water continues straight down, in a repeating pattern, the mills being as close as water power allows. The town stream has an underground exit, also in the old pattern (and in the town is partly underground, partly above ground where it was formerly used). Upstream is a lesser equivalent — there is less grand housing, it is smaller, etc.

Ellingen, by the Regnitz, is a typical relic settlement. The old bridge crosses the moat to a fortified gate leading to the Lord's place. The moat is supplied by a small tributary, now piped underground. The water is for fortification and ornament in front, and behind for the duck (formerly the moat here was wider and defensive). The village is beyond. Water is for (ex-) supply, defence and food (fishpond too), all combined. This can well be studied as early and very efficient planning.

### Other types

Nienburg by the Weser shows an early pattern. It has a canalised tributary beside, formerly navigable, and away from the centre (it is not a trading-town). It did not expand to the river bank — but, well downstream, there is new riverside industry. Presumably a smaller tributary led from the town to the canal (cf. Lippborg, Fig. 9.1). The canal has a ruined lock, and former industry beyond. The housing is now redeveloped, and the canal ornamental.

Tübingen, on a tributary of the Neckar still has the tributary down the old main street. The reconstruction shows the former use (see also Chapter 3). This is less hygienic than one could wish, but a source of much civic pride! Most towns later put such streams underground but some (see Lyon, Fig. 9.7) did not. Many villages

(e.g. Fig. 9.13) left streams beside the roads. Development followed in phases here.

Treutlingen and Pappenheim are small places on either side of the Altmuhle. The river-based Treutlingen, with a much larger quay, contrasts with the defensive and aristocratic Pappenheim, clustered round a hill with a castle on top, and no interest in the river. One is business, the other not.

Three nearby villages on the Main show a pleasing variety. Munsterschwarzach has the Minster, with a typical monastery layout: mills to the side, supply through the centre. Munsterstadt is a non-river-based settlement beside, separated by a small stream, while, over the river, Munsterschwarzenau was a trading-settlement, with much quay, though with little wealth. Once more, now trade has passed by, the place has acquired pleasure craft.

Rotenberg, on the Würme, has old docks in the town centre (like Lochem, Fig. 9.5), showing how a town of modern type can have remaining features of old river-use.

Also see Fig. 9.11e for the river-based distribution patterns of Rhein towns such as Mainz, Wurms.

Hill settlements of the southwest are of considerable interest. Blaubeuren is on limestone, so it has a fairly gentle flow even though it is among hills (Haslam, 1987). The river is in four channels, with (ex-) mills: that of the picture shows the traditional village duck. Settlements on Resistant, or similar rock, have streams with fierce flow. Wildberg on the Nagold has mills outside the village. The old centre is away from the river, but the old access from this and the old water-house are still there (its notice mentions 1446). It is not impossible that boats came here in the Middle Ages. Wildberg is now a tourist town. Nagold, from which the river takes its name was much more wealthy and is, still, more self-sufficient, with less need of tourists. Upstream again is Rohrdorf with a mill leat, so that there are two parallel channels in the town. Mills are frequent, and water is retained (ponded) within the town. Sawmills still exist, but they are not water-powered.

Moving to smaller settlements, where *Heim* and *Dorf* are common ancient names, a characteristic '-heim' village is shown in Dottenheim with two rows of houses and the (former) stream in the street between. Itzing illustrates the '-dorf' typical pattern, as a Cluster rather than a village Street (though it does not have '-dorf' in its name). Nuttelm has houses in two rows, but set back a fields' width from the stream (Figs 10.4, 9.11g).

**Double-Channel towns** *(Fig. 9.12)*
The final German examples cited are to show the Double Channel (see Chapter 8). Warendorf on the Ems is a demonstration piece, the outer river used now for recreation, though formerly it was little used. The inner river has the mills and the old town access for boats and water supply; the mill is now redeveloped for non-water power; and the Wasserstrasse leads to the Old Centre. Verden on the Aller shows the same pattern.

Itzehoe on the Stor in Schleswig Holstein (the pattern extended into Old Denmark) has the same basic pattern. Here, though, the inner channel has not been maintained — it has been converted to a very nice town ornament. The outer channel is the (large) river and as usual is without any relics of town use. But there is now much new riverside industry, away from the town. Kellinghauser is a smaller and poorer, upstream version of Itzehoe (as so often). It is on the same plan — except that here the inner channel was filled in and is gone.

# Czechoslovakia
## *(Fig. 9.13)*

The town of Trebon is the only one described here: a fishpond town, on the Golden Canal. The canal was dug for new fishponds and town access in the fourteenth century. The town is still (semi-)walled, the access gate from the canal is fortified and there used to be a drawbridge for better defence. The Czech town square is often large, as here, and has pleasing fountains. The moat on one side is the canal, and on the other is dry (dry moats were common, as in Augsburg: Fig. 8.2). The town has not expanded much outside its old walls, except on the drawbridge side.

Many Czech villages preserve the old stream pattern. (Most new housing is concentrated in the cities.) A small brook ran through the High Street, or the road leading to it (see Chapters 3 and 12). If in the High Street, the channel (at the side) is usually cobbled or stoned; in side streets it is more likely to be grassed over. Typically the channel is bridged to the old houses, but not to the new ones —

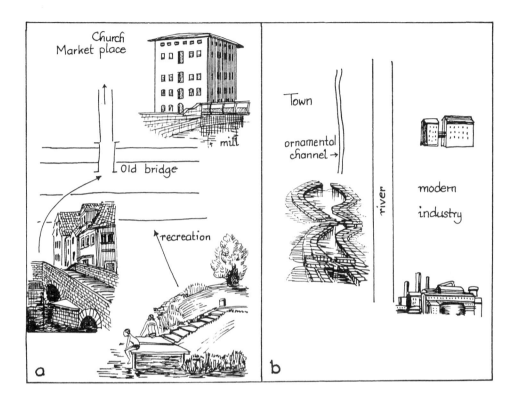

Fig. 9.12 The Double Channel or Town Island. a) Warendorf, b) Itzehoe, Germany.

Fig. 9.13 Czechoslovak towns and villages. a) Trebon. Moat is partly the Golden Canal, originally for access to town and fish-ponds, and partly dry. b) c) Villages. d) Ponds.

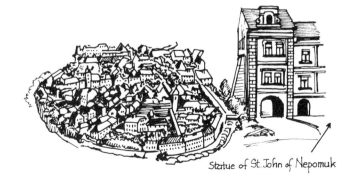

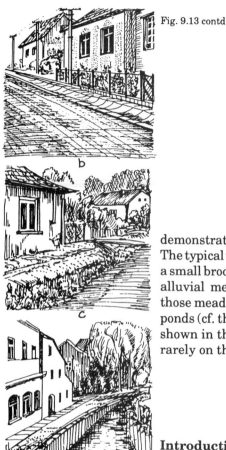

Fig. 9.13 contd

"Sky fed"

P   Fish pond
V   Village

d

demonstrating the recent lowering of the water table. The typical village is clustered, with a stream below, and a small brook through. Until the 1940s village houses by alluvial meadows held a strip of land down through those meadows. Many villages are associated with fishponds (cf. the town of Trebon, above), and the pattern is shown in the Fig. with a chain of ponds. The village is rarely on the upstream end of the chain.

# Denmark
*(Fig. 9.14)*

## Introduction

For most of its history, Denmark has looked out to the sea more than in to its rivers. There were flourmills on the rivers, but little other industry until recently (see also Chapter 5). The north-central infertile heath was developed in the nineteenth century, with much more industry, but by then with less reliance on water for communications.

## Aristocratic towns

Viborg has a very small wharf area (on a lake),

Fig. 9.14 Danish towns and villages. a) Viborg. b) Ribe. c) Varde. d) Skjern. e) Lovtrop.

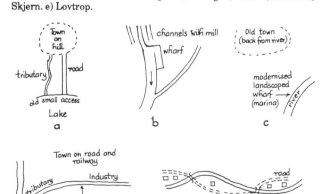

now used for pleasure craft. The small size is because, like Rastatt, this was a Court town (the capital from about 1000-1600 A.D.), with little trading or exports. It has the usual town stream (dirty and ornamental below — if that is not a contradiction in terms).

Ribe, though likewise an ex-royal town and a Bishop's Seat, is also a trading-town with the outside waterways and inner stub-canal (i.e., a canal to the middle of town and no further) to the harbour in the town centre, as, basically, in Middleburg (though here without much fear of inland attack). It is sited between the Ribe and a major tributary of that river, giving by nature three moated sides (and the fourth is not joined). The other ancient towns of Jutland are on hills. Water is here used for defence, instead. With natural boundaries, not ones taking much manpower, time and wealth to dig, Ribe has been less cramped in its ring than, say, Strasbourg. Lades from the river run through the town with good-quality old mills.

**Other patterns** *(see also Chapter 10)*
Varde was a commercial centre from ancient times, set well back from a (formerly flooding) river. Its new marina looks suspiciously as if it was redeveloped from an old harbour! Skjern is another town with much nineteenth-century expansion. The town is on the railway and road, as predictable. But there is a town stream (to the Skjern River) suitable for boats, leading out of the industrial part of town — and with a boat factory outside the town. Grinsted, on the inland heath, has less suggestion of old use, but has the town stream, with the main river below, and the new industry beyond the river — a simple expanding small-town pattern. Holsterbro is the basic plan, on a tributary at right angles to the stream. Brande is another settlement on a rise, the stream backing onto the town. The stream had mills. This is a decayed, formerly rich, market town, redeveloped industrially with the old pattern still showing.

South Denmark has an ancient village pattern, quite unlike the cluster-villages to the south. The houses, as in Lovtrop, are scattered lengthwise and mostly between the stream and the road, with therefore an unusually great length of stream per house. Villages such as St Jyndevad, more developed, now have houses on both sides of the road, with the stream beyond: a common pattern (see Chapter 10).

# Britain
*(Fig. 9.15)*

**Introduction**
Settlement development depends on both natural and human factors. New or tiny settlements may develop through quite fortuitous circumstances. The decayed Yorkshire town of Hedon was built (by the Lord of Preston) as a new river-port in the twelfth century (with *c.* 780m of harbour frontage and three docks in the town centre; cf. Fig. 9.4, Lochem). It did well for a time, but competition from Hull and Ravensford (now decayed) and the silting of the River Hedon, caused its decline in the fifteenth century. Human and natural factors were adverse (Beresford & St

Joseph 1979). Stourport was a little alehouse in a sandy waste until the Stafford-shire and Worcestershire Canal was completed, when a new town shot up by the junction with the Severn. It quickly had wharfs and docks, boat-building yards and warehouses, becoming the main emporium for the West Midlands. Stourport survived the decay of the canal trade, and is still a busy town (Hoskins, 1953).

Torksey, on the other hand, had even better communications but declined on their loss. This was a busy and prosperous port, 60 miles (96km) inland along the Trent, and on the junction of the Roman Fossdyke leading to Lincoln and the south (Chapter 6). It was of crucial importance. The Anglo-Saxons had no main sea port in Boston; Torksey was developed in the Norman period, and by the late thirteenth century replaced Lincoln as the wool staple market. In 1237 Torksey could be described as the key of Lindsey (Lincolnshire) just as Dover is the key of England. The Fossdyke was smaller than the Trent, and larger boats increasingly needed trans-shipment at Torksey (see Chapter 6 for the hindrance this can be to trade — Denver sluice). In spite of repeated reconstructions of the waterway, trade declined, the main decline being in the fourteenth century. A major reconstruction was done

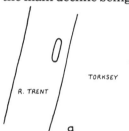

in the Canal Age in 1740 (in 1735 loaded waggons could drive along the silted channel). Torksey is now a small, remote village with little left of its former glory (Beresford & St Joseph, 1979). There is, however, an island in the Trent opposite the village. The Trent is wide here, so this is perceived as a river island rather than a bridged double channel. But a 'double channel', an old slit-harbour, it surely is (see above and Chapter 8).

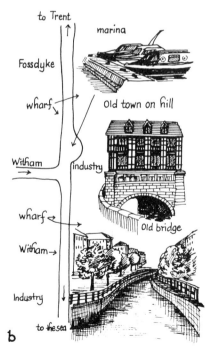

## A city with two waterway patterns

Lincoln is a Roman site connected south by the Romans via the Witham to Cambridgeshire and west by the Fossdyke to the Trent. Defoe (1724-7) describes it as ancient, ragged and decaying, with the ruins of religious houses. One part is, as he says, flat in the bottom, so that the Witham sometimes flows in the street; the other part is on the top of a high hill with a cathedral. The steepest slopes are best for trade and business. His conclusion is that Lincoln is a dying and dirty town. Two and a half centuries later, it is neither! Lincoln now has two main points of interest: a housed bridge and the waterfronts. As we approach

Fig. 9.15 British towns and villages. a) Torksey. b) Lincoln. c) Bury St Edmunds. d) Newark. e) Llanfair Ceireinion. f) Godmanchester to left, Huntingdon to right. g) Yeovil. h) Bruton. i) Burwell. j) Little Misbourne. k) Otmoor. l) Hurstbourne Tarrant. m) R. Yar, Isle of Wight. n) Barrington. o) Much Hadham (and see Fig. 13.3).

the city, the Witham waterfront is, as expected, redeveloped from river-based trade and industry. To the west, however, is a second waterfront and a larger harbour. That is the Fossdyke connection, the earlier harbour, pre-dating the main trade down the Witham to Boston. The harbour is now a marina, the Fossdyke still being a functioning canal. Once more the old priorities remain and can be found.

## An Abbey river-town

Bury St Edmunds is an Abbey town dominated by the Church. Defoe (1724-7) comments on its gracious living and sweet air. He describes the river Lark as a small branch of a small river (Little Ouse) which the town and gentry had made navigable to where it joined the main waterways, so that coal, wine, iron, lead and

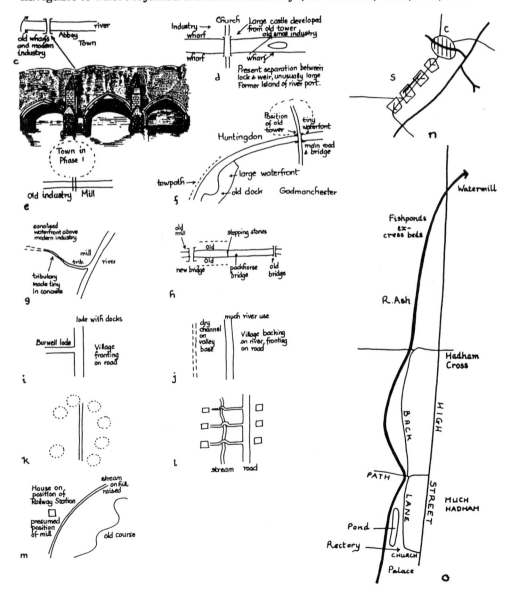

other heavy goods could (in Defoe's time) come from Kings Lynn. As usual, further reconstruction took place, though, as noted earlier, pound-locks were never introduced here. Trade decayed in the later nineteenth century, also as usual in Britain.

Downstream from the old town is the new industrial estate: exactly where expected. The Abbey gate is splendid, a fortified entrance (see Fig. 8.2: Fortified Bridges; and later entrance-bridges, Figs 2.4 and 2.8). Although the main wharf was later outside this, boats naturally passed within the entrance — where intruders could be halted and tolls paid.

### A castle river-town

Newark-on-Trent is described by Defoe (1724-7) as a handsome, well-built town with a noble square (still there). 'The Trent divides itself here', Defoe writes, 'and makes an Island, and the bridges [plural] lead just to the foot of the castle wall, so that while this place is in the hands of any party, there was no travelling but by their leave.' But all the travelling into the north at that time was by Nottingham Bridge (well to the west). The present island, used for the lock, is thus the remnants of a larger island: the Double Channel island as in, e.g., Warendorf (Fig. 9.12). The Old Tower by the crossing has been developed into a noble castle. The (sole) bridge leads to the square.

### Defensible border towns

Llanfair Ceireinion on the Welsh Marches (borders) is a town stuck in Phase I (Fig. 8.2, the *Nuremburg Chronicle* phase: Chapter 8), a defensible hill which never grew, having no good communications or resources. It was just a necessary town for Border warfare. The fortifications have gone. The mill was opposite the town, and downstream of the crossing are the descendant buildings of water-dependent industry. Welshpool, downstream and close to the much-navigated Severn, developed industry (many woollen-mills), and throve rather better. Here, as often in Britain, the poor end of town is downstream on the river — avoided by choice by the better-off (it was damp and polluted, so unhealthy; and often overcrowded, aggravating both dirt and disease).

### A capital and trading-town pair

Godmanchester and Huntingdon are on opposite sides of the Great Ouse, both chartered in the thirteenth century. Defoe, writing in pre-railway Britain could still describe both as 'good towns'. He praised Huntingdon, the county seat, more. This had higher social rank, a bridge, and an Old Fort guarding the crossing (which developed to a Norman keep and later decayed). Huntingdon has not, and clearly never had, much in the way of a waterfront. It was a County seat, and on the Old North Road from London to Edinburgh (so with a central Street, see the Rib, Chapter 2. This Old North Road is the ancient Way, Ermine Street). River trade in England might have been owned, but was not run, by the socially high.

Godmanchester was a trading-town, with a long waterfront, good harbour, possible docks, etc. The harbour is now ornamental; trade is decayed; the town is decayed to a village, with facilities for just a few pleasure craft. Huntingdon, independent of river trade, flourished, Godmanchester, recently, has not.

## A craft and a clerical town

Yeovil is on a tributary to the (Somerset) Yeo and was an industrial centre, and in a small way it still is. This tributary is now canalised upstream, towards the present Industrial Estate, near houses. Downstream the stream has recently gone to a narrow concrete channel; after all, centuries have passed since water access was needed by the town's industry (if this possible interpretation is correct!)

Bruton has a very old layout, venerable on both sides of the Brue, with a Packhorse Bridge and stepping-stones across the centre. Upstream is the (fairly) Old Bridge, downstream is the new one on the by-pass. The Old Mill was downstream, ponding the water into the village. There was a twelfth-century Benedictine monastery, and a prosperous wool trade. A Grammar School replaced the monastery after the Dissolution.

## An old river and newer canal-village

Batheaston and Bathampton are a close pair of villages. Batheaston on the (Bristol) Avon, east and upstream of the High-Society Spa town of Bath, is old and rather stately. Bathampton, on the other hand, developed on the Kennet and Avon canal in the eighteenth century. It is a pleasant village, certainly not poor — but with lower-grade housing.

## Other village patterns

Burwell, like Lochem and Rotemburg (above), has many old docks. Like Reach (Chapter 6) Burwell had a lode (a canal on an old stream) giving access to the Great Ouse and the North Sea, and was a trading-port. It had boat-builders and merchants — most houses to the west of the village street belonged to merchants, most having docks at the back (Hoskins, 1973).

Little Misbourne is a village with a stream (the Misbourne, a tributary of the Colne) along the back of the houses, obviously formerly much used. However, this stream is not the original watercourse at the base of the valley, it is an artificial channel. There are frequent mills requiring diversions and also the valley base would have been too wet for building on.

Much Hadham on the Ash (a tributary of the Lea) has another variant on the standard village pattern. Two villages, once separated by a hill, have now coalesced. The village is a Street one, on an old main road. Much Hadham proper had the church and the Bishop's Palace at the upstream end (he was the Bishop of London). Fig. 13.3 shows the pond, now used for ornament, which might have been the clerics' fishponds. The Ash runs parallel to the High Street with the Back Lane between. Direct from the centre of the High Street a lane runs to the old village supply area where the Back Lane and Ash River meet, forming a crossroads where a footpath goes up the hill. Village children still use and enjoy this part — a continuity of pattern. At a later stage, pumps appeared along the High Street. The downstream village, Hadham Cross (crossroads) has a similar pattern, however, access to the stream was here behind rather than beside the village centre, but again at a crossing (a road this time, not a path). This is the more obvious position. In Much Hadham the Rectory grounds occupied that area. The Maltings were close by. Further downstream is the fish farm, probably on an old fishpond area (the village ponds?) and downstream again the watermill, with a ford, typically placed just below it.

Barrington, by a tributary of the Cam, is another typically English pattern. The village is on a small stream, but has spread out parallel to the main tributary and is off the main road. As in Little Misbourne, the main stream is a diverted channel — the earthworks shoring it up from the lower (valley) side are considerable — and there is no stream in the valley base. As at Much Hadham, the stream is away from the main village and parallel to it.

Many villages had a stream along the high street small enough not to be very dangerous in flood and large enough still to survive. Hurstbourne Tarrant, on a Dorset Stour tributary is one such village. Yet another type is that of Fritham, on a Dorset Avon tributary, where houses surround a rather steeper valley.

A site on the Yar in the Isle of Wight has unusual channelling. Winding down the valley base is the Old Course. There is a straighter and larger channel on the slope to the left, man-made. Where one would expect to find the Old Mill, however, there is a very different type of building: an old railway station (*Victoria County History,* 1900-12); the water runs along the old railway line. However, that is not why the stream was diverted! The railway was presumably laid, for convenience, along an Old Mill leat — with the station on the mill site, and the water running beside, not on, the tracks.

Finally Otmoor, a small wetland on the Thame. Such areas have their settlements on higher lands around — uplands, non-flooded lands. There is a ring of old villages here dating back to Roman and Saxon times, and a Roman road, paved and bridged, passed through the centre. The wetlands were profitable to the Poor but unhealthy. The Seven Towns had grazing-rights of cattle, sheep, pigs and geese, and peat rights. After the Enclosure Act (1815) there was much poor grassland and some arable. This was converted to intensive farming with pump-drainage in the 1960s. The rules of use of the wetland were, as usual, extremely complex (Bond, 1981b).

# Sweden
## *(Fig. 9.16)*

Uppsala is on the river Fyris. The old town has, predictably, the cathedral. This church is on a small hill, from which the old market place leads to the old wharf. Just downstream of the wharf is a mill: it is unusual in having two wheels, one each side of the building, with a channel led off to the inner one on the town side. Where, just downstream of this, the old tower would be expected, is a larger, yellow-coloured fortification with a fortified gate, guarding the Old Town on and near the river. Just downstream again, and outside the old city wall, is the later wharf, now a car park and road. The Fyris is channelled and stoned, and shipping no longer comes this high. A little downstream is another, rather newer, and this time aristocratic, centre. An old royal palace crowns a hill — on the same side as the old town — with appropriately stately buildings around. Here, though, the wharf is on the opposite side of the river. Merchants wish to have goods conveniently near their houses, and Uppsala, as a semi-trading town, had sizeable wharfs. Nobles prefer to be apart from the messier processes of life, and their larger wharf was opposite the castle. (The castle could, of course, guard both sides). This wharf is also small (mainly for passengers and incoming goods), as is typical of aristocratic towns (see Viborg and Rastatt, above).

Pleasure cruisers now ply from this castle wharf.

The tributary for the old city is no longer obvious, though St Erik's fountain graces the side of the old market place (Fig. 14.3b: a spring arose where St Erik was killed). The stream watering the castle, though, is of some size and has been diverted and dammed to form what is now an ornamental lake called (predictably) Swan Damm.

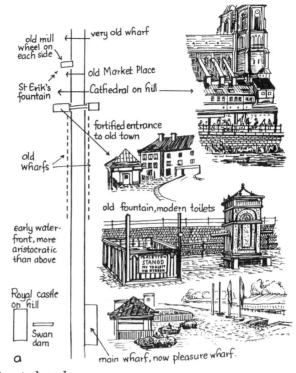

In the Uppsala area (Uppland), settlements are typically on raised areas. The land is now much drained, to an extent more resembling England than most Continental countries. Summer flow has always been very slow in the streams, and snow-melt floods were considerable. It is not surprising settlements were sited off the damp. The Fig. shows a series, in space, of the possible development of villages from farms, over time. Buildings increase, churches come, a High Street develops. Along the High Street, though, buildings are likely to be separate and at varying distances from the road. In the largest settlements here shown (Sweden is a big country, with only eight million people, so villages are small) open space is still abundant. This pattern is of particular interest to the English, as it is the same pattern

Fig. 9.16 Swedish towns and villages. a) Uppsala. b) Villages and smaller settlements, Uppland.

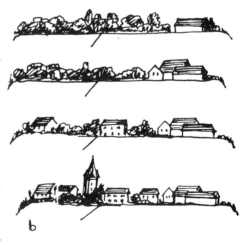

that, for example, Beresford and St Joseph (1979) describe for the development of the English village. The next stage is the High Street with (most) houses close to, and facing, the road (the crofts behind being infilled yet later).

The settlements, as always, needed water and were sited with easy access to this. The streams leading away from the settlements are now much channelled and straightened. (Incoming water was presumably springs in the hills.) These straight, 'dry' field-tributaries are almost farcical descendants of the village streams. There may be diversion channels to farms, as usual (e.g., a tiny stream being brought to the farm, and a larger one being near enough to carry from when needed).

## Mallorca
### *(Fig. 9.17)*

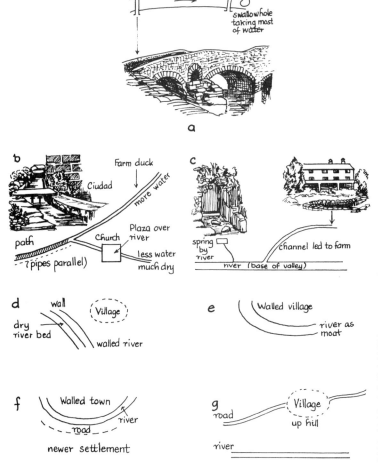

Lowland rivers now bear little more than storm run-off and in this Mediterranean country would never have had perennial flow. The mountain rivers had, and (even with reservoirs) have, much more water. Two river towns are on them. Pollensa has a Roman bridge. As so characteristically, the later settlement is beside the bridge (in fact

Fig. 9.17 a) Pollensa, Mallorca. b) Soller, Mallorca. c) Mountain farm, Mallorca, re-built on old site —stream water diverted to buildings above main river level. d) Llosetta, Mallorca. e) Villafranca, lowland Mallorca. f) Mercadal, Menorca. g) Madeira.

downstream of it), not centred on it. There is a ford downstream and a swallow hole into which river water falls, giving less flow. Sited above the swallow hole, the town is thus on the maximum river supply close to (5km from) the coast. The river was of but minor civic use and the town remained on one side of it. Soller, with a better supply, has the remains of an excellent ancient water-supply system in the Ciudad, with channels, controls and fountains. There is also still minor farm use (duck, etc.) of the stream at the outskirts. Soller has two streams: this one, with considerable water, and another, with much less. Unusually the city square and church are built *over* this second one. Downstream of the Ciudad the position changes. Here there is secondary development, though still mostly on the same side of the river. There is a path beside the river — 3km from the sea: was this perhaps a towpath? Modern pipes use the course for easy laying, and there are road-drainage channels.

Smaller mountain settlements, villages and farms are also on or near running water. Lowland villages, however, are on underground water, well use still being abundant, in addition to mains supplies.

An occasional river bending past a village suggests possible earlier defence (cf. Fig. 2.8). Partial or complete concreting may have been done following severe floods: not the best treatment for the environment, historical or natural.

## Menorca
### (Fig. 9.17)

Unlike Mallorca, Menorca has no rain-attracting mountains and so no long-flowing rivers but settlements on underground water. Mercadal though, has a (now) fully lined river in a defensive position.

## Malta
### (Fig. 9.17)

Malta again has no summer-flowing rivers (though there are good springs), and settlement sites were chosen for a combination of underground water (spring, well, etc.) plus defensibility. Occasionally rivers here can aid defence (Fig. 2.8).

The ancient capitals of both Malta and Gozo had good springs under limestone caps. Gozo is the better watered and has no place names to do with cisterns. In Malta nearly a quarter of place names (about 800 out of 4,000) are connected with water, about 160 with cisterns, about 200 with rivers (*Wieds*), about 50 with springs and others with dams, lakes, waterlogging, spouts and oozes. Only a quarter of the water-place names are thus associated with rivers, and only three of these refer to settlements or dwellings (G. Wettinger, personal communication). River-dependence, of course, decreases as rivers decrease in the Mediterranean climate. Water-dependence is everywhere, river-dependence is not.

# Madeira
*(Fig. 9.17)*

As described in Chapter 3, Madeira has running water by *levada* to all the coastal land, and *levadas* or good rivers in inland settlements (Fig. 3.21). There is no obvious evidence for river transport except just beside river mouths in the capital, Funchal.

There is no clear division between this chapter and the next: farms are excluded from this one, towns from Chapter 10, but villages are included in both. The emphasis of the text differs, but the separation is arbitrary.

# 10

# River-farms and Villages

## Early days

A French fifteenth-century village is shown in Fig. 10.1. It has a castle, with a fortified bridge, and the thatched houses and church of the rest of the community (this castle was not just a fort; it was a dwelling for many inhabitants). The village bridge is wooden, earthed above. In the larger and walled settlement of Fig. 13.14 more is shown, a pleasure boat, fine stone and wooden bridge. Other similar pictures show access steps, women collecting water from such steps, and farming close to river and settlement. Fig. 10.2 in sixteenth-century Germany shows more activities. The bridge is a simple wooden one. The stream has fish-nets, then has hides downstream on the far side (polluting below the fisher). The far bank is eroded because of people going in and out of the stream. The church is up the hill on the far bank. On the near bank is the well, a large one showing a commendable care for hygiene. Buying and selling are in progress.

A seventeenth-century English trading-village is described in Fig. 1.8. Fig. 10.3, an early nineteenth-century English Valley Farm, is not too clear in black and white. However, the stream is actively used, explaining the shortage of vegetation. The banks are satisfactory: it is the centre which is disturbed. Cows walk along it, perhaps for milking; waterfowl are present; boats are quanted along it — the farm owns at least two boats. Washing-water is collected. The house is *c.* 0.75m above river level, so within the flood zone. The ground story differs — did the household live upstairs, or was it just that from the fifteenth century, houses could be rebuilt under existing roofs? A farm of this size

Fig. 10.1 French fifteenth century village (from illumination, by permission of the Fitzwilliam Museum, Cambridge).

was wealthy: however unhealthy the site may look (for pre-pesticide days), the enterprise was successful.

At the turn of the twentieth century Williamson & Williamson (1907) describe Dutch (Friesland) canal life: 'Always going from one meer into another, there were charming canals, decorated with pretty little houses in gardens of roses and hollyhocks, and emphasized, somehow, by strange windmills exactly like large, wise grey owls, or, in the distance, resembling monks bearing aloft tall crosses. It was exquisite to glide on and on between two worlds; the world of realities, the world of reflections. Villages were far separated one from another, on canal and meer, though there were many farmhouses, walled round by great trees to keep cool the store-lofts in their steeply-sloping roofs. Gulls sat about like domestic fowls, and perched on the backs of cows, that grazed in meadows fringed with pink and purple flowers. Men and girls rowed home from milking, and hung their green and scarlet

Fig. 10.2 German sixteenth century village (from woodcut).

Fig. 10.3 Early nine-teenth century valley farm (J. Constable, by permission of the Tate Gallery).

milk-pails in rows on the outer walls of their farmhouse homes. Fishing-nets were looped from pole to pole by the water side, in such curious fashion as to look like vineyards of trailing brown vines; and as we drew near to Sneek, where we planned to stay the night, we began to meet quaint light-ers, with much pic-turesque family life going on, on board; children playing with queer, home-made toys; ancient, white-capped dames knitting; girls flirting with young men on passing peat-boats — men in scarlet jerseys which, repeated in the smooth water, looked like running fire under glass... every heavily-laden peat-boat, or brightly painted eel-boat....'

The life is water-centred, fishing is good for both ordinary fish and eels. Peat boats bring the fuel. There are scattered farms between villages, and scattered houses on canals. Clearly a living can be made from fish and eels. People still live amid abundant wildlife, as is described for earlier centuries in Britain (Friesland was then still sparsely populated). A boat culture also existed until recently in the Vendée, France.

Parker (1975) describes a tiny village stream. The Brook belonged to the community and was necessary for its existence. In four parishes, no village house was over 80 yards (*c.* 73m) from the brook until after 1800. This gave easy access for supply, etc. Water use was strictly regulated. In the fourteenth century fines were payable in Foxton for (a) making ponds for watering; (b) widening the brook or diverting it by at least 6in (15cm); and (c) for letting the bank fall in, or allowing it to be widened by neglect by at least 2ft (*c*. 60cm). This was before made roads or concrete and if these sins had been allowed, parts of the High Street would have fallen in. Also, the downstream end of the village would have had its water reduced.

In the fifteenth and sixteenth centuries offences included: allowing dunghills to drain into the Brook; allowing waterfowl or pigs in it within the village; failing to clean and scour the part by one's own frontage (effectively keeping vegetation as well as silting down); diverting water; and, before 8pm, washing clothes or letting gutters or cesspits drain in. The eighteenth century brought less individual care, ditching being done by someone paid by the parish. Late in the century controls were abandoned, and farmers dug ponds up to a size for eight horses to drink together. The brook was dirtier. As people no longer brewed their own beer (which was a sterilised drink), other drinking-supplies were desirable. Wells were sunk in gardens. As supply decreased, with abstraction and drainage lowering ground-water levels, farm boreholes were dug 1830-70, and two large boreholes for village supply followed in 1873, water-carts bringing the water to houses. As the brook became too dirty for supply, its sole village use became waste disposal. The stream gradually dried up and in about 1960 was put in pipes underground: the final indignity!

In this village, therefore, the history of the brook is known. It illustrates many points:

(a)     Regulations are needed to keep a settlement stream in good order.
(b)     The parishes were skilled in physical stream management, but not in the control of chemical management — waste put in at the allowed time of 3.30am will not leave the stream clean for drinking at 4am. Many pollutants, including disease micro-organisms, are not visible in poisonous concentrations!
(c)     Supply went from brook to wells to boreholes (with water-carts) to mains.
(d)     Waterfowl were kept, but the stream was too small (contrast, e.g., Figs 9.10i, 10.13c) for the birds to be on it in the village (they would have caused damage).
(e)     That which is needed by man is maintained; that which is not may easily be lost.


## Patterns
*(Figs of Chapters 9 and 10)*

There are many English village patterns.

(a)     The simplest type of stream village is a line of houses on the river from which many villagers derived a living.
(b)     In the next type, houses are built on banks on both sides (Hurstbourne Tarrant type: (Figs 9.15l, 2.1) — the German '–heim', often; see Chapter 9).
(c)     Bridgehead — or stream-crossing — villages are another type (Fig. 7.4 shows the old ford pre-dating the bridge).

(d)   Villages parallel to, but further from, the main stream with ordinarily a minor brook running to the main stream.

(e)   A cluster of farms, round a brook (the German '–dorf', often).

(f)   Farms between road and brook, however these cross (Fig. 9.14e) (partly from Beresford & St Joseph, 1979).

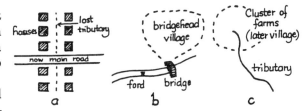

Fig. 10.4 a) Houses both sides of a stream, Dottenheim, Germany. b) Bridgehead, previously ford-sited village, Llanystumdwy, Wales. c) (Originally) cluster of farms etc. round brook, Itzing, Germany.

Although villages vary more than towns (see Chapter 8), once a pattern is set, it takes a major necessity for it to be changed: war, natural disaster, much incoming wealth or resources (e.g., the arrival of a railway, the discovery of minerals), or conurbation. Of the countries surveyed for this book, the English are the most likely to change an old pattern, the Germans the least. Piecemeal rebuilding, the commonest type, preserves patterns, total rebuilding loses them. Toddington (Fig. 10.5) is cited by Beresford & St Joseph as an example of stable pattern over four centuries. This has had rebuilding. Ellingen (Fig. 9.10h) is more fossilised.

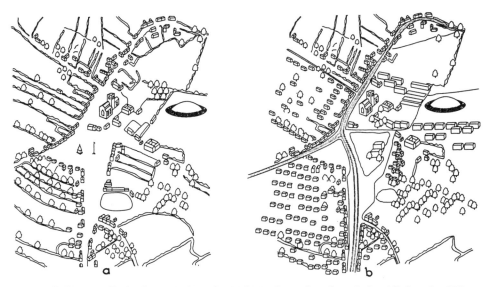

Fig. 10.5 Toddington, England, in 1581 (a) and 1962 (b) (re-drawn from Beresford and St Joseph, 1979).

For convenience, stream sizes may be divided into size, A, brooks, typically now tiny, up to 0.5m wide, or depressions, or lost; size B, typically 1-3m, or now lost, or underground; size C typically 4-8m, rarely lost, formerly available for transport

Fig. 10.6 Duck shooting in a wood, 1730 (I.J. de Troy, by permission of the Fitzwilliam Museum, Cambridge). Detail.

and undershot mills; size D, typically 10-25m wide; and size E the large water-courses.

Summing up the settlements described: villages on the tiniest brooks (size A) are on sources apt to dry, and so have another and larger stream, e.g., size C (or other source) nearby. Often this is in a valley formerly liable to flood, the settlement being above main flood points. The larger stream may have been available for transport. When settlements were on small (size B) streams rather than tiny brooks, their streams were less liable either to flood or to dry, and the Foxton pattern (Parker, 1975) is frequent. On size C streams settlement may be primary or secondary, secondary settlement being that spreading over and down the valley side. The smaller streams may supply water for processing and, locally, mills (e.g., Quantocks, Fig. 5.4: overshot mills), but the main mill distribution is usually on size C.

Size B streams in the past could usually also be used for transport. The settlements may also have had a size A stream, but not necessarily. Size C is liable to flood in many types of valley. Size D or E rivers are definitely liable to flood the waterside. Settlements are on hills, or were developed after flood-protection works — or, of course, were regularly flooded. They had, or have, water transport (except if the stream is torrential, dry in summer, etc.), but their settlements are based on smaller tributaries (Chapter 8). Many variants occur of these basic patterns. In spite, and perhaps because, of these variants, as Rodgers (1947-8) points out, rivers and streams have in the past controlled settlement design and size better than any modern planning authority can do.

The number of people working in, on and by the village stream has dropped over the centuries. Now the water authority appears in emergencies and otherwise — annually? five-yearly? Even in eighteenth-century Foxton, when villagers had stopped attending each to their own piece of stream, someone was employed by the *parish,* locally, not coming from far away, to manage the watercourse. Now children may play in the stream but pollution and broken glass often make this undesirable. Only if the settlement has turned to tourism will many people be there: but even then only to look and to add to the damage, not to maintain the stream. The stream used to be part of life: water supply, duck, swan, fish, eel, watering stock, laundry, milling, industrial processing, transport. Now it is an irrelevance — part of the background (even farming, which may still want river water, employs so few people that its river activities barely impinge on the village).

Village streams used to have continual disturbance (see above). Streams in the open country had less. (Damage from transport, swans, fisheries, etc., was, overall, less than settlement damage.) Now the farmland stream has had much more alteration: straightening, deepening, embanking for drainage and flood protection. People are not abundant, but the result of their efforts is.

Woods had less disturbance than open country (particularly if and when preserved for shooting), and better vegetation could often grow in woodland glades than in the open country or settlements (e.g., Fig. 10.6). Over recent centuries traditional woodlands — and some plantations — have retained their minor brooks where these have vanished from the farmland beside, and the woods may have retained them in little-altered shapes. This can be seen across Europe from Britain and Norway east to at least Czechoslovakia. Lachat (1988) cites a French example with, in equivalent areas, about three streams in farmland and about ten in woodland.

## Stream-Farms

Farms may be found singly, in small groups, in larger groups (hamlets), in villages, or in towns. The pattern varies with the terrain and the social conditions. Crofters in Highland Scotland can be widely separated. In eastern England there was co-operation in communities, which is more necessary for arable farming, and separate, isolated farms generally arrived only after the Enclosure Acts. At that stage allocated lands could be well away from the village, and new farms had to be built. Isolated farms are now scattered over much of Europe. In Germany, south of Hannover, farms are mainly concentrated. In the French Camargue the old farm complexes (*Mas*) are scattered, and larger than single farms.

Before mains supplies, farms were sited for water. The recently drained Dutch polders are perhaps the largest area of new farms without this constraint: siting here is for the convenient division of the land.

Water is essential, but floods bring damage and disease to man, beast and land (Chapter 12). Both, therefore, influenced farm distribution. Drainage, flood protection, sprinklers and mains water, etc., lessen dependence on natural water supply. On very small brooks the risk of flooding is low, but that of drought may be high. Many little brooks have been lost (dried or piped underground) with the general fall in water level; e.g., half the minor streams on the Stor, Denmark, have disappeared since 1876 (F. Jensen, personal communication). The larger the stream the more the risk of drought lessens and that of flood increases. Consequently farms — and likewise villages — may be built on seepage areas or tiny brooks above larger streams, so avoiding floods, and making supply possible in drought. Farmers water land, stock and dwellings. Where water is short (as in much of Malta; and, for some

while post-Enclosure, on the Dorset chalk (Hoskins, 1973)), dwellings may remain in villages, and
just the farm buildings be out on
the land — where the water supply is less, or dirty. Stock need
continuous and plenteous water.
Crops are less dependent. (Plough-
ing with animals, though, needs
water supplies.)

Fig. 10.7 Alpine chalet home and farmstead. Note stream and pond.

Old Alpine chalets (Fig. 10.7)
are independent farmsteads, and
may have a small stream running under and through the chalet, filling a small,
stoned pond on the downstream side, for watering stock and fowl.

Farms on drying tiny brooks are shown in Fig. 10.8. Patterns are similar, but
they have to be: tiny brooks are similar. The examples are from Czechoslovakia,
Belgium, Denmark, Luxembourg, Wales, Germany and England. The German
farms here may be in clusters (Figs 10.4c, 10.9d). Some plans show the way waters
have been diverted to reach each farm. Streams this small need upkeep for

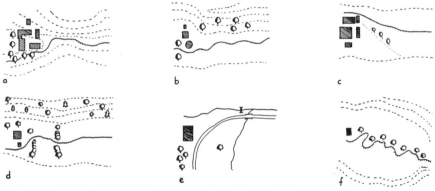

Fig. 10.8 Farms on tiny streams. a) b) Czechoslovakia. c) Belgium. d) Denmark. e)
Luxembourg. f) Wales. g) h) Germany. i) England, 1930s stream pattern.

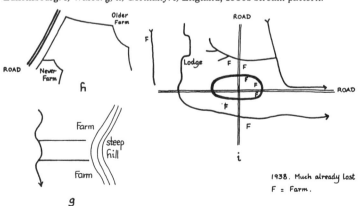

diversion channels
but not massive
upkeep. Fig. 10.8g,
in lowland Ger-
many, shows
farms changing
over the centuries
from being close to
the stream to be-
ing close to the
road. The Luxem-
bourg example
(Fig. 10.8e) has the

brook now straight-
ened, because the old
narrow track has be-
come a road. A French
farm near Villeneuve
has a stream much al-
tered after it stopped
being the main farm
supply (it has been
drained: i.e., deep-
ened, etc.). However,
beyond, the stream
has been altered yet
more, being straight

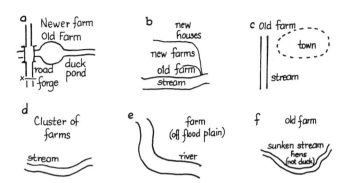

Fig. 10.9 Farms on small streams. a) England. b) Belgium. c) d) Germany. e) Denmark. f) Czechoslovakia.

with a straight row of poplars. The new houses beside are quite separated from the stream.

Farms may, secondly, be on small, rather than tiny, brooks (Fig. 10.9). There is again much similarity between countries. Fig. 10.9a, Lydyeard St Lawrence, England, is the farm in the village. The oldest buildings, not inhabited, are close to the stream. The newer and larger ones are increasingly far off (and less stream-dependent). The stream is dammed to give a pond for duck and for watering stock in the field. One from Belgium, has like Comberton (above), a stream diverted to supply houses, and a branch diverted to a farm. The diverted stream along the back of houses was seen in Fig. 9.15: Little Misbourne, there on a larger scale.

In Pleinfeld, Germany (Fig. 10.9) the old farm is at the head of the stream, and the village is on the rise of the valley at the side. The farm needed a good water supply enough to risk flood. The village did not. Drainage has now lowered the water level, so that flood risk is negligible. Supply is less but it is needed only by farms. Another German example shows a straightened and low-quality stream. Upstream an old bridge and an old farm complex have — fortunately — prevented straightening and the old winding course is preserved. A typical north German pattern is a cluster of farm buildings of different ages, at the bottom of a valley. A Danish example shows a farm on, but above, a previously much-flooding river. The Czech example shows an on-river pattern, with a footbridge and fowl. The fowl are now hens, not ducks: but the water level has been much lowered and access for duck would be more difficult. Fig. 2.8 shows a typical Maltese river-farm, beside the river, which formerly flowed (and now has ponded water) for most of the winter.

A large Menorcan farm complex includes the well-house (the well is enclosed because of the windy climate), water-storage tank and cattle-troughs: the farm is well-based, not stream-based (Fig. 3.8e, f). A Mallorcan lowland farm is likewise on wells with a water-tank (cf. Fig. 3.22), but a mountain farm has stream access.

There are also non-water-based patterns. A Dutch example is a dwelling, not a farm, and the stream beside it is irrelevant — except for Auld Lang Syne (Fig. 9.4k). The English farm in Fig. 10.10d is old enough to have used the stream, but drainage has recently removed the stream from the orbit of the farm. This is not now a river-based farm.

On the Rhine — quite a different scale of river — are isolated farms, (e.g., Fig. 10.10f), often with the vinery above. Such had, and earlier used, their own wharfs. The German and Welsh river-farms in Fig. 10.10g have added tourism to their enterprises. Both have placed the caravans further into the valley than their own buildings are! Of course drainage has lowered the risk of flood, and the caravans are for summer use, but does a slight danger remain?

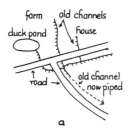

## Small village supply channels
### *(Fig. 10.10)*

A nice old supply pattern of tiny brooks was shown in Jilowice (Czechoslovakia). Unfortunately 'was'; as, when the writer saw it, pipes were being laid to put them all underground. This, however, is the old European pattern: supply/drainage channels everywhere for dwellings, farm and village pond. It becomes unsatisfactory when the drainage is for other than run-off water, as the incoming supply is then contaminated, or is inadequate (too many houses), or demand increases, (e.g., baths, water-pressure wanted for water at sink level and upstairs), or when the brook is lost with drainage.

A similar but simpler pattern is shown in the preserved eighteenth-century part of Buckler's Hard (England). This is a simple settlement pattern, just two rows of houses on a good slope. The brook splits into two above, one watercourse going down the back of each row. Buckler's Hard was a shipbuilding settlement, and the old dock is seen below the houses, on the bank of the Beaulieu estuary.

Fig. 10.10 Villages. a) Jilowicz, Czechoslovakia. b) Bucklers Hard, England. c) Winkle Street, England (place for sheep-wash in foreground). d) River farm now divided by drained stream, England. e) f) farms above normal flood level, with holiday caravans below. e) Wales. f) on the Rhine. g) Bad Salzuflen, Germany. h) Sallanches, France. i) Les Contamines, Alpine France. j) Beaufort, Alpine France.

Fig. 10.10 contd.

Fig. 10.11 Duckponds.
a) Czechoslovakia. b)
France. c)-d) England.

Similar little channels are seen in Winkle Street, a stream-hamlet (of Calbourne, Isle of Wight. A little depression — a drain — still runs *from* each house *to* the stream. This is discharge-drainage. Where channels run on to other houses, water must be kept clean!

Some rather indeterminate channels are on the Green in Brockenhurst, England. Brockenhurst also has an old stream and wharf access with several newer developments on roads of various ages. A village has expanded into a town.

## Duckponds
### *(Fig. 10.11)*

Village duckponds — or farm duckponds, but in a village — are still frequent, particularly perhaps in England and Czechoslovakia. Of course they may — as in Czechoslovakia still — be used for fish, but 'duckpond' is the traditional English name, showing their primary English use. Duck on village streams are seen in Figs 4.7, 9.10i. Traditionally, it is the women who look after ducks.

## Village siting and development
### *(Fig. 10.12)*

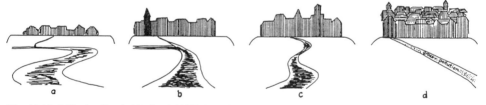

Fig. 10.12 a) Thorley Brook, England. b) Wecker, Luxembourg. c) Near Sens, France. d) Mnisek, Czechoslovakia.

One pattern is shown nicely in Fig. 10.12, of four villages from four countries. All started above a *c.* 2-6m stream with, presumably, a tiny brook passing through for immediate supply. These, therefore, had two supply streams for different purposes. Within this pattern, those differ. The English one (Thorley Brook) is a hamlet, so without a church, and it has stayed small. The Luxembourg example, Wecker, is now elongated along the contour. The French example has grown further into the valley. The Czech settlement has become a town (Minisek), with The Village Stream becoming The Town Sewer — still used over-much for sewage disposal. The stream has gone from lifeline to rubbish dump (as described above for a different village pattern, by Parker, 1975).

Villages again, may be on canals or big rivers (e.g., Figs 6.1, 12.6). Canal-village life has been described above, and in the description of Makken (Chapter 9). Belgian Damme, like Makken (Fig. 9.3), is along a canal (on the canal to Bruges), not the road. So is Dutch Waddingxeen on the Gowe. It fronts the canalised river with housing at this high river level. The church is set a little back (as usual). The

Commercial End is away from the residential part. Now, of course, both have road communication also. Beckdorf in Schleswig Holstein is a different matter. The old waterway is present, embanked and raised. It is, however, polluted and smelly — and with sparse housing. The Rhein villages on a primary waterway which had vagaries of flow and course (Fig. 6.17f), have much old wharfing. The villages have former walling, underground exits of tributaries (cf. the *Nuremburg Chronicle*, Fig. 8.2), ex-ferries, hill-forts above (behind is a plateau, not a mountain range). Profondeville on the Meuse is more of a minor watering-place. The better buildings typically front either the stream down the village centre (older) or the main river (less old). To all, the waterway was the prime source of transport and trade.

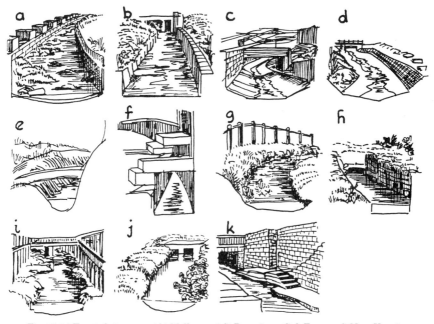

Fig. 10.13 Treated streams. a) b) Mallorca. c) St Romain en Gal, France. d) Near Voznice, Czechoslovakia. e) Wrestling-worth, England. f) Ghajn Qajjied, Malta. g) Rhein-bischofsheim, Germany. h) Criccieth, Wales. i) Balmont, France. j) Peene, England. k) Grundhof, Luxembourg.

The village stream, the former lifeline, is now treated in various ways. It may be lost altogether or put in an underground pipe. This is possible only when the stream is, or has been made, small — small even in flood. Various treatments and beauties are shown in Fig. 10.13. The first two could have been much improved by prettier footbridges. The first Mallorcan stream would be all right if unpolluted. The second, completely lined — well, is better than being put underground, but not much. The river is caged to an unacceptable degree. The French one has a pleasing bridge and bank. The focal point of the (new) Czech village street has been made, to the writer's eye, unnecessarily ugly. Beauty lies in the eye of the beholder, though, and to the inhabitants it may be beautiful. To the writer, erosion protection should, and can, be done better. Malta has a prettiness of its own, even with a concrete channel! Rheinbischofsheim, Germany, a typical '–heim', has old housing on both sides of the stream. Criccieth, Wales, is also meant to be ornamental and to some degree succeeds. Blamont is French, like Sallanches below, with the same central stream pattern: but it is not ornamental, and past use cannot even be seen. The final two are very nice. Even putting the river underground can have a charm, as in Bad Salzuflen, Germany (Fig. 10.10g). The stream used to flow *through* the square but even now adds to the picturesqueness. In Sallanches, France (Fig. 10.10h), although the stream is unnaturally straight, it is pleasing with the fast flow and varied substrate, the greenery and the bridges. (This is just outside the centre). Malta has a prettiness of its own, even with a concrete channel.

Three French alpine villages can be contrasted (Fig. 10.10i, j). Les Contamines is a mainly-new tourist village, built with chalets for late-twentieth-century tourist preferences. It is on a ridgeway above the Bon Nantes, with only a depression remaining in the centre to show where the tiny brook, which supplied the first houses, lay. The Bon Nantes is used as a tourist attraction: for the view and for walking beside it. St Gervais-le-Bains, a minor watering-place, has French terrace housing — the preference for tourists earlier (when chalets could be considered 'rough'). This also was developed for outsiders. But here it is built around the rim of the river, nearly in a horseshoe shape: the fashion has changed. Visitors before wanted housing like the lowland cities they knew. Now they want something different. Thirdly, Beaufort, which existed in its own right as a local centre, has a bridge leading to the church and a cluster of good central housing. The housing was built to show the solid worth of the inhabitants, not to attract tourists. Beaufort stopped growth in the Phase I stage (see Chapter 8). When a good road was built it could not go through the old town — so it was put on the other side of the river where a 'new town' grew up along it. The river still has a sawmill and was of course used for supply, but the town was too remote and small to develop much industry. Water-dependent village industry is varied (e.g., Fig. 10.14; also Figs in Chapter 5): (a) a sawmill, (and stable), formerly water-powered; (b) an old industrial Luxembourg village with many mills. This one is worth a closer look. There are old access steps, too big and grand just for collecting water. This was boat access. The main wharf, now a car park, is just upstream. Manufactured goods were exported by water down the Attert, which leads to the Alzette, connecting both south to the capital, Luxembourg City, and north to the Moselle and Rhine — to half Europe, in effect; (c) an old French example has a formerly-used stream emerging from a house, and steps opposite; (d) Clausen (near Luxembourg: now a suburb) where the old brewery with its steps, is on the right. On the left is housing trying to distance itself from the river: correctly, as there is now severe pollution. (e) shows Dutch village industry. Other types are numerous!

Until fairly recently, farmland was included within the city walls (see, e.g., Fig. 8.2). With increasing population and land values and indeed more settled times, it became more profitable to build within, and farm without. It is now difficult to find farmland within the settlement. Mellieha, Malta is an incomplete example, as the farmland is in a valley liable to storm flood, and so not suitable for building, but it shows this pattern. (Flow is channelled to the side where containers also collect run-off water for irrigation.)

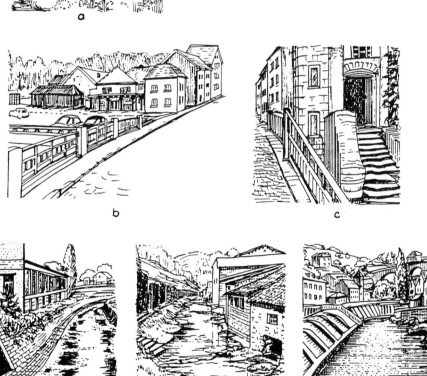

Fig. 10.14 Water-dependent village industry. a) Sawmill, French Alps. b) Bissen, Luxembourg. c) Satillieu, France. d) Clausen, Luxembourg. e) Terborg, The Netherlands.

# 11

# Waste Disposal: Pollution

...the picturesque little cottages where the refuse had to be pitched out at the back, and the slops chucked out in front, and where the general arrangements for health, comfort and decency were such as one must forbear to speak of, since, on such matters, our ears — Heaven help us — have all the delicacy which seems denied to our noses. (Ewing, 1876)

> In Köhln, a town of monks and bones,
> And pavements fang'd with murderous stones
> And rags, and hags, and hideous wenches;
> I counted two and seventy stenches,
> All well defined, and several stinks!
> Ye Nymphs that reign o'er sewers and sinks,
> The river Rhine, it is well known,
> Doth wash your city of Cologne;
> But tell me, Nymphs, what power divine
> Shall henceforth wash the River Rhine?
>                                         (S.T. Coleridge)

*[Nearly two hundred years later, we have but a partial answer to this question.]*

## The river for cleansing and dumping

When anything is cleaned by man, the dirt, together with any substance used in the cleaning, must go somewhere. So must human waste: sewage, unwanted materials and the by-products of making wanted goods. Today, this 'somewhere' is for liquids most often rivers, secondly the seas and thirdly the lakes, and for solids dump sites and the seas, though regrettably rivers are still used. The waste may drain into, or be dumped straight into, streams, or reach them by open channel, pipe, or run-off. The waste may be, though should not be, sewage, factory effluent, mine effluent, farm slurry and silage liquor. It is likely to also be direct run-off from the roads and other built-up surfaces, soil washed from farmland, fertilisers and biocides put on the land, aquatic herbicides, fish-farm effluent and such-like. The waste may reach the river indirectly, having gone by pipes to a sewage-treatment works (Table 1.2) and then in various degrees of water quality (none as good as natural river water), by pipe to the river — the word 'sewer' has changed its meaning. It now usually refers to pipes for sewage disposal, particularly to those for the treatment works. Originally it meant a fishpond drainage channel, then wetland drains (it is still used in this sense in S. England marshes), then an artificial waste channel, usually underground, and finally the sewer became the main piped sewer of the town. The name has meant, therefore, the most prominent type of drain of the period.

Fig. 11.1 Road run-off
channels. a)-g) Malta. h)
i) Mallorca. j) k) France.
l) m) Madeira. n) o) Eng-
land.

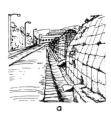

Human waste has increased enormously for two reasons: firstly through increase in population numbers (Chapter 1). People do not always appreciate that the sewage from 1,000 people is about 100 times more than that from 10. Housing has increased more than numbers — houses now contain fewer people — but more houses mean more waste. Wealth has increased, also more than numbers, and so has technology. This means the number of possessions increases, the by-products in their making and the dirt from their maintenance increases and the pollution from some possessions — whether detergents, or fuel-driven vehicles — also increases. The problem of waste disposal is more acute than ever before.

To take a simple action: washing clothes (see Fig. 3.13 for some earlier structures). When these were washed in the stream by banging a small stone on the clothes laid on a flat surface, only the dirt in the clothes polluted the river. Fullers earth, particularly in small quantities, is hardly harmful. Soap is not too bad. Detergents, however, are more persistent and toxic.

Sewage-treatment works were designed to do just that: treat sewage. The trouble with sewage is its quantity, not its quality. It does break down to relatively innocuous substances (which do, though, increase the amount of nutrients). Add other substances, and treatment works have difficulties. Detergents, like many other substances, come through into the river. There are newer detergents, which are phosphate-free and break down more easily, but these are used as yet sporadically (e.g. much in Germany but only slightly in Britain). The number of clothes to be washed has increased because population has increased and fashion has changed; they are washed more often; and each wash is far more poisonous than it used to be. The more elaborate early clothes were not washed, they were — eventually — unpicked and the bits re-used. In the days of everyday working-clothes and Sunday best, people had only the two sets of clothes (see, however, the Swedish example in Chapter 3 for much washing).

From houses also come disinfectants; bleach, ammonia and such-like (these kill micro-organisms, useful ones as well as pathogens:

that is their function); hair shampoo; soaps; salt; polishes; whiteners; medicines; food additives; and heavy metals (metals with a density of over 5, such as nickel, mercury, etc.)

From houses also come the additives put in by the water companies or the residues later resulting from those: chlorine or other disinfectants, aluminium, etc. The chlorine can form trihalomethanes (chloroform and such-like) with organics in the water. These can produce cancer — and both enter and leave our houses. From urban and road run-off come rubber, bitumen and other tyre derivatives, heavy metals, petrochemicals and other hydrocarbons from exhaust fumes, petrol and oil, glass, aggregate, tarmac derivatives and particles, derivatives from shoes, de-icing salt in winter, dead leaves and animals, and spills from any type of load (n.b., though all known that cyanide is poisonous, it must also be remembered that, say, milk is also — a load of milk is as bad as a load of sewage when tipped into the river). Go back a bit, and road pollution was negligible. Traffic was minimal compared to the present, and horse dung, dead leaves and animals, and the occasional small spill (small because loads were small and few) were all that the rivers had to cope with. Present country-lane run-off is reasonably innocuous but that from motorways destroys fragile stream types (Haslam, 1990). Urban run-off increasingly goes to the treatment works. Where it is not so treated, it can be more harmful to the river than treated sewage, as now in Aberdeen. Provision for purifying run-off from busy roads in the country, though, is woefully inadequate. There are a few settling lagoons, but these are not enough. Purification as well as settlement is needed (see below for purification by vegetation). Run-off pollution is particularly bad in Malta, since Malta combines (1) dense roads and much traffic; (2) inadequate dilution in the Mediterranean climate (n.b., dilution renders substances less toxic, but does not, of itself, destroy or detoxify) and (3) re-use of surface water on the land, compounding the contamination.

Built-up surface and intensive farming increase the flash floods and so the need for provision for run-off. The variation to be found in such a simple matter as road run-off channels is enough to be quite interesting (Fig. 11.1). Heavier rain and greater areas of road require larger channels. (Not all run-off is dirty; that from roofs, if they be clean and air pollution little, is clean, and has traditionally been used

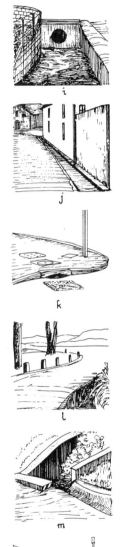

for supply — earlier for drinking, later for watering. Rainwater is soft water, and without tap water's additives.) Rubbish dumped in watercourses will be carried away in flow, but left for other collection in usually-dry channels without force of flow, or little-flowing canals or dykes (Fig. 11.2).

Fig. 11.2 Rubbish dumps. a) Madeira (from Haslam, 1990). b) c) Malta. d) Gozo.

a

## History of Pollution

In earlier days, say the thirteenth century, complaints about pollution were that mess had accumulated and it should be dug out, and allowed to flow down the river; e.g., Rodgers (1947-8) quotes that the London Fleet in 1307 'by filth of the tanners and such others, was sure decayed'. The river did not improve over the centuries, Dean Swift's eighteenth-century comment being:

Drowned puppies, stinking sprats, all drown'd in mud
Dead cats, and turnip tops, come tumbling down the flood

(Later that century this water course was built over, becoming, in modern parlance, a sewer: see Chapter 8.)

In major settlements, edicts against dumping were frequent, e.g. Acts such as those of 1372 and 1552 forbidding the casting of dung and refuse into the Thames. In 1519 Oxford University complained to Cardinal Wolsey that the city drains could not be cleared, because the water level in the Thames was too high for gravity-drainage (being dammed by obstructions), and so plague infested the city in warm spells (Rodgers, 1947-8).

These 'major settlements' were in themselves tiny compared to the present times; the City of London was perhaps just over 3km along the river, Greater London is now perhaps 45km.

Ancient waste was of quite a different order from the present day: only where it originated did it need to be considered. Once away from there nature could and would do the rest. Now an unpolluted river in lowland Europe is a thing not to be found. The question is the degree of pollution, not whether it exists. (E.g., the writer analysed samples from around 500 small English streams. All lowland and most highland streams contained detergent. There is only one way detergent now comes

into streams — and it does not come alone. It comes with sewage, bleach, cleaners, toothpaste and many other pollutants.) Pollution must be regarded as a whole: undestroyed substances go somewhere, destroyed ones still have their breakdown products, even though these might be safer.

Industrial river pollution was little until woolmills and other mills became common after the tenth century (Chapter 5). From then on industrial pollution became serious locally, before the Industrial Revolution (e.g., Quantocks, Fig. 5.4) and after (e.g., S. Wales Coal Valley streams). After this, however, it became much worse, both in type (it was more non-organic: simple organic material like sewage and paper breaks down more easily), directly due to the growth of industry; and in quantity, indirectly so, due to the expanding population (see Warren, 1971; Haslam, 1990; Hynes, 1960).

Older sewers were designed for storm and drainage water, and it was only when population, and hence waste, became excessive that practice changed. It was forbidden to discharge human waste to sewers until 1815 in London, 1823 in Boston and 1880 in Paris. In 1847 the cesspools of London houses could be required to connect to sewers. In the 1850s, two American towns had a water-carriage system, bringing fresh water and disposing of waste water (Warren, 1971). It took even longer for industrial discharge to rivers to become legal. The 1847 (British) Gas Works Act prohibited effluent discharge, and it was not until 1937 that British industry had the right, under certain conditions, to discharge to sewers (Hynes, 1960).

Until very recently those dealing with nuisance from waste were primarily concerned with solid waste. The collectors of night soil have been important in cities for most of history. Country practices varied. Manure is used in farming and before household chemicals became abundant human manure was more acceptable, especially round cities. Indeed, China had long-term, large-scale waste disposal on land (Warren, 1971). Crowded conditions mean awful rivers (Figs 3.2, 11.3). The waste had got way beyond the capacity of the rivers to cope. However, the problem

Fig. 11.3 a) Nineteenth century industrial waterfront (from Haslam, 1990). b) Nineteenth century industrial hill river, Wales (from Edwards *et al.*, 1984). Showing the exhilaration felt by many at the sight of what we consider appalling pollution: compare Towerblocks of flats in the 1960s.

was still local. In S. Wales the rivers were dreadful, in W. Wales they were largely clean (apart from some mine and local town pollution). (Now, the one is rather less dirty, the other less clean.) It is not that nothing was done. Table 11.1 shows how in the nineteenth century even in then-remote country areas, outbreaks of disease were attended to, and hygienic practices recommended. These were, though, mainly concerned with getting clean water to the house and clean practices within it, not with cleaning up the river. The rivers got worse during this period. Eventually, but not until 1898, the Royal Commission on Sewage Disposal was set up, which was (in ten reports) to do such sterling work. This set a

*Table 11.1*
*Nineteenth-century reports on disease and sanitation.*
Reports to the General Board of Health, and Local Government Board reports
*(Extracted from Whittaker (1921) for part of Norfolk, England)*

*These increased during the nineteenth century, as water-borne illnesses became understood, then decreased, after clean water had been provided.*

Lee, W. (1849). *Report to the General Board of Health on a Preliminary enquiry into the... supply of water... of Swaffham.*

Law, R.B. (1893). *Report... on an outbreak of typhoid fever in the borough of Kings Lynn, Norfolk. No. 63.*

Lopeman, S.M. (1895). *Report... on an outbreak of enteric fever at Loddon... No. 95.*

Low, J.S. (1907). *Report... upon the sanitary circumstances... of the... Thetford Registration District... No. 256.*

b

standard, the Royal Commission Standard: that an effluent diluted at least eight times in a river should have a Biological Oxygen Demand (dissolved oxygen absorbed in five days) of not over twenty parts per million, and suspended solids of not over thirty parts per million. This is known as the Royal Commission 20/30 standard. It has been used longer and more widely than any other standard and is still the basis of other standards. However, it does refer just to sewage. In the early twentieth century, the effluent might be in just too great a quantity for the river, in many places the treatment works might be overloaded, or otherwise inadequate, but it could be envisaged that with a little more time, trouble and money, pollution could be almost eliminated. Then came twentieth century wealth, technology and the Consumer Society. A second treatment revolution is needed, and there are indications of its beginning. It should return waste to industry: recycling, not new collection and dumping, should be required by Governments.

There are three main sources of pollution: domestic, industrial and farming. The first two have point-source effluents, which in theory can be purified — though road run-off approaches the diffuse in distribution. Farming pollution is diffuse from the use of chemicals on the fields (as well as point-source pollution from slurry, etc.). Farming pollution used to be very little. Nutrients were in deficit rather than surplus, and the extreme leaching of fertilisers that now occurs was impossible. Modern biocides did not exist, and few chemical treatments were available at all. Table 11.2 shows the diffuse effects of pollution. The Rhine drains water from five countries and from important industrial areas of, particularly, Germany, France and Switzerland. Though the Rhine has enormous self-purifying power (e.g., Friedrich & Müller, 1984), and its purity is improving, it is very far from clean. And a river cannot destroy lead. So when Rhine water gets to fields, lead gets to the fields too, and to the stock grazing on those fields. Cows filter out lead from the grass to some extent, but far from completely (more gets into the kidneys than the other organs or milk: but then far more milk is drunk by man, so that milk is actually the more poisonous). The Dutch are a nation most careful of pollution — see their *Environmental Statistics of The Netherlands*. They can prevent contaminated milk being drunk by man. They cannot prevent lead being in the Rhine. What a change since Izaak Walton wrote in 1653. He could then cite a German proverb to describe the best of food — 'More wholesome than a perch of Rhine'!

Hence from all sources pollution has increased in the past two centuries, becoming greater ever faster. (The exception is mines, if these are considered separate from the gravel extraction that is now so polluting in Italy. Mining in Europe is decreasing, and purification of its waste has much improved.)

*Table 11.2*
*Where mercury is found in cows grazing on the Rhine flood plain in The Netherlands*
*(From Jansen et al. (1979))*

|  | **Mercury in ppm** |
|---|---|
| Rhine water | $4 \times 10^{-4}$ - $2 \times 10^{-3}$ |
| sediment | $2$ - $90$ |
| grass | $10^{-1}$ - $2 \times 10^{-1}$ |
| cow milk | $10^{-4}$ - $6 \times 10^{-4}$ |
| brains | $2 \times 10^{-4}$ - $1 \times 10^{-3}$ |
| meat | $1 \times 10^{-3}$ - $3 \times 10^{-3}$ |
| liver | $3 \times 10^{-3}$ - $5 \times 10^{-3}$ |
| kidneys | $1 \times 10^{-2}$ - $2 \times 10^{-2}$ |

## Cleaning the river

Rivers are cleaned in two ways: by the self-purification of the river, and by the purifying of polluted water before it reaches the river. In the distant past, the former was adequate in most rivers. It does not destroy pathogenic micro-organisms (typhoid bacteria for instance) and is exceedingly slow for many, particularly newly released substances such as organochlorine biocides (now largely banned). (Self-purification is now woefully inadequate, but should be encouraged to its limit — it is, after all, free.)

Ponds were, and in remote areas still are, used for purification. This is dangerous when more than a trivial amount of sewage is concerned. Natural wetlands are, of course, as effective as artificial ones (see below), but should not be used, as the wetlands become polluted, and water-level control is needed.

In sewage treatment works (Table 1.2), primary treatment is a settling tank, where solids are screened out and are usually taken to be dumped: except by a few efficient authorities who recycle much or use the material for fuel generation, hot-water systems and the like. Secondary treatment is by activated sludge or biological filter, allowing the breakdown of much sewage and other organic matter. The best biological treatment gives as good effluent as tertiary treatment. Tertiary is done sporadically, with microstrainers, sand filters, or chemical-biological treatment lagoons. The Dutch have the declared aim that waste waters should have little or no impact on receiving waters: would that all would achieve this!

In theory this effluent is now potable, and many are the photographs of water-authority heads drinking a glass of clear liquid emanating from their new treatment works (whether it was further treated first, and whether they would feed their children on it permanently, are questions not raised at such functions). Water coming into waterworks is usually treated, and is always treated when it is recycled water. Treatments include storage (so that temporarily polluted water need not be used), coagulation (of pollutants), sedimentation (of solids), filtering through for example sand filters (to decrease nitrates and ammonia), carbon absorption (to eliminate bad tastes and odours, and to provide emergency disinfection), aeration, and disinfection (usually chlorine) (Water Research Centre, 1977). Aluminium or other compounds may also be added to make the water look nicer. (Aluminium is now thought implicated in Alzheimer's Disease, and so is less welcome to consumers.)

A new, properly designed and working sewage treatment works gives reasonable effluent. Soon, all too soon though, it receives more than the design standard (in volume or in type), or stops working well, and the effluent is no longer clear but visibly polluted on leaving the works. Relying on downstream recovery may not be enough — the English Welland, in the 1970s, was badly polluted from an upstream town. There is some 45km before the river, on entering the Fenland, slows quite enough to purify treated effluent from a smallish town. But along this length over 50 villages discharged into the stream, and coupled with the upstream pollution, the river was too overloaded to recover (Fig. 11.7). It was, however, used for water supply.

Treatment can remove all solids and suspended matter, in theory. In practice, though, treatment is usually inadequate or nil. Gravel-works pollution in Italy is a good example. It causes severe damage on a large scale.

Micro-organisms can change almost anything into something less toxic. They are in sewage-treatment works, which rely on them heavily. They are in the river, in water, in soil and around plants. Purification is particularly potent around plant roots — though the root effectiveness varies with species, the reed *Phragmites communis* being exceptionally good. Reed beds are used for purification. One most effective commercial method of water purification is the Root Zone method.

---

*Table 11.3*

*Purification by Phragmites Root Zone treatment*

*(Examples from, or cited in, Lawson (1985); Reddy & Smith (1987); Winter and Kickuth (1985, 1988, 1989))*

| substance | % loss | substance | % loss |
|---|---|---|---|
| Phosphorus | 98 | PCB Clophen A 60 | 0 |
| total Nitrogen | 90 | Naphtalin | 99 |
| Ammonium-Nitrogen | 93 | Monochlorbenzol | 99 |
| Sodium | 7 | Benzene | 95 |
| Potassium | 21 | Toluene | 99 |
| Chemical Oxygen Demand | 76-93 | Chloroform | 89 |
| Biological Oxygen Demand | 96 | Iron | 98 |
| Sulphur | 80-85 | faecal coliform bacteria | 99 |
| 2-Chlorphenol | 92 | suspended solids | 76 |
| Pentachlorphenol | 58 | | |

N.B. Compounds may be broken down to less harmful compounds or individual elements. These may be incorporated into soils, taken up by plants, or leave in the effluent water, etc. The elements themselves such as phosphorus, cannot be destroyed. Eventually, a given soil may be filled to capacity. Without a change of, e.g., soil, the method may be more appropriate for disposing of complex poisons and bacteria than of individual nutrients.

---

Fig. 11.4 A typical effect of increasing pollution on plant community. a) clean. b)-e) Increasing
pollution. Species present a) *Ranunculus* sp (abundant), *Apium
nodiflorum, Callitriche* sp,
*Myosotis scorpioides, Phalaris
arundinacea,      Potamogeton
crispus, Rorippa nasturtium-
aquaticum,        Sparganium
emersum, Sp. erectum, Veronica
beccabunga.* b) *Callitriche* sp,
*Myosotis scorpioides, Phalaris
arundinacea,      Potamogeton
crispus,    Ranunculus    sp,
Sparganium emersum, Sp.
erectum,* Blanket weed (long trailing filamentous algae). c)
*Potamogeton     crispus,    P.
pectinatus,        Sparganium
emersum, Sp. erectum,* Blanket
weed. d) *Potamogeton pectinatus*
(abundant), Blanket weed. e) No
larger (macrophytic) plants. (P.A.
Wolseley in Haslam, 1990).

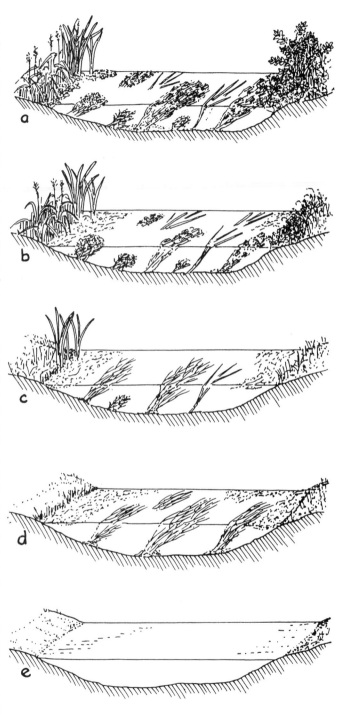

Another      effective
method further south is
by the floating Water
Hyacinth. (E.g. the mas-
sive symposium volume
edited by Reddy &
Smith, 1987, and that
by Athie & Cerrie, 1987;
Kickuth, 1976, 1984;
Lawson, 1985; Winter &
Kickuth, 1988, 1989,
1991; Haslam, 1987
(summary)). These plant
beds take more space
than conventional treat-
ment works, but can cost
much less, down to a
third of the cost to build,
and a tenth to run. The
method seems generally
as good as conventional
methods, for liquid ef-
fluents, with some spec-
tacular success stories
at German chemical fac-
tories (places where ef-

fluents are indeed nasty). Sulphur and persistent organics may be removed much better from Root Zone tanks than from ordinary treatment works. The reeds, of course, remain. It takes about three weeks for the micro-organism population to change, to become adapted to purify (i.e. to feed on) a different composition of effluent. So plant methods are adaptable to new types of effluent.

Some substances are, however, less degradable than others. Organochlorine biocides, alkyl benzene sulfonate detergents, and heavy metals (being elements rather than compounds), for example, cannot be eliminated, but can be changed to less toxic forms. Also, degradation means breaking down, but does not mean breaking down into safe substances. The degradation products of some biocides (e.g. fenitrothion, simazine) are unpleasantly toxic. While nitrogen can eventually be turned into gas and be released into the air, there is no such pathway of loss for phosphorus. It is absorbed into the soil, but when the absorption capacity is used up, something different is needed.

Most research has been done on emerged and floating plants, and all tested have been effective. (e.g., Table

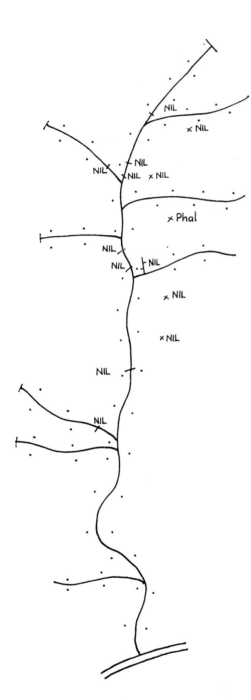

Fig. 11.5 River map, Lower Neckar, Germany. Gross pollution, devoid of macrophytes. Keuper, Lias etc., Lowland 1978 (L) (from Haslam, 1987).

The river maps are presented in a stylised format for easy comparison. The flow is from top to bottom of the page (unless otherwise marked). The abbreviations used for the species names and the order in which the species are listed are given in the Appendix. Rock type is listed, and boundaries (solid line across river) are marked only where they cross the river (sometimes giving a misleading impression of rock distribution in the catchment). The landscape is indicated by the density of dots along the river (plain, lowland, upland, mountain and alpine). L indicates large rivers, over c. 50 km long. M, medium, c. 25-50 km long, and S small, c. 10-25 km long. The records refer to the year and sites of survey only.

Fig. 11.6 River map, Skjern, Denmark. Fairly Clean. Fluvial sand (mainly), lowland, 1977, 1978 (L). 'L' indicates ochre — lignite — streams. See Notes Fig. 11.5 (from Haslam, 1987).

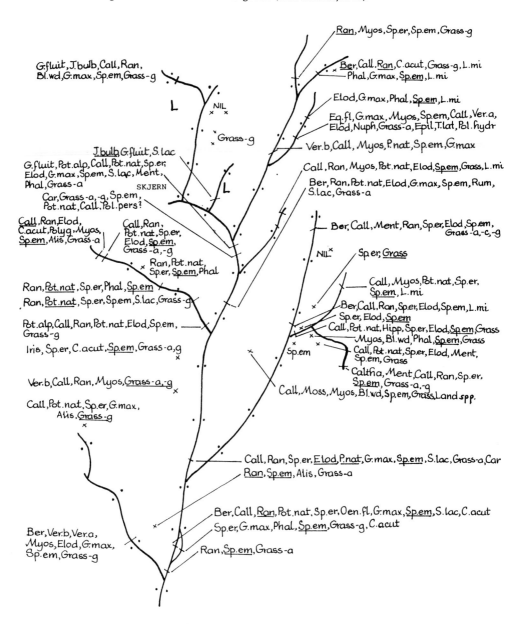

11.3). The bacteria *E. coli*, *Salmonella* and *Enterococcus* are eliminated to different degrees by *Mentha aquatica*, *Alisma-plantago-aquatica*, *Iris pseudacorus* and others, petrochemicals and toluene are broken down best by *Eleocharis palustris* and *Juncus inflexus*, and worst, of those tested, by *Typha latifolia*, *A. plantago-*

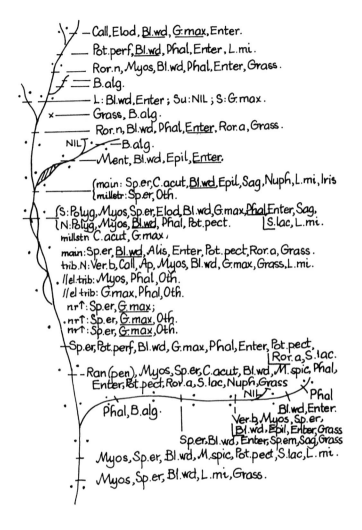

Fig. 11.7 River map, Upper Welland, England. Polluted from source, slight recovery, then many small effluents. Clay (limestone), lowland, 1980 (S) See Notes Fig. 11.5 (from Haslam, 1990).

*aquatica* and *Phragmites*. So species vary in their effectiveness (which depends on their root microflora), and *Phragmites*, though overall the most useful, is not the best in all circumstances.

Even simple 'safe' breakdown products may be, in quantity, polluting. Downgrading organic compounds to nitrates and such-like still leaves the nitrate as a pollutant (and appropriate other measures may be needed).

Channels with tall plants could take more heavily polluted water than empty channels, and this would be advantageous — for dealing with road run-off, for example.

In the river, self-purification takes place by this means, too. There are microorganisms everywhere. But to encourage the most self-purification of an effluent there should be firstly plenty of vegetation, with tall plants at the sides. (The most effective purification is in the soil, though.) There should be as much vegetation as possible without its causing damaging floods. Secondly, there should be no pollution other than the specified effluent. If the purifying powers of the river are already largely engaged in dealing with an upstream discharge, the effluent under consideration will be dealt with less effectively. It will take a longer length of river to purify to the same degree. Here land management by the river is important (Fig. 15.1). In unmanaged marsh, or traditionally managed grass or woodland, no chemicals are added, no additives reach the river. The natural leaf fall from

Fig. 11.8 River map, Dyle/Dijle, Belgium. Grossly polluted. Mixed rock types, lowland, 1980 (L). See Notes Fig. 11.5 (from Haslam, 1987).

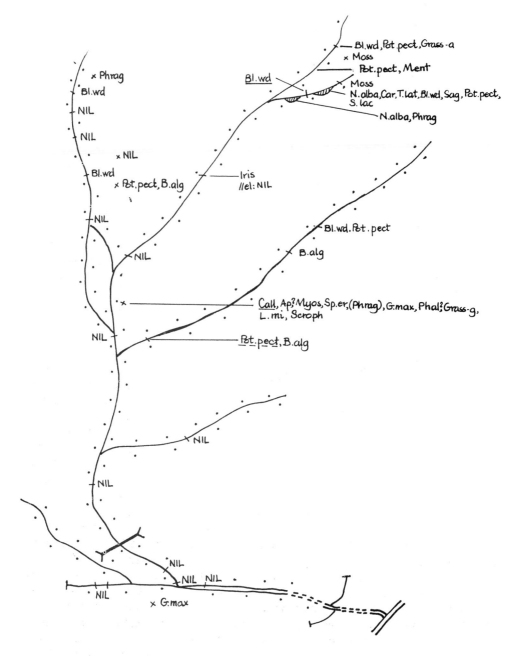

riverside trees may prevent much algal growth and the breakdown microorganisms may help purify. Rainfall from the land percolates to the rivers with little or no pollution — the pollutants having been filtered out in the fields. When arable land reaches to the riverside, however, the run-off contains fertilisers and biocides. Even without other discharges, this can slow recovery (P.A. Wolseley, personal communication).

## Pollution assessment with vegetation

Even the best purified water is not stream water, and will alter the receiving river (Hynes, 1960), i.e. pollute it. Streams are of many water types: the Alpine snow-melt torrent; the bright chalk stream; the sluggish dull clay one, etc. Some contain much higher concentrations of natural substances than others. The lower reaches of clay rivers, for instance, are solute-rich and organic-rich and are well buffered. They are slow to be altered by minor pollution. Others, such as acid bog streams and some chalk springs, are solute-low (and may be organic-low) and are very fragile. Just a little pollution completely alters the water type and so the aquatic life. The various robust stream types do not contain the same plant and animal communities. Still less do all fragile ones. There is a diversity of communities. Pollution tends to reduce to uniformity — no life is no life, whatever the original stream type and whatever the killing pollution.

Some rivers are now composed largely of effluent, because of the increased waste water and greater drainage of recent decades (e.g., the English River Glen). These differ chemically and so in vegetation too, from when they had their natural water.

The typical effect of pollution is shown in Fig. 11.4. As pollution gets worse, first the sensitive species disappear, then the tolerant ones.

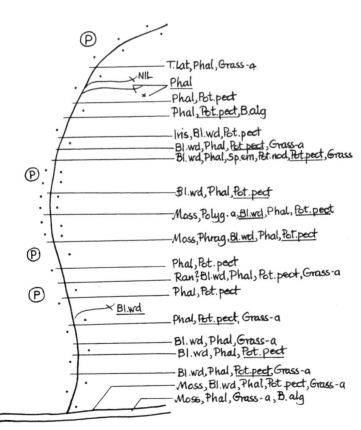

Fig. 11.9 River map, Alzette, Luxembourg. Severe pollution. Sandstone etc., lowland with local gorge, 1980 (S). intermittent slight improvement. P = pollution. See Notes Fig. 11.5 (from Haslam, 1987).

Fig. 11.10 River map, Great Stour, England. Unsatisfactory and threatened. Two pollution-fa-
Clay above, chalk below. N.B. flows from lower left to upper right. Lowland, voured species may
1986 (M). See notes Fig. 11.5 (from Haslam, 1990).

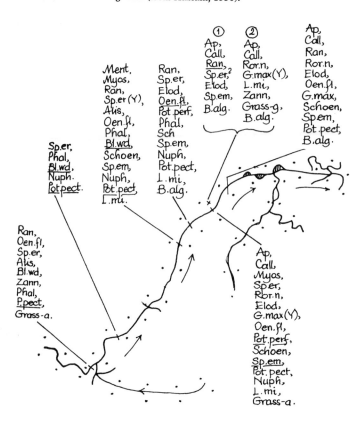

enter but finally, in gross pollution, no plants grow. In the Figs 11.5-11 series, each name, e.g., 'Ver b' means a plant species, and the Latin names are given in full in the Appendix. The Danish Skjern is a reasonably clean river: species lists at most sites are long. The German Neckar is the reverse: species lists at most sites are 'nil'. There is heavy and complex industry upstream in Stuttgart, a high population, and inadequate purification. The English Welland, referred to above, is medium; the quality varies. (On a vegetation scale where 'a' is good — many sites are 'a' in the Skjern — and 'h'

is bad, the main Welland sites are *e, d, b/e* (two channels), *d, b, c, d, e*.) The Luxembourg Alzette is worse (*f, g, f, g, e, g, g, g, f, e, g, g, g, g, g. 'e'* here represents improvement between discharges.) Just to show that monitoring has some difficulties, the Tauber does not get suddenly cleaner at intervals. Instead there are fords, where vegetation grows much better on the shallow gravelly bottom than in the deep muddy water in between. The grades are a *damage* rating, damage from physical as well as chemical causes, and care is needed to distinguish them (see, e.g., Haslam & Wolseley, 1981; Haslam, 1990; *Methods for the Analysis of Waters and Associated Materials 1985:* Haslam *et al.*, 1987). With this warning, though, a quick guide to pollution can be used by the general reader. If there are eight or more different kinds of river plant present at one place (of 4m or more stream width), then there is not much wrong with the river. If less, there is damage — by pollution, by Alpine flows, by navigation, or whatever (see Appendix for a short outline of method).

More pollution assessments of rivers by authorities are done by the water insects (macro-invertebrates) than by the water plants. However, the method is

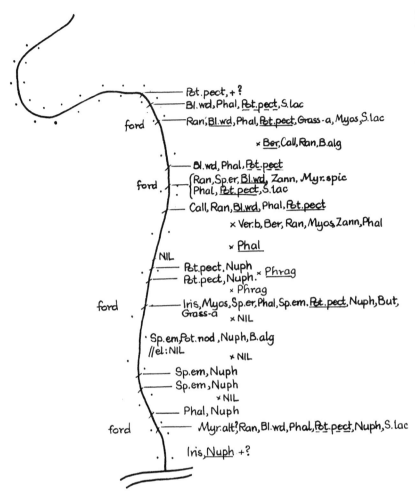

Fig. 11.11 River map, Tauber, Germany. Bad pollution. Old fords provide good physical habitat (shallow, gravelly, well-oxygenated), and vegetation there increases. Muschelkalk (sandstone below), lowland, upland above. 1980 (M). See notes Fig. 11.5 (from Haslam, 1987).

less suitable for the non-specialist, partly due to the spread of water-borne (pollution) diseases, including the potentially fatal Weil's disease (see Chapter 13) — invertebrates must always be collected from within the water — and partly because methods are more complex.

Man's use of rivers for chemical-waste disposal is better demonstrated in vegetation than in buildings.

## The European Community and clean water

It is very easy to get used to seeing rivers in the state they have been in for the past few decades. The impetus to clean is rare and local, and is often stimulated by something much worse than normal — a massive fish-kill, a new, unpleasant smell, a typhoid outbreak. This is due to inertia and the wish not to pay higher taxes to

Fig. 11.12 Fish recolonisation between 1974 and 1980 in the Ebbw, Wales. Fish present in tributaries and upstream of the town in 1974 and gradually colonising nearer the town, from downstream (from Edwards *et al.*, 1984).

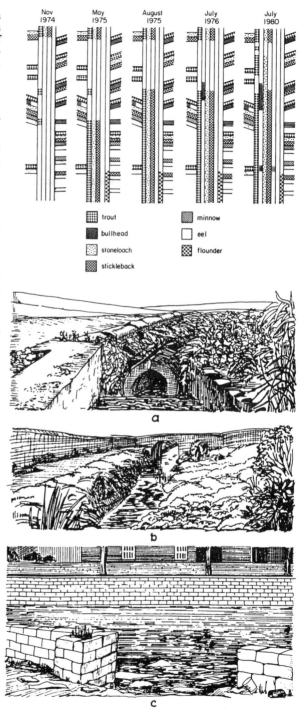

cure something 'which hasn't done any harm since I can remember'. It is also due to the ignorance of what constitutes a good, healthy river (Fig. 15.1). These are now so rare in lowland Europe that most people, even most river specialists, have never seen one (even the writer, with records of over 30,000 sites, has found only a handful, and none in England). If no one knows what to aim for, how can it be achieved? And how easy to acquiesce in further lowering of quality, too slow to be noticed on an annual basis. From 1980 to 1990, British rivers, overall, have deteriorated (some bad areas have been improved, but better ones have worsened. The tendency is towards uniformity, and hence further loss of the knowledge of the good).

EEC directives on water quality in the tap and in the river are compulsory. Working outside any one region or country with an overview it is easier to detect the bad. However, EEC standards are minimal. Even when all rivers meet these standards, they will be far from clean. Only a few substances are assessed, out of the thousands of pollutants that enter the rivers (Water Research Centre, 1984). Also, the difference between stream types, the robustness, the buffering against

Fig. 11.13 Some pollutions. a) Town, Mallorca. b) Town, Menorca. c) Urban run-off, Malta: in summer a football pitch.

chemical change, is not yet accepted. Fragile stream types need, and do not yet have, more stringent pollution standards than robust ones. It is to be hoped that standards are tightened, and promptly. This seems the best hope for European rivers.

## R. Ebbw (Wales)
### (Fig. 11.12)

The tale of this Welsh river is that of many of those affected by the Industrial Revolution. It was clean, with splendid fisheries and other wildlife, up to the late eighteenth century. In that century the coal seams began to be exploited fully (a pump was now available for deep mining; see Chapter 1), and iron works developed along the northern rim of the coalfields at the head of the valleys. By 1841 population and industry had much expanded, few houses had privies or sewerage, and filth was excessive, leading to outbreaks of cholera and other disease. Pollution was gross in 1861, though a few last trout were still there. In 1912 there was a trunk sewer to the coast (no treatment), but it ran beside, and overflowed into, the river. The replacement started in 1971. The steelworks effluent was not fully treated until 1973. By this time — in fact by two decades earlier — industry was turning away from the coal valleys. The rivers certainly improved greatly — but it was as much a result of industrial decay (and so less pollution) as of purification. Fish returned remarkably rapidly as the pollution lessened, quickly colonising the main river from such tributaries as had remained clean (Edwards *et al.*, 1984). This last shows the importance of *part* of a system retaining plants and animals: colonisation from other river systems is much slower. The new twentieth-century pollution is more pervasive.

## R. Great Stour (England)
### (Fig. 11.13; Table 11.4)

This is from an area to which later twentieth-century industry is moving. Until recently the main pollution was domestic — of course becoming worse with detergents, after the Second World War. Indeed the East Stour is still polluted by septic tanks and such-like from villages without, or with inadequate, sewage treatment. The East Stour is now the worst part of the river: site species lists are short. The main town grew, industry came and outgrew its treatment works, and by 1965 the river was appalling for a short way below it — as bad as the Ebbw, but for a short distance only, as self-purification in the river was possible. The new sewage works led to a major improvement. But industry continues to come, the river deteriorates and the Channel Tunnel is expected to bring more pollution, both directly and through attracting yet more industry and traffic. This river is not bad, therefore alarm bells do not ring. It is not what it should be, is getting worse and is under threat. It is endangered by the turn of the twenty-first century, not, like the Ebbw, ruined by the nineteenth century. Fortunately, if treated right, rivers can recover very quickly (as long as refuges for their species remain). But will they be treated right? People can do it if they will. Only *if* they will (Fig. 11.13).

*Table 11.4*

*River and fish pollution over thirty years in the Great Stour, England*

(*From D.S. Martin, personal communication*)

| date | history | fish | invertebrates | vegetation |
|------|---------|------|---------------|------------|
| 1951 | Crystal clear, clean gravel, little sign of pollution | Numerous trout | Fly hatches profuse | Good |
| 1958 | Detergent foam increasing | (decrease) | No mayfly. Other ephemeroptera decline | Blanket weed increases spreading downstream. Other macrophytes decline |
| early 1960s | Poor | Trout decrease | No ephemeroptera in Blanket weed reaches | Blanket weed stretches downstream of sewage works |
| 1965-6 | No gravel seen | Upstream, only a few sickly trout; downstream trout rising | Upstream, no fly hatches | Upstream, Blanket weed; downstream, Blanket weed patches |
| 1966 and later | New sewage works, bare gravel increases | Trout improve | Fly hatches return | Blanket weed decreases, other macrophytes increase |
| 1970s to early 1980s | Improves | Good | Mayfly hatches return and spread, less than 1950s, but good in part | Improves |
| mid-1980s | Pollution incidents | 80% loss trout in part of river (1985) | | Decline |

# 12

# Threats from the River

In danger from rivers... (2 Cor. 11.26)

A plague of rain and waters. (*Book of Common Prayer*)

The flood was rising and pursuing them... and behind... the great silver sheet of water spread and spread. (Sayers, 1934)

That alarming malady [of cholera in the 1830s]. (Holmes, 1974)

When our great seat of learning smells as it does smell under the noses of the professors. (Ewing, 1876)

From the wrath of the Norsemen, Good Lord deliver us. (Merovingian — N. France — addition to the Litany)

> Every pelting river made so proud,
> That they have over borne their continents.
> ... the green corn
> Hath rotted, ere his youth attained a beard;
> The fold stands empty in the drowned field.
> And crows are fatted with the murrain flock.
> (W. Shakespeare, *A Midsummer Night's Dream*)

## Introduction

Nothing, here below, brings unalloyed good. This includes rivers. Like electricity and gas, rivers can kill, but continue to be necessary. All the danger rivers can hold for man tends to be forgotten because modern technology, and modern social patterns (no Viking raiders) have much diminished them. This decrease is hard-won: it has taken centuries.

## Water-borne and water-linked disease

The association between water and illness has been known for a long time; for instance, in 444 B.C. an epidemic in Greek Sicily was checked by draining two river valleys (Potter, 1981). Malaria is perhaps the foremost of the water-borne diseases. The *Anopheles* mosquito may be confined to watercourses — as recently in Malta — although it is most often associated with large areas of wetland, right across

Europe. The Po Plain drained in classical times (Chapter 4) was largely abandoned for nearly two millennia with malaria. The South Hungarian swamps were bad until the nineteenth century (Y. Bower, personal communication). The French coastal wetlands were malarial; so was the Thames-Medway area in England. The 'Fen Ague' plagued the English Fenland to the end of the last century, and was considered to have been a form of malaria. Sicily in fact had bad malaria until the mid-twentieth century. Drainage and DDT rescued Europe from malaria. The mention of DDT is important. Temporary use of this dangerous substance for a disaster is valuable. Complaints about biocides are about their routine over-use for just a little higher crop yield — for well-fed Europe.

Many diseases are spread by man-infected house-water, e.g. cholera, typhoid, bacillary and amœbic dysentery, polio, parasitic worms and other gastric ills (Hynes, 1960). It took long before the importance of cleanliness was understood — that clean, boiled water for human use, and clean personal habits, would eliminate most of these ills. Yonge (1886) charts the nineteenth-century British progression: 'now [1880s], tidings of a visitation of cholera are heard with compassion for crowded towns, but without special alarm for ourselves and our friends, since its conditions and the mode of combating it have come to be fairly understood. In 1832, however, it was a disease almost unknown.... We had heard of it in a helpless sort of way... and thought of the victims as doomed. [By 1849] there had been some experience.... On the alarm in that year there was a great inspection of cottages.' Some of the dirty practices have been described earlier (see Chapters 3 and 11).

A description of the even worse conditions in industrial towns is given by Gaskell (1848) for Manchester: '[They] lived in a cellar in Berry Street. [The street] was unpaved; and down the middle a gutter forced its way, every now and then forming pools in the holes with which the street abounded. Never was the old Edinburgh cry of "Gardes l'eau" more necessary than in this street. As they passed, women from their doors tossed household slops of every description into the gutter; they ran into the next pool, which overflowed and stagnated. Heaps of ashes were the stepping stones, on which the passer-by, who cared in the least for cleanliness, took care not to put his foot. ...You went down one step even from the foul area into the cellar in which a family of human beings lived. ...the smell was so foetid as almost to knock the two men down... three or four little children rolling on the damp, nay wet, brick floor, through which the stagnant filthy moisture of the street oozed up. ...a door... led into a back cellar, with a grating instead of a window, down which dropped the moisture from pigsties, and worse abominations. It was not paved; the floor was one mess of bad smelling mud.' Note here: a street gutter, no cesspits or sewers, all waste thrown into the street, the street unpaved, no swift water-flow removing waste, fire waste, ash abundant (as everywhere until recently), dwelling-rooms below street level, no drainage to keep these rooms dry or free from street filth, pigsties allowed in such streets.

For water-borne disease, the village brook by the stream ceases to be the object of interest described heretofore and becomes the agent of doom: when the brook is not maintained clean, but, as in nineteenth-century time particularly, allowed to become a dump for waste. Ewing (1876) describes: 'children playing happily with their mimic boats on the open [village] drain that ran largely under the noontide sun, by the footpath of the main street, were coffined for their hasty burial before the sun had next reached his meridian [during a cholera epidemic]'.

Other illnesses are less dramatic than cholera. The endemic ones need continual vigilance. Mains water is disinfected at the waterworks nowadays, which makes these diseases even rarer (though minor water-borne ones are still extant in South Europe).

Secondly there are the diseases due to the consumption of chemically polluted water, not infectious ills, but lead poisoning and such-like in the past and including, e.g., biocide poisoning now. Thirdly, there are also the ills arising from the water itself, and what it contains irrespective of man. These are less easy to identify.

The floods in Bristol in 1968 caused, among those whose home had been flooded, a 50% increase in deaths, a 53% increase in those consulting doctors, and a doubling of hospital admissions (Bennett, 1970). While some of this may have been due to chemical or microbiological pollutants, much was surely due to the trauma of flood, and lowered resistance from damp. The 1850s considered various ills to be aggravated, perhaps altogether caused, by cold and damp in undrained valleys. These ills could include: malaria, fevers of severe and even malignant kind, chronic disorders of the digestive organs, those tedious liver complaints so prevalent, especially near rivers, scrofula (pulmonary and glandular modifications), disorders of the alimentary canal or liver, rheumatism (acute and chronic, and the premature infirmity it so often entailed) (Clarke, 1854-5). Of course the list also contains infections. The damp Nene Valley was one of the last refuges of intermittent and marsh diseases left in Britain. It was a local saying that 'they destroy more lives than the Danes and Saxons of old.' Northampton (in that valley) had one of the six highest mortality rates in the kingdom. With draining, the mortality rate in the Isle of Ely dropped, between 1796 and 1825, from 1 in 31 to 1 in 47, about the average of the country. Similar improvements occurred in Buckinghamshire, Huntingdonshire, Norwich and Colchester. In Bath, the 'cheerless and inactive Avon' made so by weirs, 'has the air impregnated with the most noxious vapours, in the warmer months, killing hundreds who court that retreat of fashion' (Clarke, 1854-5). Other sluggish rivers, like the Great Ouse, are also noted as deadly (it sounds like disease and pollution). A common English street name for overcrowded industrial-revolution development on damp valleys (see Chapter 9) was Waterside. Waterside inhabitants were often reported as pale and diseased. Once squalor sets in, it is perpetuated, and disease follows. Earlier, as already mentioned, water-millers were often referred to as pale and dour, unlike their jolly red-faced counterparts of the airy windmills. Damp traditionally favours rheumatism; damp houses, whether through siting or inadequate heating, increase this formerly widespread and crippling complaint. When river levels are too high for open sewers and drains to run into the river, this makes them even more a source of disease, as in Oxford University's complaint to Cardinal Wolsey in 1519 (Thacker, 1914).

From a mixture of causes, damp led, and where relevant still may lead, to disease and early death. Increased mortality was not due solely to the presence of the river. The trading-towns like Bruges, Antwerp and Namur show that. They flourished. Good building, good drainage, airy siting (compare present Namur, Fig. 9.4 with an enclosed valley mill, e.g. Fig. 10.3) and the absence of malaria may have much to do with it. Trading towns presumably, though, imported foreign diseases, liable to be virulent in a community without immunity. The contrast is with the Po plain (above). Another example is the English Fenland, traditionally considered unhealthy. Defoe (1724-7) comments on its base and unwholesome air, and nineteenth-century descriptions are of an ague-ridden and, consequently, opium-eating population. The opium-eating continued into the early twentieth century.

Several people (e.g. Granville, 1841) have recorded that communities bustling, active and joyous may thrive in unhealthy (particularly polluted) places, where the reverse is expected, and usually happens. This effect must be considered too.

# Crops and stock

## Crops
Crops are harmed (the yield being lowered) and killed by flood. They are most sensitive in summer (when they are growing and require much oxygen, etc.). In summer, though, the land dries out more quickly, so a flood may have worse effects in winter (for winter-growing crops). The harm varies with the crop. Potatoes and wheat in ear are sensitive and cannot stand more than about two days of standing water. Grass can tolerate much more, particularly in winter and spring. Watermeadows and floodmeadows are flooded for management; grass being benefited by the silt and water — for a short period. Watery meadows, because of the water, might carry diseases (Chapter 4).

## Stock
Apart from the obvious danger of drowning in flash floods, stock can be adversely affected by water in various ways.

*Damage to pasture:* regular flooding removes many nutritious plants and grasses from grazing-lands, and nutritionally poorer species take over, leading to a downgrading of the pasture. Stock kept on poor pasture loses condition and is more susceptible to infections. Leeching-out of trace elements such as copper can also cause disease.

*Poisoning:* various substances that pollute streams can be harmful to stock. Fluorine from rainfall contaminated by factory smoke, when taken up by plants or in run-off in streams, is toxic to cattle over a 0.09% level. A 0.25% contamination of Dieldrin, or a 0.05–0.1% of Benzene Hexachloride can cause death in cattle, sheep or goats. Fertilisers, such as nitrates are also poisonous in high concentrations (100g of sodium or potassium nitrate for cattle and horses, and 30g for sheep or swine, can be lethal).

Some plants poisonous to stock, such as Horse tail (*Equisetum palustre*), are found in regularly flooded wetlands; some, like Hemlock water dropwort (*Oenanthe crocata*), grow on the banks of streams. Some fungal diseases, such as footrot in sheep, are mainly found in stock kept on wetlands.

*Infections:* micro-organisms causing infectious diseases in stock are often spread by water. Streams can become infected with Anthrax (*Bacillus anthracis*); emphysematous gangrene (*Clostridium chauvoei*) is confined to wet areas as its spores require water for survival. Water also aids the viability, and consequently helps the spread, of bacterial diseases. Tuberculosis bacilli survive for 687 days, *Brucella abortas* for 114 days, in water (Cameron, 1932), though they soon perish in dry conditions. (Though both these diseases have been virtually eliminated from the British Isles, they are still present elsewhere in Europe.) *Cocciotia,* causing red dysentery of cattle in wetlands, survives in water for 2-2.5 months.

Many internal parasites require water for part of their life cycles: the eggs hatch in water, where the larvae in their first stage or stages remain until ingested by livestock. Parasites can cause loss of condition, serious illness or even death in cases of heavy infestation. The remedy lies in regular dosing and moving of stock (which is expensive and time-consuming) to avoid build-up in the pasture, but again some parasites can survive a surprisingly long time in water: *Trychostrongylas,* for instance, for seven months in standing water, *Haemonchus* for nine months on regularly flooded areas. Lately the presence in some rivers of toxic blue-green algae has added another danger to stock.

Finally, increased levels of nitrogen fertilisers may not be entirely without effect. Hatyra could write in 1938: 'carcinomas... have little clinical importance', a statement which could not be made in 1990, as cancers of all sorts have greatly increased in livestock. Correlation between increased use of fertilisers in Western Europe and the increase of carcinomas might well repay study.

## Floods

Floods are aggravated within the river by winding channels, silting, obstructions (weirs, sewage, trees, nets, fords, shoals, etc.), and beyond the river by built-up

Fig. 12.1 Flood. a) 1570, Antwerp (woodcut). b) 1990, St Ives, England.

*a*

Fig. 12.1 contd.

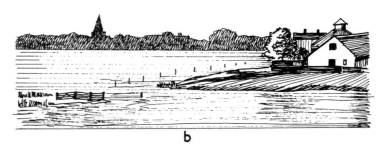

surfaces and
intensive farm-
ing. They are
alleviated by
removing these
by flood-protec-
tion works,
flood-relief cuts, washlands and drainage.

Flood-protection works have, after many centuries, insulated Europe from the
worst effects of flood. Fig. 12.1 contrasts the effect of an — admittedly exceptional
— sixteenth-century flood with that of 1990. One shows extreme damage to house,
man and beast, the other, water quietly sitting on grassland below house level.
(Elsewhere there was minor house-flooding in England in 1990.)

Floods into villages and towns used to be commonplace. Villages on the Nene,
a particularly bad area, were often flooded and barges could be held up by floods for
up to thirteen weeks (Clarke, 1854-5).

Early embankments tended to be piecemeal, protecting towns and settlements and, later, drained areas. They served three purposes: (1) keeping water
within a known channel, so helping navigation — their principal early purpose; (2)
preventing flooding to town and land; and (3) preventing the natural movement of
the course of the river (a perpetual nuisance to river users — except any who might
gain from having their boundary moved). The Loire may be used as an example (Fig.

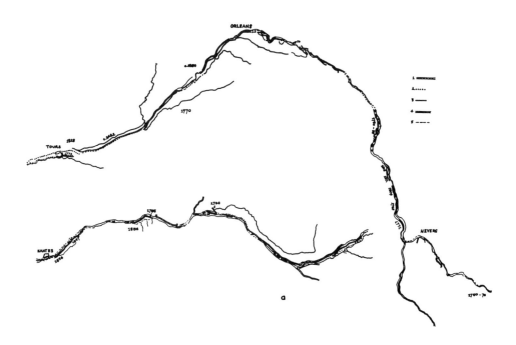

12.2a). Navigation was, as usual, the primary early concern. The first charter (Henry II) was in 1160 (followed up in 1268 and 1275). Catastrophic floods still occurred regularly, as protection was but local, and broken embankments caused much devastation. After the 1709 inundation, plans were made to alleviate flooding by regulating water above the flood plain. Barrages were built (Pinay, La Roche and Saint Maurice). These led onto the reservoirs for summer irrigation, described in Chapter 4. As long as the dams hold, all is well. However, when the Pinay dam broke in 1946, 100 million cumecs of water caused mass destruction and this was not the only break (Wolseley, 1987). Dams may also be broken on purpose, in war or by terrorists, in order to cause mass destruction.

Draining is the second part of flood prevention, lowering ground water level and facilitating speedy removal of excess water.

Embanking and draining cause restriction of channels. Fig. 12.2b shows the alterations in part of the Rhône channel: a change from braided (that is, divided) winding channels, to straight, fast, deep ones (with much loss of river habitat) (Wolseley, 1987). Flooding is now occasional, not normal. Dorothy Sayers' *The Nine Tailors* describes, as late as the 1930s in the Fenland, the frantic activity to sandbag the banks of the swollen watercourses and to remove the population to high ground — and the loss of life and property. 'The whole world was lost in one vast sheet of water, and the Fen reclaimed its own.' The activity was, however, practised and disciplined. Thanks to greater drainage and flood-protection works, such floods are no longer expected — but if they occurred would be more destructive from the lack of preparation. Sea-facing Dutch towns might — and may still — be closed from the sea by sluices during very high tides, e.g., Haarlingen.

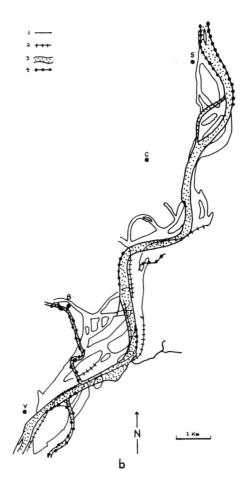

Fig. 12.2 a) Embankments of the Loire between Nevers and Nantes. Section of river downstream of Tours: 1. before the thirteenth century; 2. thirteenth century to 1460; 3. 1460-1707; 4. 1707-1856; 5. mediaeval embankments of indeterminate date (from Wolseley in Haslam, 1987). b) Change in the channel of the Rhône between Soyons and La Voulte, 1856-1950. 1. Rhône in 1856; 2. embankments in 1856; 3. Rhône in 1950; 4. embankments since 1856; 5. Soyons; C. Charnes; B. Beauchastel; V. La Voulte (from Wolseley in Haslam, 1987).

Defoe (1724-7) frequently mentions flood damage, e.g., on the Yorkshire Don, bridges, wharfs and mills destroyed, and on the Chester Dee, a new wharf and landing-place lost with the warehouse contents.

Table 12.1

*Flood levels for Tewkesbury, on R. Severn, 1882-1976*

(From Wood (1981))

| level (metres above ordnance datum) | dates |
|---|---|
| 11.5 | 1880 1946 1988 |
| 11.6 | 1912 1915 1925 1939 1945 1950 1965 |
| 11.7 | 1875 1881 1882 1889 1895 1910 1919 1958 1959 |
| 11.8 | 1862 1901 1954 1955 |
| 11.9 | 1929 1940 |
| 12.0 | 1877 (also 1990) |
| 12.1 | 1860 1924 |
| 12.2 | |
| 12.3 | |
| 12.4 | 1886 |
| 12.5 | 1947 |

In England floods in the Severn Valley are shown in Table 12.1. Recent floods have been particularly high in 1947, 1953, 1968, 1978 and 1990. After 1953 (which broke the east-coast sea defences) damage has been minor and even the 1947 floods were nothing to those of 1852 (almost the wettest year of the century). That flooded the Severn Valley; parts of Wales; all of the Vale of Gloucester; Bath, and central Somerset into the West Country; Oxford was in a sea of water; and the Thames valley was under several feet (1-2m?) of water — the floods extended from west to east (Clarke, 1954-5). The term 'uplands', now used for hills, then meant land above normal flood level. Bad floods in Cambridge occurred in 1796, 1862, 1875, 1914, 1915, 1919, 1928, 1937, 1947 and 1978. The works undertaken since 1947, which include a 'cut' around the outer edge of the Fenland (Fig. 6.13), a relief channel to the sea for storm flows, ensure that future floods remain local (Greenhaugh, 1980).

Floods caused damage to buildings, bridges and mills, as well as drowning man, beast and crop.

Floods were much increased by the miller's need to pond the water, and to a lesser extent, the watermen's need for deep water: but this latter can be obtained by dredging as well as by ponding. Silting impedes flow and needs removing. Silting increases with more intensive farming, and flood protection means that the natural changes of river course do not take place.

Arterial drainage on major rivers is to remove obstructions (including removing or lowering dams and weirs), straighten and excavate (to lower the bed), so that water flows freely. This, as a major enterprise, started in the mid-nineteenth century. (Keeping outfalls clear had been attempted — and done — for centuries before.) The numerous old laws against the kiddles (fish-weirs), which impeded navigation rather than drainage, will be remembered from Chapter 1. Arterial drainage is now done over most of lowland Europe. The next stage is field drainage, similar schemes on the smaller streams. This has been mentioned as ecologically doubtful (or worse!) in Chapter 4. The importance of flood protection for settlements has never been in doubt. Dense vegetation in rivers aggravates (or causes) small floods, but makes little difference to the water spread and damage in major floods.

Flood-protection work continues (Fig. 12.3). Eastern England is slowly sinking. Banks do not last

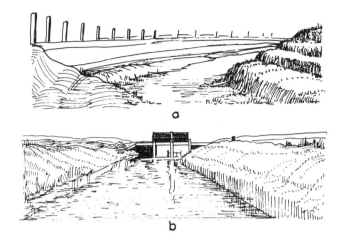

for ever. London-on-the-Thames is now at greater risk from high tides (because of this sinking and the greater population on low ground), and the Thames Barrage

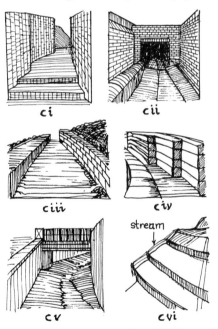

has been constructed downstream at Woolwich. Ordinarily it is down, and ships may pass. But in over-high tides it can be raised and prevent water going up London. (To show contrasts, the *Anglo-Saxon Chronicle* notes for 1113, that the river dried at ebb tide so it could be crossed on foot! Not since.)

Floods, in effect, store water somewhere until the river can move it to the sea. Hence 'wash-lands' can be provided to store the water where convenient to man. In Lincolnshire some riverside farmland is let on the understanding that it will be used to store floodwater if need-ed. In Italy there is a mountain tunnel from Adige in the Alps to L. Garda, so that some water can be diverted from the Verona region.

Roads were so often flooded that white-painted posts to mark roads near rivers were

Fig. 12.3 Flood Protection Works. a) High-banked rivers, Czechoslovakia. b) Balancing drain, fen to left as a Wash, farmland beyond bank to right, pumping station centre. Woodwalton Fen, England. c) Lining. (i) Funchal, Madeira, (ii) Haverhill, England, (iii) San Vicente stream, Mallorca, older lining, (iv) same, newer lining, (v) Mercadal, Menorca, (vi) Rhine vineyard, (vii) Herts., England. d) Flood relief channels, (i) English Fenland, (ii) Arve plain, France. e) Dutch drain. f) Reservoir-controlled, R. Sure, Luxembourg. River can be bank-full because the dam above prevents natural flooding. g) Waal embankment, The Netherlands. h) Village on fishpond on small stream, Czechoslovakia. i) Walled streams, Mallorca. j) Thames barrage, London. Can rise and close the river to high incoming tides.

Fig. 12.3 contd.

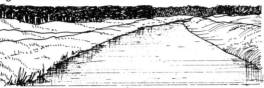

di

plentiful. They can still be found, but are rarely used — now they are just a reminder of common road conditions in the past. Road floods became much less acceptable with the coming of cars; 30cm of water can present a major and possibly insuperable hazard, where before carts and horsemen could pass easily.

The danger of swollen rivers and flood to travellers by land is well summed up by Defoe. 'I mention so often the safety of travelling... because... the commissioners for these repairs of the highways have order'd, and do daily order, abundance of bridges to be repaired and enlarg'd, and new ones built... which not only serve to carry the water off, where it otherwise often spreads, and lies as it were damm'd up upon the road and spoils the way; but where it rises sometimes by sudden rains to a dangerous height, for it is to be observ'd that there is more hazard, and more lives lost, in passing, or

dii

attempting to pass little brooks and streams, which are swell'd by sudden showers of rain, and where passengers expect no stoppage, than in passing great rivers, where the danger is known, and therefore more carefully avoided. In many of these places the commissioners have built large and substantial bridges for the benefit of travelling... and in other places have built sluices to stop, and open'd channels to carry off the waters, where they used to swell into the highway.' Defoe does not mention the mud. Unmade — or un-macadammed — roads were easily turned into quagmires.

A great debt is owed by modern travellers to the highway and flood-protection authorities!

e

Drowning was a routine hazard for watermen, particularly at flash-locks (Chapter 6), when boats were smaller, and river passages more difficult, and there were no lifebelts. The Thames was noted as perilous to passengers, in the sixteenth century (Thacker, 1914). Drowning was far from impossible for travellers by road (see above). Even in the nineteenth century rivers were considered a common way of death, by accident or suicide (e.g. the novels of George Eliot and Charles Dickens: the latter's *Our Mutual Friend* (1865) describes those who made their living from drowned bodies in the Thames). Though very much fewer, river drownings do still

f

occur: about one a year in the Cam, the tidal Blackwater and Medway, one in three years in tidal Stour (Y. Bower, personal communication). Bad storms make large rivers very rough, which, together with the wind, can damage boats; e.g., in 1703 the Thames was blocked by wrecked shipping (Boyer, 1703-13).

Arable and farms, water kept out

Grassland, may flood

9

Various illustrations of flood protection have been shown earlier, e.g., embanked rivers (Figs 6.1, 6.10, 6.17, etc.), including those embanked above ground level (whether or not drained), where ground water has to be pumped up to the river. Fig. 12.3 shows a wider range; first is shown a high-banked river. These may be embanked, drained, or both. The pattern in detail differs with country as well as with topography and stream size. Next is a balancing drain taking water from higher land, using the fen to the left as a wash, and with a pumping-station in the distance to raise drainage water from the farmland on the right. Following, are varieties of protection within the channel — various linings of bank and bed. These

h

are, regrettably, found widely in settlements. Many are ecologically disastrous — those completely lined are especially so. The Haverhill one was the old Town Stream, formerly industrial. It now flows, unwanted, through the modern industrial area. The walls of the San Vicente stream were broken by flood in 1985, and the second Fig. shows the replacement channel. This degree of caging of the river leaves no flexibility. The Rhine vineyard stream is straightened and, on such a steep slope, necessarily stoned to prevent scour.

The next two (in Fig. 12.3) show flood-relief channels: those of the English

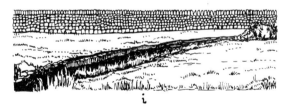

i

Fenland, and of the French Arve flood plain. The latter is a smaller wetland, easier to see. The cut runs along the edge of the high ground taking water to the river downstream (and even here is polluted, bearing algae (Blanket weed) as the only prominent vegetation). Settlement used to be at the edge but, with better flood protection, is encroaching into the plain (see Chapter 9, Fig. 9.8). (Diversion channels for other purposes have already been shown, e.g., Fig. 3.20 for watering a village, Fig. 2.6 to power a mill, Fig. 6.15 for a navigation canal, etc.)

The Dutch illustration shows a drain that is full to the bank (it is wide, so it must have been constructed recently). These have 'grazed edges' in contrast to the 'dredged edges' above. The water table is high, and the crop is grass, not arable. This is undrained, but within a protecting embankment. The next, from Luxembourg,

is also bank-full, as in the past, with cattle grazing the edge and drinking, etc. There may be minor flooding, but upstream is a main reservoir, with controlled water release. Both these have

j

a

b

Fig. 12.4 In danger of Flood. a) Madeira. Clearly unsuitable in a valley leading from high mountains. b) Malta. Protected by dam above, but of dubious wisdom.

flood protection, but not in the channel itself.

Another Dutch example shows the Waal embankment. On one side is ditched grassland, on the other arable and farms. Ground level is similar, but only the former is liable to flood.

The Czech fishpond is on a tiny stream, so there is little fear of flooding. Thus even the church of the village — which is the most usually on high ground (see Chapters 9 and 10) — is beside the pond.

Mallorcan rivers are unusual in being walled: almost all, large and small (from about 1m wide), are walled. (For a large one, see Fig. 6.4e.) This walling is still being renewed.

Finally, buildings liable to flood, without protection, are hazardous. Fig. 12.4a from Madeira is all too obviously unsafe. Fig. 12.4b from Malta may escape.

# War

### Introduction

Rivers can be used for defence unmodified. Many Anglo-Saxon settlements, for instance, were in river bends (e.g., Durham) or confluences (Limbrey, 1983, who notes the remaining side could be a marsh, cf. Ribe, Fig. 9.14). Rivers can be diverted, or ponded (as moats) for defence. Moats are also effective when dry or drained. Fortifications can be placed overlooking, by, or on, the river crossing, round the settlement, and across the valley. Flooding can be used to deter an enemy, and either side can cut off, or poison, the water supply of the other. Invasion can be along the river; or by land, but needing to cross the river.

### The flood

Using the flood in war has been the speciality of The Netherlands, the only nation with so much of its land below sea level. In the seventeenth century, William of Orange could create, then flood, a Water Line against the French. On the opening of the sluices, there was water from the Zuider Zee (now the Ijsselmeer) south to

Dordrecht, so that the heart of the nation was moated off. There were a few causeways, and five garrisons to command the lines of the rivers. Numerous boats were needed to maintain and guard this, and to supply the garrisons (Robb, 1962). His sixteenth-century predecessor broke the banks of Alkmaar and later of Leiden, hoping to allow the water-borne relief force in, and to hamper and starve the Spanish (Parker, 1977). Releasing flood is a drastic, but valuable tool.

---

*Table 12.2*

*Viking and later river movements as recorded in the Anglo-Saxon Chronicle*

A.D.

| | |
|---|---|
| 787 | Three ships. |
| 794 | Northumbria ravaged by heathen. |
| 845 | Battle at mouth of R. Parrett, Somerset. |
| 851 | Overwintered for the first time. |
| 870 | King Edmund (later canonised) killed. |
| 875 | Winter quarters on R. Tyne |
| 881 | Up R. Meuse (France); remained a year. |
| 882 | Up R. Scheldt (Low Countries) to Condé (France); remained a year. |
| 883 | Up R. Somme (France) to Amiens; remained a year. |
| 885 | Up R. Seine (France). |
| 886 | Up R. Seine (France) through the bridge at Paris, up R. Marne to Chezy sur Marne and R. Yonne valley. Two winters in these two. |
| 893 | Into Pevensey Levels, Kent (by boàt). |
| 896 | Built a fort on R. Lea, 20 miles north of London. King Alfred-the-Great built forts both sides of the same R. Lea; the Danish host could not bring out their ships and they abandoned them (Londoners collected them). |
| 913 | King Edward the Elder built forts on both sides of R. Lea, at Hertford. |
| 919 | King Edward the Elder occupied the fort on the north of R. Great Ouse at Bedford (town on north) and built a fort on the south. He constructed forts on both sides of the same river at Buckingham. |
| 921 | King Edward built a fortress on the south of R. Nene at Stamford — and accepted allegiance from the existing north fortress. |
| 924 | King Edward built a fortress on the south of R. Trent at Nottingham, opposite to the existing one on the north (where the town was), and a bridge to connect the forts. |
| 1002 | Vikings up R. Yare; sacked Norwich. |
| 1009 | Danish fleet down R. Ouse, past Bedford, etc., and home. |
| 1012 | Danish King Swejn along R. Trent to Gainsborough. Many later drowned in R. Thames because they did not cross by bridge. |
| 1013 | Danish King Swejn on Thames. |
| 1016 | Besieged London, dug great channel on south bank (London was on the north bank), dragged their ships west of the bridge and built earthworks. By ship into Orwell; into Mercia; to R. Medway. |
| 1070 | Hereward (not accepting authority of King William-the-Conqueror) by boat to Peterborough and plundered monastery; treasure taken to Ely. Danes from R. Humber to R. Thames, then Denmark. |
| 1071 | Earl Morsa to Ely by ship. |
| 1072 | King William-the-Conqueror built causeway to Ely and called out naval levies. Other forts by river. Hereward escaped, but King William seized his ships, weapons, etc. |
| 1076 | Danes came but did not dare join battle with King William and went to Flanders. |
| 1085 | Many preparations for a Danish invasion, which did not materialise. |

Other forts by rivers, e.g. Towcester, Tempsford, Colchester, were built by Anglo-Saxons and Danes.

The Chronicle shows that Alfred the Great successfully used (and the phrasing suggests, introduced) the principle of the river defended by two opposite forts. Edward the Elder extended the practice in his successful war with the Danes. Although Hertford, Bedford and Nottingham subsequently developed on only one side of the river (the normal pattern), various main east-facing cities (York, Norwich, etc.) are now based on fortified rivers, the town developing from that pattern.

Fig. 12.5 Defence by moat. a) Homestead moat, R. Rib (Chapter 2), England. b) Sixteenth century siege, German woodcut.

## Invasion by river

The pre-eminent example of invasion along the river is the Vikings from Scandinavia. They first raided, then conquered, Normandy in France, the east of England (the Danelaw) (Table 12.2), and settled also in much of the west and north of the British Isles (Orkneys, N. Scotland, Lancashire, etc.). They came up rivers, and up streams which are now barely 2m wide and which, though wetter (being undrained), may not have been much wider than now (Chapter 6).

## Moats

Julius Caesar knew the value of moats, using trenches filled with water to defend his camp, in Gaul. Moats are (artificial) bands of water hindering crossing (e.g., Fig. 12.5). In the later Middle Ages, there is typically a fortified bridge, perhaps with a drawbridge. Moats may be dry as well as flooded (Figs 8.5i, 9.13a) — the attackers have to go down into a dry moat and face the defenders above, who are able to pour boiling oil or throw stones or whatever (cf. the Anglo-Saxon Offa's Dyke, Fleam Dyke, etc., with a ditch facing the invaders, and a bank facing the defenders). Water is a great protector. So, however, is hastily draining the water. A knight in armour is much hampered by thick, sticky mud! Kuklik (1984) records a drained fishpond being a complete obstacle to armoured men, deceived into entering it by women's scarves laid on the mud, around 1400 A.D.

In England, fifteenth-century castles, like their predecessors, were built for defence, perhaps with moats (the Wars of the Roses were 1450-85). The great houses and the lesser country houses built later might have moats, but for ornament (and perhaps food). Moats could be mined, that is, have tunnels dug under them. Prince Rupert of the Rhine introduced this art to England (it was developed on the Continent), mining Lichfield in the Civil Wars of the seventeenth century (Morrah, 1976).

Ornamental moats could be unhealthy from pollution, too. 'It was a fine old place; the dyke surrounding it... was of remarkable width. It was filled in... and fine pleasure grounds might be seen now where unwholesome water had once stagnated. Possibly that water had been the... unsuspected cause of the dying of so many of the houses' children' (Mrs Henry Wood, *Oscar Gray).*

## Forts

Fig. 12.6 Hill (and river) forts (also see Chapters 8-9). a) Small hill fort, Rhine. b) Hill fort larger. Note small old tower by river, Rhine. c) Hill fort. Old tower more developed, Rhine. d) Hill fort more developed, Luxembourg. e) Tuddenham, England. f) Guarding the Loire, France. g) Hill fort fully developed, brooding over village and river below. Windsor Castle, on River Thames, England (*Girls' Own Paper,* 1887).

*a*

*b*

*c*

Fortifications are expensive, and so are usually built only with good reason. Remains tend to be more on the Continent than in more peaceful England (and see Fig. 12.5b for depictions of a siege). The means to resist invasion, i.e. fortifications, are shown in Figs 8.2, etc., 12.6, etc. Hill-forts are shown in various stages of growth and decay. These were above the crossing, forming watchtowers, with men available to go to the crossing, or elsewhere, as needed. Hill-forts on the edges of plateaux (Rhine, Black Forest, Dinant, etc.) are there to defend the river below, for which they are well placed on steep slopes above the river. They are more vulnerable to attack from the plateau above.Hill-forts may develop into grand castles, or chateaux, the culmination in this series being Windsor Castle, England.

Fig. 12.6 Contd.

d

The Old Tower guarding the crossing is a separate development (Figs 8.1 and 8.3). Romans fortified above (e.g. Lyons, Chapter 9), but others (Chapter 8) first put the fort on the crossing. Both towers are, therefore, in the more recent European tradition. If useless and a ruin, the riverside tower is more likely than the hill-fort to have been taken down and the site redeveloped

e

(the land being more valuable and useful than the hill-top). Like the hill-fort, it also may develop into, for instance, the Norman keep (e.g., the Tower of London, later developed further but still primarily defensive) or the later castle, such as that at Newark (Fig. 9.15).

## Other fortifications

Defensible walls, city gates and bridges have been shown in various stages (e.g, Chapters 8 and 9). The cruder massive walls at, say, Arles are more recent, being cannon-defensible. Breda was considered a supreme example of military engineering of the early seventeenth century, with two large scarpes and a moat between them (Ashley, 1973). (When it was taken, bundles of twigs were used as floats to cross the moat. Shades of armies in classical times! See Chapter 7.)

The feat of keeping the bridge was an ancient one, and could still be envisaged by Macaulay in the nineteenth century (*Lays of Ancient Rome*).

[*Horatius speaks:*]
'Hew down the bridge, Sir Consul,
With all the speed ye may;
I, with two more to help me,
Will hold the foe in play.
In yon strait path a thousand
May well be stopped by three.

Now who will stand on either hand,
And keep the bridge with me?'...

But all Etruria's noblest
Felt-their hearts sink to see
On the earth the bloody corpses,
In the path the dauntless Three:...

But with a crash like thunder
Fell every loosen'd beam
And, like a dam, the mighty wreck
Lay right athwart the stream:
And a long shout of triumph
Rose from the walls of Rome,
As to the highest turret-tops
Was splashed the yellow foam....

'Oh, Tiber! father Tiber! [*says Horatius*]
To whom the Romans pray,
A Roman's life, a Roman's arms,
Take thou in charge this day!'...
And with his harness on his back,
Plunged headlong in the tide....

But fiercely ran the current,
Swollen high by months of rain:...

Never, I ween, did swimmer,
In such an evil case,
Struggle through such a raging flood
Safe to the landing place:...

With weeping and with laughter
Still is the story told,
How well Horatius kept the bridge
In the brave days of old.

In the Second World War, Luxembourg blocked the German advance with a lorry on each bridge — a token that sovereignty was breached, but one unlikely to attract much retribution from the German army.

*a*

It was not only in olden times that battles were fought over rivers: the Battle of the Somme in the First World War, the fighting around the Rhine in the Second World War (and, for example, in that war, the Allies' difficulty in crossing the Sche-

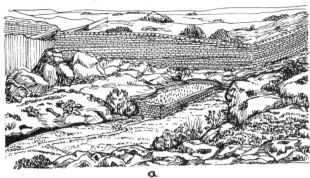

Fig. 12.7 Dwejra Lines, Malta.

a

ldt and the Rhine enabled more V2 rockets to be launched into England in 1944). The post-Second World War British Army of the Rhine is not named lightly. In the 1991 (Persian) Gulf War, bridges over the Euphrates river were destroyed by the Americans, trapping Iraqi forces on the wrong side of the river, with no supplies or easy way home.

When armies invade overland they must cross rivers and so control crossings. This may mean a major battle or a minor hindrance.

Valleys can be fortified by being walled or otherwise guarded — the sides as well as the river. This may be done as part of a larger exercise, e.g. Hadrian's Wall in N. England, the Duke of Wellington's early nineteenth century Torres Vedras Lines in Portugal, and the Malta Dwejra Lines (Fig. 12.7, not intended as full fortifications).

### River defences

The river itself may be protected. The Thames (according to Bede, the *Anglo-Saxon Chronicle* and twelfth-century Geoffrey of Monmouth) was staked to hinder Julius Caesar crossing. Bede, writing in the eighth century, reported traces of these stakes still present, cased in lead and as

b

Fig. 12.8 To sum up many features: a) Echternach, Luxembourg. b) Hesperange, Luxembourg.

Note fortification of different ages, village and town plans, former water gate, etc.

thick as a man's thigh, fixed in the river bed. As well as stakes, chains were widely used for centuries (Fig. 8.2: *Nuremberg Chronicle*). They are flexible fortifications, as they can be raised for defence, and lowered to let ships pass. The mouth of the Medway (junction of Thames) was chained, to protect the navy lying upstream. 1667 saw the greatest humiliation of the British navy: the Dutch fleet (under de Ruyter) sailed up to Chatham. Pepys' diary for 12 June reads '…ill news is come to Court of the Dutch breaking the chain at Chatham, which struck me to the heart, and to Whitehall [King's Palace] to hear the truth of it…. For the news is true that the Dutch have broke the chain and burned our ships.' Booms were used for the same purpose, both being in place in the Napoleonic Wars.

A more elaborate defence, found in Italy for example, was artificially narrowing the river bed, which increases water force and so slows invading boats, coupled with building forts on both sides upstream.

### Water shortage

Cutting off water supply is a traditional means of reducing siege, recorded in Old Testament times. In the (sixteenth-century) Great Siege of Malta, the defenders poisoned the coastal spring outside the fortifications (at Marsa) to prevent its use by the Turks (Chadwick, 1884).

### Wars for water

Up to now, wars for water have been mainly small skirmishes for wells, or the use of rivers as frontiers. With increasing water consumption and therefore shortage, especially in arid and semi-arid lands, major wars seem, regrettably, not impossible in the future.

Finally, to sum up many points, Fig. 12.8 demonstrates, from Luxembourg, defence — and other features such as the wharf area, underground streams etc.

# 13

# For Ornament and Recreation

The poplar is most beautiful by the rivers. (Virgil)

Sitting by the river's side is... the quietest and fittest place for contemplation. (Walton, 1653)

## Introduction

Rivers have been used for ornament and recreation for time out of mind, but the twentieth-century use for recreation is far greater than before, due to increased population, wealth and leisure. Fashion also influences the use of leisure time — sport fishing, for instance, only became widespread in Britain in the nineteenth century, though available and done for centuries before.

There is, as always, an arbitrary division between chapters, some material found here being also appropriate elsewhere (and vice versa). The distinction between ornament and recreation is also artificial. There is no law saying that the functional must be ugly; it is recent experience which makes us expect it to be. Fountains have been things of beauty since they were first constructed. The classical lion's head fountain (see Fig. 1.3 for a modern one) and the elaborate huge bowls with arches around, as in first-century Corinth, were ornaments to the cities they served.

## Ornament

The Arab culture in S. Europe had much running water in gardens. The Spanish Alhambra is an extant example, with many fountains and streams in its splendid grounds. The eighteenth century was when this became fashionable in Europe and then fashionable among the nobility rather than the common folk. Versailles, built by Louis XIV at the turn of the eighteenth century, is perhaps the grandest. Water was taken from the Seine by a large, initially horse-drawn, engine, for use in the river park with its fountains (Fig. 13.1), basins and canals for river parties. Water diversions without care, though, often cause disputes. The Versailles' works led to an acute water shortage in and around Paris (downstream) (Haldane, 1970). This might have been thoughtlessness — the idea that 'a big river cannot be harmed by what I do' is commonplace down the centuries. But the malaria from the marshes which, before the works, surrounded Louis' other palace at Marly, causing many deaths, should have been foreseen and avoided. That Palace had an aqueduct of three-storied arches, with fountains, lakes and canals (Haldane, 1970).

Fig. 13.1 Versailles, seventeenth century fountain.

Other lesser eighteenth-century water-gardens were — and are — spectacular also. Wilhelmshöhe Castle (Kassel, Germany) has a staircase cascade and a splendid water show. The tank on the hill takes three days to fill from the spring, so shows are held twice-weekly. Hercules stands at the top with water-gods, nymphs and satyrs in grottos. The water pressure forces air into a horn held by a satyr, blowing a penetrating wail during the show. Since the water pressure varies a little, so does the tone, making the horn-call sound live. As the water descends, so the various fountains rise up, and finally the high fountain (about 40m) erupts from a lake behind a grove of tall trees. The effect is spectacular. This has been a public garden since the First World War (A. Tyndale, personal communication; Modrow, 1989). The other Kassel palace, Karlsrave, was built in river-meadows as a rural retreat open to the public. At first, in the sixteenth century, there was a rectangular lake here. In the eighteenth century three canals radiated from a floral carpet, the central one being filled in later. Ornamental water, in some form, has remained (A. Tyndale, personal communication). A similar staircase and fountain in Mannheim was recently restored in 1989 at the back of an 1812 water-tower. The fountain pattern is now computer-generated with hundreds of variations in size and angles, so, as is rare, going beyond the original design (Y. Bower, personal communication).

In sixteenth-century German Darmstadt, the Darm was dammed to make a lake for courtiers to punt in and enjoy. The lake still gives pleasure. The lower end has a swimming-area, with a shallow part, and changing-cabins. Darmstadt also has a new adventure playground, through which little rills run, diverted here and there, with plank bridges over them. The stream is an integral part — the rest being sturdy wooden play-structures, swings, rockinghorse, Hansel-and-Gretel House (Wendy House), etc. In wet weather there is a mud paradise for enthusiastic children. Lower, the Darm has what were allotments but are now nice gardens with weekend chalets, undoubtedly giving much pleasure also (A. Tyndale, personal communication).

At Chatsworth (Derbyshire, England) the cascade (water-stairs) was begun in 1694; the canal and cascade house date from 1702, but — unusually late — the tall Emperors' Fountain was only finished in 1843. Studley Royal, in Yorkshire, has notable hydraulics, moving large volumes of water to, and keeping them on, different levels. These achievements, done without electricity, can be startling. This one was made in the 1720s and still works well (R.M. Haslam, personal communication). The Serpentine lake in London's Hyde Park also dates from the early eighteenth century (Burton, 1967). Such boating-lakes, for the pleasure of the upper classes, were frequent. London's Vauxhall Gardens were famous for their water attractions (cascade, etc.).

Fig. 13.2 Ornamental fountains. a) Floriana, Malta. b) Lyon, France: note functional water supply in foreground. c) Trebon, Czechoslovakia: note goldfish. d) Funchal, Madeira. e) Strasbourg, France. f) Megève, France. g) Valletta, Malta. h) Monte, Madeira.

A range of ornamental fountains are shown in Fig. 13.2. Also see Figs 3.8 to 3.11, etc. Note that goldfish may be present (see Chapter 14). Well-designed fountains, small or great, are pleasing. Fountains erupting from the water itself are often modern (as in Strasbourg, Funchal).

Water to enhance beauty is shown well in Fig. 13.3. This (see Chapter 9) may be on the site of an old fishpond. It was put into the present shape in the early nineteenth century. The pond is parallel to the river and was used for boating and skating, etc., as well as for the view. The Dutch have of course developed the art of gardens on canals. Moats may be ornamental (Fig. 9.10h) and later English ones were intended primarily for ornament (Chapter 12).

Repton was one of the great English landscape planners and his formal designs have much charm as do those of Capability Brown. Several in Fig. 13.4 show water redeeming what would otherwise be ugly, like the boating-lake and the old used channel. Sometimes not even water can help (Fig. 15.1b). Regrettably many think — as do the owners of Fig. 13.4f — both that river vegetation is weed and that weeds should be pulled up in a well-conducted garden. The bank to the left is adequate, that to the right is not! Some people plant 'garden species' in their piece of river. Native species in the 'wrong' habitat may mislead botanists (and may be difficult to propagate). Ornamental rivers are shown in Fig. 13.5, where man has tried to enhance the beauty degraded by village or city use. This is sometimes successful, perhaps in unexpected ways, as in the Madeira river covered by creepers — successful simply because it disguises the ugly river bed itself. (It is a good compromise, since flash floods are frequent, and stringent flood protection is necessary.) Fig. 13.5b looks beautiful if the eye is kept to the bridge with its pretty flowers. The polluted water spoils the effect. Fig. 13.5d was, I was told, done for ornament! Beauty may indeed lie only in the eye of (some) beholders.

In earlier days the effort to make pockets of civilisation fighting against the encroaching wood, heath and waste, against nature red in tooth and claw, was such that, for pleasure, man often wanted something as different as possible from that seen in the Wild World.

Fashion also changes. Shakespeare could praise the bank whereon the wild thyme grows and, through many voices, other natural beauties. The Romantic late eighteenth-century movement could praise the wild and free. (Jane Austen's *Sense and Sensibility* contrasts one character's view that the good life was tidy, happy villagers and good roads — the nineteenth-century Reformer's view — with the Romantic one of *banditti* and dead leaves driven in showers.) For Bath, Rodgers (1947-8) sums up the earlier view. Natural river scenery takes second place to the beauties of architecture, although going down the river to Bristol was considered a pleasant excursion (e.g. for Princess Amelia, in 1728, in a wherry). On the whole, though, those who came to take the waters in Georgian Bath felt little admiration for the Avon — remember, though, Clarke's description of the deaths it caused (Chapter 12), which may be relevant. Horace Walpole wrote: 'The river is petty enough to be the Seine or Tiber [!]. Oh how unlike my lovely Thames.'

The buildings put up by the river were different: those of the Great were expected to look Great from the river (see Figs in earlier chapters). As Admiralty Secretary (the first and last) Samuel Pepys had over his main door a shield with the

Fig. 13.3 Water enhancing beauty of building. Much Hadham, England.

Lord High Admiral's anchor and, above it, the Royal Arms, so 'all the boats on the river could see who and what dwelt therein' (Bryant, 1938).

New developments, for instance the Lea Valley Park, built on disused gravel pits, put much less emphasis on beauty, and more on immediate return on investment: the difference between a commercial enterprise and a wealthy man creating his ideal garden. Fig. 13.6 shows an interesting historical village pattern destroyed by planners interested in prettiness but not in heritage.

The depiction of rivers in art has been considerable. A few are shown in Chapter 1 and Fig. 13.7. Millais' Ophelia is very good botanically, as well as artistically! And so, in fact, are Constable and most other non-impressionists. (When identifying species from the original pictures, stand well back from the pictures.)

Rivers have been the inspiration of other Arts. For song and verse, the Rhine is pre-eminent (Friedrich & Müller, 1984; e.g., in English, 'Lorelei', 'Bingen-on-the Rhine'). Table 13.1 gives some extracts from English verse. Claudius of Darmstadt wrote of the river. Handel composed for a procession on it ('Water Music'). Madrigals are sung on the Cam in May Week. Waterways are important in some films, such as *The African Queen* about a boat on an African river; *The Third Man*, with important scenes in the sewers of Vienna, and various Westerns, such as *The Big Sky*, *River of No Return* and *How the West Was Won*. Novels are sparse, but include ones of stature, e.g., Mark Twain's *Huckleberry Finn*, Dickens' *Our Mutual Friend*, Jerome K. Jerome's *Three Men In a Boat*. Dante's future worlds contain

Fig. 13.4 Water enhancing beauty (and see Figs. 1.5-1.10, 13.7). a) Cambridge, England. b) Brandon, England. c) Cambridge, England. d) Alcudia, Mallorca. e) Belfast, Ireland. f) Essex, England.

a

b

c

d

e

f

Old mill. Restored and converted
into restaurant. Note the careful
tending of the water to 'belong to'
and enhance the total scene. A
pleasant place to live or visit.

many rivers, of water and of light, some with peculiar properties (petrifying, red-sulphur, forgetfulness of guilt, Good Remembrance, seeing Heaven truly, etc.).

The use of the river in biblical language and metaphor is discussed in Chapter 14.

## Fishing

O the gallant fisher's life
It is the best of any
'Tis full of pleasure, void of strife,
And 'tis beloved by many:
        Other joys
        Are but toys;
        Only this
        Lawful is;
        For our skill
        Brooks no ill
But content and pleasure
        (Cited in Walton, 1653)

Sport fishing is of early origin, recorded at least from Roman times and solitary anglers are depicted commonly in pictures from the sixteenth century. Clergymen, forbidden to hunt by Church canons, were allowed to angle (Walton, 1653). Cardinal Wolsey, in the early sixteenth century, fished in the Gade (Victoria County History, 1902-14), and Elizabethan statutes, by implica-

Fig. 13.5 Ornamented rivers. a) Cromer, England. b) Dormancy, France. c) Funchal, Madeira. d) Usseldange, Luxembourg. e) Irrigation stream (intermittent flow). Botanic Gardens, Madeira.

tion, favoured angling (Walton, 1653). Izaak Walton's *The Compleat Angler*, the foundation of modern (British) angling, was written in mid-seventeenth century. It describes river fish, their habits, angling-tackle, and where, how and when to catch fish. As mentioned above, sport angling greatly expanded in the nineteenth century, except that, as usual, there are differences between countries. Hungary, with its large rivers, never developed the sport in the same way (it is less pleasant) (Y. Bower, personal communication). The fishers for coarse fish, may sit close, only 15-20m apart if absolutely necessary (such as for a competition), but preferably more. In contrast is the isolated salmonid angler, casting his line along his beat, his beat varying from about 0.5 to 2 miles long (0.8 to 3km), the beat being usually

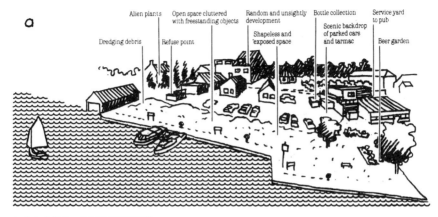

Analysis of village waterfront environment

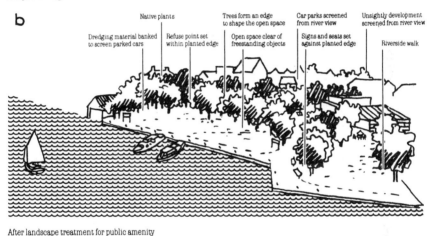

After landscape treatment for public amenity

Fig. 13.6 How to lose heritage with good intentions. a) Shows former large wharf, suitable for storage of bulky cargoes (e.g. reed, peat), the old market place leading from the wharf, with houses around it. b) After landscaping, is devoid of history and interest. To destroy is easy, to conserve and enhance requires thought, (reproduced by permission, from a leading conservation organisation).

measured by pools, so that it is shorter in lowland chalk than in fast mountain rivers. (There are usually one to three people per beat. There can be up to, say, three shifts a day, moving between short beats.) Within the groups, anglers may vary for the species they catch. Coarse fishers may confine themselves to perch or pike, game fishers to trout or salmon. The coarse fisher is the more damaging to the habitat. He makes sitting-places, may erode banks and may even put herbicide around him. There are also more of them: always most significant in damage. The total damage, though, is low — if only anglers were around there would be no complaints from ecologists. Other means of sport fishing are various, and include tickling, children's string, worm and jam pot (now, alas, an infrequent sight, pollution and damage having rendered catches too low), fishing from boats, etc.

Fig. 13.7 Rivers in Art.  a) St John Baptising, Domenico. b) Ophelia, J.E. Millais.

Fig. 13.7 contd. c) On the Dart, de Wint. d) Port Marly, Sisley. (a), c), d) by permission of the Fitzwilliam Museum Cambridge; b) by permission of the Tate Gallery.

*Table 13.1*
*Rivers in rhyme*

Great and small, anciently and recently, rivers have been a valuable part of the rhymester's repertoire. There are two main categories, the descriptive, those describing the beauties — or unpleasantnessess — of nature, and the moral — those using streams to point a lesson (see also Table 14.1 and text, Chapters 13 and 14). Only a few examples can be given:

**(a) Descriptive**

Think a little, while ye hear
Of the banks,
Where the willows and the deer
Crowd in intermingled ranks
As if all would drink at once
Where the living water runs! —
Of the fishes' golden edges
Flashing in and out the sedges,
Of the swans on silver thrones
Floating down the winding streams...
And the lotus leaning forward
To help them into dreams
                    (Elizabeth Barrett Browning)

For deeply hid with lovely Thames
Are the haunts my heart loves best
Fair jewelled stream
Of flash and gleam
Where banks are a brede of wildflower gems;
Oh if I might rest
                    (Cited, F.S. Thacker, 1914)

...The small round basin, which this jutting stone
Keeps pure from falling leaves! Long may they Spring...
Send up cold waters to the traveller
With soft and even pulse! Nor ever cease
Young tiny core of sand its soundless dance
        (from S.T. Coleridge, 'Inscription for a Fountain
                    on a Heath')

The River flows so gently by
It seems so sad and lonely
The willow leans right over it,
And weeps so sad and slowly
            (from Postbag, *The Brownie*)

The floods' queen, Thames, for ships and swans is crown'd;
And stately Severn for her shore is praised;
The crystal Trent, for fords and fish renown'd;
And Avon's fame to Albion's cliffs is raised.
Carlegion Chester vaunts her holy Dee;
York many wonders of her Ouse can tell;
The Peak, her Dove, whose banks so fertile be;
And Kent will say, her Medway doth excel,
Cotswold commends her Isis to the Thame;
Our northern borders boast of Tweed's fair flood;
Our western parts extol their Willy's fame;
And the old Lea brags of the Danish blood
                    (M. Drayton)

Where Tivy falling down, makes a high cataract...
Here, when the labouring fish [salmon] does at the
        foot arrive,
And finds that by his strength he does but vainly strive,...
Then springing at his height, as doth a little wand
That, bended end to end, and started from man's hand,
Far oft itself doth cast; so does the salmon vault
                    (M. Drayton, 'Poly-olbion')

The treasure of its infant springs
With flag-flowers fringed and whispering reeds
Along the many-coloured meads
                    (T.C. Peacock)

The moory soil, the wat'ry atmosphere,
Thick stinking fogs, and noxious vapours fall
Agues and coughs are epidemical;
Hence every face presented to one's view
Looks of a pallid or a sallow hue
                    (A Fen Parson)
                    [*Wetland ill-health*]

A sudden little river crossed my path
As unexpected as a serpent comes,
No sluggish tide congenial to the glooms;
This, as it frothed by, might have been a bath
For the fiends' glowing hoof — to see the wrath
Of its black eddy bespate with flakes and spumes

So petty yet so spiteful! All along,
Low scrubby alders kneeled down over it;
Drenched willows flung them headlong in a fit
Of mute despair, a suicidal throng:
The river which had done them all that wrong,
Whate'er that was, rolled by, deterred no whit.

Which, while I forded — good saints, how I feared
To set my foot upon a dead man's cheek,
Each step, or feel the spear I thrust to seek
For hollows, tangled in his hair or beard!
— It may have been a water-rat I speared,
But, ugh! it sounded like a baby's shriek.
                    (Robert Browning,
            'Childe Roland to the Dark Tower Came')
        [*What the Industrial Revolution did to rivers!*]

**(b) Moral**

What was he doing, the great god Pan
Down in the reeds by the river?

He tore out a reed, the great god Pan
From the deep cool bed of the river.
The limpid water turbidly ran,
And the broken lilies a dying lay,
And the dragon-fly had fled away,
Ere he brought it out of the river...

Yet half a beast is the great god Pan,
To laugh as he sits by the river,
Making a poet out of a man:
The true gods sigh for the cost and pain, —
For the reed which grows nevermore again
As a reed with the reeds in the river.
                    (Elizabeth Barrett Browning,
                    'A Musical Instrument')

You steer out straight through many a gale
As down the stream you fall,
God send you cleanly navigate
The last lone lock of all
(Cited in F.S. Thacker, 1909)

From reveries so airy, from the toil
Of dropping buckets into empty wells,
And growing old in drawing nothing up!
(W.S. Cowper, 'The Task', book III)

And still, when mob or monarch lays
Too rude a hand on English ways;
The whisper wakes, the shudder plays,
Across the reeds at Runnymede.
And Thames, that knows the moods of kings,
And crowds, and priests and such-like things,
Rolls deep and dreadful as he brings
Their warning down from Runnymede!
(Kipling, 'The Reeds of Runnymede')

Finds tongues in trees, books in the running brooks,
Sermons in stones, and good in everything.
(Shakespeare, *As You Like It*)

Thou has taught me, Silent River,
Many a lesson, deep and long,
Though thou hast been a generous giver,
I can give thee but a song.
(Longfellow)

I steal by lawns and grassy plots
I slide by hazel covers,
I move the sweet forget-me-nots
That grow for happy lovers....

And out again I curve and flow
To join the brimming river,
For men may come and men may go,
But I go on for ever.
(Tennyson)

*[With twentieth-century technology, and drainage, rivers, like men, may come and go!]*

And see the rivers how they run
Thro' woods and meads, in shade and sun
Sometimes swift and sometimes slow
Wave succeeding wave they go;
A various journey to the deep,
Like human life to endless sleep
(J. Dyer, eighteenth century)

A wanderer is man from his birth
He was born in a ship
On the breast of the River of Time
Brimming with wonder and joy
He spreads out his arms to the light,
Rivets his gaze on the banks of the stream.
(Matthew Arnold, 'The Future')

Go up and watch the new-born rill,
Just trickling from its mossy bed,
Streaking the heat-clad hill
With a bright emerald thread...

Canst thou her bold career foretell
What rocks she shall o'erleap or rend,
How far in Ocean's swell
Her freshening billows send?...

Perchance that little brook shall flow
The bulwark of some mighty realm,
Bear navies to and fro,
With monarchs at their helm...

Or canst thou guess, how far away
Some sister nymph, beside her urn
Reclining night and day
'Mid reeds and mountain fern...
(*The Christian Year*)

Let me live harmlessly; and near the brink
Of Trent or Avon have a dwelling-place,
Where I may see my quill or cork down sink
With eager bite of perch, or bleak, or dace;
And on the world and my Creator think:
Whilst some men strive ill-gotten goods t'embrace,
And others spend their time in base excess
Of wine, or worse, in war and wantonness
(Davors, in Walton, 1653)

When some river slides away
To increase the boundless sea
Think we then how time does haste
To grow eternity at last
(Lady Winchlsea, eighteenth century)

Still glides the stream, and shall for ever glide
The Form remains, the Function never dies.
(Wordsworth, Valedictory Sonnet to R. Duddon)

*[Would this certainty could obtain, two centuries later!]*

### (c) Miscellaneous! (just a few)

Milton had four rivers in Paradise Lost.

Children's (folk) singing-games: 'London Bridge is falling down'; 'Milking Pails'; 'Down the river every day', etc.

Gilbert and Sullivan's *The Gondoliers*.

The *Romaunt of the Rose*, *Piers Plowman* and *Parsifal* all start with running water, green grass and a dreamer.

Charles Kingsley's *The Water Babies* - has a world under the river quite separate from that described in Chapter 14.

In Xanadu did Kubla Khan
A stately pleasure-dome decree:
Where Alph, the sacred river, ran
Through caverns measureless to man
(S.T. Coleridge, 'Kubla Khan')

Rodgers (1947-8) notes the solitary angler is not the independent he appears, though. First, the right to fish from the bank belongs to the riparian owner, the owner of the bank, and permission has had to be sought — and usually paid for. There are other restrictions: close seasons, during which fish may not be caught (for conservation of stock); for migratory fish, times when they are absent; and rules as to the size of fish which can be removed from the river (no small ones: conservation again). Trout, particularly, are often too few, and stocking is common, either on a replenish-the-natural-stocks basis, or what is expressively called put-and-take. Over-fished rivers, and ones where pollution, deteriorating physical habitat (including decreased water) and disturbance have between them lowered fish populations, are all too common. The degree of plenty described before 1800 (see Chapter 4) is rare indeed. Friesland (The Netherlands) can still advertise: 'Pike or eel, rudd or bream, pike-perch or fat tench, they all live in the unspoiled Frisian waters. Over 1200 registered fishing waters... as always, a fishing licence may be bought at any post office.' But this is exceptional. Salmonids attract much higher licence fees, and so are the ones more usually boasted of: the Irish Shannon is well known for salmon, like the Norwegian rivers and the large east-flowing Scots rivers; in Denmark sea trout are plump and plentiful; while the Welsh Wye has the most salmon of all British rivers. To take a lesser, but still lucrative example, nine authorities advertise fishing on the Welsh Dyfi - hotels, the Electricity Generating Board, the fishing-tackle shop, and angling clubs and associations (Y. Bower, personal communication).

Anglers (and keepers, if any), and more especially salmonid anglers, since they move around more, usually know most about a river, its moods, scenery — and changes. Unlike the busy water-authority official, they have leisure to examine and notice. They may wax lyrical — '[the river] fleeting over golden shallows and swinging round deep curves, watering many meadows and turning many mills.... Lastly come the smooth glides where streams break.... In a streamy water they [trout] lie near the surface, with fins a-quiver, an air of expectancy running over them.... But now at evening they [May fly] had awakened and collected together and resumed their dance.' (Hills, 1924). Not the usual language of the water authority!

Descriptions of fishing abound in older — and newer — books, e.g., such as the accounts of fishing in the Avon in *Tom Brown's Schooldays* (T. Hughes, mid-nineteenth century). Fishing also has a literature of its own, good in both quantity and quality. Izaak Walton has already been mentioned. More recent are the journals such as *Coarse Angler, Trout and Salmon, The Trout Fisherman, Trout Rod and Line*, and books such as Anon. (1979), *The Fisherman's Guide to Coarse Fishing* (Marshall Cavendish: London); L. Head, (1985), *River fishing* (Crawood: Marlborough); C.F. Walker (ed.) (1963), *The Complete Fly-fisher* (Herbert Jenkins:).

Coarse fishing led to a serious decline in English mute swans. Nylon line became very cheap, so it was easier to leave it and its lead weights behind in the river than to pick it up. The line gets tangled round any suitably sized animal, and may injure or strangle (in addition, polythene bottles suffocate and empty tins and broken glass cut, and all may get stuck on limbs or head). Lead weights have an additional danger for swans. They look like small gravel and are eaten as gravel, causing poisoning and death. In 1953 the Thames swan-upping (see Chapter 4) recorded over 1,000, in 1984 under 200. Lead weights, under public pressure, were used less, and banned in 1987. In 1987, swan numbers on the Thames increased by 53% over 1983-5, and blood lead content was down (RSPB, 1988a), with another decrease in 1988 (Sears, 1989). (Whooper swan deaths in Scotland from lead were attributed to gunshot wounds: Sears, 1989b.)

## Mock battles

Mock, as well as real, battles, took place on rivers and lakes, e.g., (Morton, 1934) Biblical Palestine, in boats; one FitzStephen, twelfth century, on foot (in shallow water), attacking a shield on a pole — as more usually on land. Rescue boats were provided.

## Two other animal sports

Shooting waterfowl used to be common, for combined sport and food. It was more often a collective sport (e.g. Fig. 10.6) than fishing. Waterfowl have now declined, and shooting them on rivers is uncommon (except in, e.g., Malta, and Italy, where migrant fowl are shot anywhere). Many now *observe* waterfowl instead; a much better practice in these days of scarce birds.

Bull-baiting in rivers is, fortunately, not now current, but for the early nineteenth century it is vividly described by Gaskell (1857) from Rochdale, England. 'The bull was fastened by a chain or rope to a post in the river. To increase the amount of water, as well as to give their work people the opportunity of savage delight, the masters were accustomed to stop their mills on the day.... The bull would sometimes wheel suddenly round, so that the rope by which he was fastened swept those who had been careless enough to come within its range down into the water, and the good people of Rochdale had the excitement of seeing one or two of their neighbours drowned as well as of witnessing the bull baited and the dogs torn and tossed.'

## Mechanical waterworks

Water-clocks were invented in early times, Charlemagne had one (given from Baghdad). They worked with dripping water, like sandglasses. There were many mechanical water-devices. The following fifteenth-century description (shortened from that cited in Vaughan, 1970) is of those of Philip the Good (M. le Voleur was paid for restoring and adding to a thirteenth-century installation). '... For making or refurbishing the three figures which can be made to squirt water at people and wet them, a contrivance at the entrance of the said gallery for wetting the ladies as they walk over it, and a distorting mirror; and for constructing a device over the entrance of the gallery which, when a ring is pulled, showers soot or flour in the face of anyone below. Also, in the same gallery, a fountain from which water spurts and is pumped back again, and another contrivance, at the exit from the gallery, which buffets anyone who passes through well and truly on the head and shoulders.

'[For the restoration of] the room before [you reach] the hermit, where water can be made to spray down just like rain, also thunder, lightning and snow, as if from the sky itself; and, next to this room, a wooden hermit which can be made to speak to anyone who enters. Also, for paving the half of this room which was not previously paved, including the place where people go to avoid the rain, whence they are precipitated into a sack full of feathers below.

'... He has also had to restore most of the ceiling of the above-mentioned room, and to reinforce the part of it which produced the rain, which had become too weak.... He also made a bridge in this room, constructed in such a way that it was possible to cause anyone walking over it to fall into the water below. There are several devices in this room which, when set off, spray large quantities of water onto the people in it, as well as six figures, more than there had been before, which soak people in different ways. In the entrance, there are eight conduits for wetting women from below and three conduits which, when people stop in front of them, cover them all over with flour. When someone tries to open a certain window, a figure appears, sprays the person with water, and shuts the window. A book of ballads lies on a desk but, when you try to read it, you are squirted with soot, and, if you look inside it, you can be sprayed with water. Then there is a mirror which people are invited to look at, to see themselves all white with flour; but, when they do so, they are covered with more flour. A wooden figure, which appears above a bench in the middle of the gallery announces, at the sound of trumpet, on behalf of the duke, that everyone must leave the gallery. Those who do so are beaten by large figures holding sticks... and those who don't want to leave get so wet that they don't know what to do to avoid the water. In one window a box is suspended, and above the box is a figure which makes faces at people and replies to their questions, and one can both hear and see the voice in this box.

'He has decorated the room in front of the hermit, where it can be made to rain, in good quality oil colours of gold, azure, and so on..., and he has done the whole ceiling and panelling of this room in azure sewn with large stars picked out in gold.... After all this was completed, my lord [the duke] ordered him to make conduits and suitable contrivances low down and all along the wall of the gallery, to squirt water in so many places that nobody in the gallery could possibly save themselves from getting wet.'

Lesser waterworks were common, as in Spring Gardens, London, where, in the seventeenth century, the unwary who stepped carelessly were sprinkled with water (Brewer, 1881).

## Service industry

Where there are many people there also are food, drink, accommodation and other tourist facilities. Inns and hotels originally used for river commerce may now be used for pleasure e.g. 'Jolly Watermen', 'Jolly Bargeman' (both names for old watermen's inns, now serving tourists) The Angler's Rest is likely to be a nineteenth-century sport hotel. Table 13.2 lists some older and newer names. Mills converted to tourist facilities are not uncommon (Cover picture, etc. and Table 13.2), or their sites may be used for other leisure activities (car parks, e.g. Almestrand, 1984). Riverside land may be used for camping, caravans or summer houses (e.g. Fig. 10.10e, f). As usual, one person going off with his tent into the wilderness is fine environmentally, but many hundreds all in the same place are not (even when proper sewage disposal, etc., is available). Fig. 1.2 shows, better than words, the damaging effect of numbers.

*Table 13.2*
*Names of Inns, Hotels, Restaurants, etc.*
*Cambridge Region*

| Type of name | No. | Examples include |
|---|---|---|
| swan | 15 | Swan Inn, Black Swan |
| navigation | 7 | Jolly Bargeman, Anchor Inn |
| mill | 6 | Dusty Miller, Old Mill |
| stream | 5 | Brook, Conduit |
| waterfowl (other than swan) | 4 | Juicy Duck, Fox and Duck |
| fishing | 4 | Pike and Eel, Jolly Fisherman |
| moat | 3 | Moat House Hotel |
| bridge | 3 | Bridge, Bridge House |
| source of water | 2 | Old Spring, Fountain |
| riverside tree | 2 | Three Willows |
| (non-mill) industry | 1 | |
| otter | 1 | Lazy Otter |
| leisure | 1 | Boat Race |

Cheddar Gorge (Fig. 13.8) is a well-known English tourist resort (also known as the place near where Mr A. Toplady, sheltering from a storm in a rock cleft last century, wrote the well-known hymn 'Rock of Ages, cleft for me,/Let me hide myself in Thee'). Defoe (1724-7), however, describes it as: 'Here is a deep frightful chasm in the mountain, in the hollow of which, the road goes, by which they travel towards Bristol; and out of the same hollow, springs a little river, which flows with such a full stream, that, it is said, it drives twelve mills within a quarter of a mile [0.4km] of the spring; but this is not to be understood, without supposing it to fetch some winding reaches in the way; there would not, otherwise, be room for twelve mills to stand, and have any head of water above the mill, within so small a space of ground.' It is a pity Defoe did not visit the place. The stream is a small limestone one, with the head (the power) coming from slope, not from winding. The mills on it would have been too small to be viable later, when in competition with the steam (and electric) power — and the place changed to tourism. Souvenir shops, etc., are on the mill sites. The stream is ornamental anyway (clear limestone water, in stone channels), and pleasantly adds to the amenities. (The main village, Cheddar, remains a country village, quite different from the Gorge.)

Fig. 13.8 Cheddar Gorge, England.

# Bathing — and pollution

There are no British standards for river-bathing water and no official bathing-places. Earlier, of course, people bathed for cleanliness, more than for pleasure (but also for pleasure — nineteenth-century swims in the river were common, cf. the still-annual January 1st bathes in the London Serpentine).

Pollution has now made bathing unwise in many rivers, particularly lowland or industrial ones. Skin rashes, nausea, vomiting, diarrhoea, sore throat, ear and eye infections, headache and fever can often occur (both the fevers developing immediately and those developing a week later). The micro-organisms cited in Chapter 12 (typhoid, etc.) are water-borne and can be present. A newer hazard is Weil's Disease, from bacteria in rat's urine. This is most common in populated and industrial areas but since it is spread by rats, not effluent, can occur widely. If not treated promptly, it can be fatal. As mentioned above, even nineteenth century pollution was still localised. It took the twentieth century to make mild pollution so widespread as to be normal; and, with the numbers of people involved, to make its results cause alarm.

Jansen, *et al.* (1979) describing the effects of polluted water on health, distinguish between direct body contact with water (swimming, water-skiing, paddling bare-legged); indirect body contact (boating, fishing, etc.); and no body contact (picnicking, sightseeing, camping). Any of these can become body contact when people fall in! When considering human health, therefore, water quality should be considered with the degree of body contact. Even polluted water can give pleasure, as the 'ornamental' waters at Tielt (Fig. 9.4), or the pleasure cruisers on the Rhine, show. A higher standard is better, though. And water that is smelly or black with indeterminate lumps in it (Fig. 11.3) is never approved for recreation! Water should be capable of supporting high-quality plant and animal life.

# Suicide

Suicide cannot be considered as a form of recreation, but it is mentioned here because it is something people choose to do. In the past, rivers were a common site of suicide. Now, the obvious choice is sleeping-pills. The river is likely to be more effective; more people are brought round from overdoses.

# General leisure
### *(Figs 13.9-13.11)*

Standing on a bridge watching the water flow by is a characteristically British pursuit. Danes and, locally, Germans do it too, but Belgians and Italians, for example, are less commonly found on bridges. Walking along the river, by field path or road, has given pleasure for centuries. Towpaths are useful. Children paddling, fishing and bathing are standard activities — in clean enough water. Comparing a nineteenth-century picture with a recent one shows similar bank erosion for similar numbers. It is as important, though, to compare the decorous Victorian picnic (Fig. 13.9a) with Fig. 1.2. Here it is not just numbers but behaviour that makes the difference. The modern behaviour is far more destructive to the river.

Children play for hours round streams, including specific games as well as paddling, fishing, etc. A favourite is Pooh-sticks (so named from A.A. Milne's *Winnie-the-Pooh* books). Sticks or other floatable objects are dropped down the upstream side of a bridge. The competitors, or single player, rush to the other side, and wait for the first and winning stick to emerge.

Fig. 13.9 Recreation, general. a) Nineteenth century (from *Girls' Own Paper*). b)-e) Modern. d) e) worn by visitors.

## Skating

Skating in rivers requires more frost than on lakes, as the water is moving — though some canals freeze easily. This, as an outdoor community sport, is in decline with the climatic warming of the twentieth century. Few winters are now cold enough in the latitudes of Britain and The Netherlands. Communal skating and watching were much enjoyed (e.g. Fig. 13.10; here also the reason for stoning banks is plain: there is too much erosion. Goods are waiting for transit). In The Netherlands particularly, skating was a means of transport prior to good roads. The same applied in the English Fenland, where Fen Runners, special long skates, were worn. The Flemings had a run from Bruges to Sluys (about 15km), the English, one from Cambridge to Ely (about 25km: described in Philippa Pearce's *Tom's Midnight Garden*), which were considered proper things to do. (At Sluys, long clay pipes were

Fig. 13.9 Contd.

presented to arriving Brugeois, which were kept as trophies if brought back intact (Sanders, 1970).)

## Frost fairs

Frost fairs were held on the Thames, which froze through a combination of cold winters in a then-cold climate and ponding of water by and above Old London Bridge. The last such Fair was in 1814 (the Bridge being removed in 1833). They occurred intermittently before then, e.g., 1676-7, 1684 (Rodgers, 1947-8). There were booths for all manner of goods — including hot chestnuts to warm the assembled company.

## Pole-vaulting

Pole-vaulting was mentioned in Chapter 7 as a means of crossing waterways. Although The Netherlands now has innumerable bridges, it can still be convenient to cross watercourses within farms in this way. It is also a sport. Winsum, Friesland, advertises: 'this is a centre for an unusual and hilarious sport, polevaulting over water.... Try it by all means, but if you end up like so many competitors, sliding inevitably down your pole into the waiting water, don't blame us....' Championships, held on the second or third Saturday in August, attract thousands of spectators from all over the world.

## Crafts

Traditional crafts — which may now serve the tourist trade — were described in Chapter 4. Other ones, like dried reed arrangements, may also be practised and the results sold.

Fig. 13.10 Dutch skaters, seventeenth century (Fouquier, Winter Scene, by permission of the Fitzwilliam Museum, Cambridge). Detail.

## Nature reserves

Visiting nature reserves is an expanding leisure activity. Reserve purposes are now conservation, education and pleasure, the proportions varying in different reserves. For all three, rivers fare badly. Rivers tend to run at the edge of a reserve (established for ancient woodland, wet grassland or whatever) and, being maintained by a far-off authority, are of little interest to the reserve. There should be specific River Reserves running along and by rivers and with suitable management! Italy has river-protection zones, giving some control. In the north, these are mainly on south-flowing tributaries of the Po; by the Ticino, down from L. Maggione, a zone (5-)10-15(-25)km wide; by the Adda, down from the lakes, *c.* 5km wide; by the Serio, from the Alps to Cremona, *c.* 5km wide; and by the Po itself, near Pavia. The tributary zones are wider near the Po confluences.) This idea should be strengthened and extended. The position at English Strumpshaw is more usual. The marsh here used to be flooded from the river, bringing water and silt in the usual way (see Chapter 4). The pollution is now so bad that the river is sealed off and water obtained from other sources instead. The river is being removed from the reserve instead of being made more part of it and so also being conserved. The marsh has lost the water regime which brought it into being.

# Boating
*(Fig. 13.11)*

'There is n*othing*', said the Rat, 'absolutely nothing, half so much worth doing as simply messing about in boats' (K. Grahame, *The Wind in the Willows*). Down the ages this truth has been attested to. Fig. 13.11 shows a happy fifteenth-century party, possibly Maying (collecting branches for May Day). Commercial boat trips on the Welsh-rising River Wye started in the eighteenth century. Those on, e.g., the Rhine are still going strong today. Water-parties were still common in the nineteenth and early twentieth centuries. For the masses (as opposed to the upper classes) the Canal Age could bring cheap holiday transport for the first time. Gaskell (1848) describes the Whitsun Manchester holiday in the woods, the people being transported there in numerous boats.

Sailing needs larger waterways — like many Dutch (and other) ones. Punting needs shallow (so mostly small) rivers, and is also now localised culturally, for instance in English Oxford and Cambridge. Rowing happens widely, both communally and in single boats, e.g., from riverside houses. Pleasure cruisers are very abundant (also see Figs 2.4, 2.6), but are necessarily confined to canals and canalised rivers where they — and their marinas — can badly erode the banks. In Britain, with narrow canals, these cruisers are small (and some are converted 'narrowboats', the old commercial barges). On the Continent cruisers can be much larger. The increase of leisure boating after about 1960 was a surprise to many, particularly British, planners. Canals disused for many years were re-opened, marinas were started and deteriorating channels renovated. (Some British waterways were first renovated for pleasure boats earlier, e.g. the Great Ouse in the 1930s (Boyes & Russell, 1977)). New housing estates on the Rhine are likely to have their own pontoon-wharf, the same type used for the Rhine pleasure boats. Boating-lakes are frequent; see above, made by damming rivers from old meanders (e.g. Lyon), from fishponds (Czechoslovakia), or from water-supply reservoirs (e.g. Grafton Water, England).

Canoeing for pleasure started mid-nineteenth century in Britain, and the Canoe Club, soon under Royal patronage, started in 1867. Canoeing much increased in the twentieth century (as usual), the pick-up being earlier in Germany. Organisation, inevitably, increased. The basic skills were worked out in the 1950s (from kayaks), and canoeing has become, for many, more of a sport than a leisure activity. White water (rapids) is preferred. Canoeing is mostly in summer on the Continent, where access is not restricted

Fig. 13.11 Boating for pleasure, fifteenth century (by permission of the Fitzwilliam Museum, Cambridge). (Also see Figs in earlier chapters.)

and large mountain rivers still flow well (e.g. Dordogne, Ardeche). In Britain, access is restricted by riparian owners — or more usually, by the angling associations to which they have let the bank — on rivers that have not (recently) been public highways, and most canoeing is done in winter, when small rivers are at their fullest, and it is close season for fishing (e.g. Dart, Exe). Czechoslovakia has much canoeing. Even Britain has one million canoeists.

The tales of canoeists in Britain are those of the old watermen, in a modern setting: disputes and hindrance with anglers (whose Associations are much richer than the canoeists and who need to preserve spawning-grounds), who complain of disturbance; disputes and hindrances at locks (when a fee is charged for *walking* round carrying the canoe); and disputes, though lesser, with riparian owners; finally, not exactly disputes, but arrangements needed with water authorities where their regulation controls the river flow. (Access officers of the British Canoe Union help to smooth the way.) Canoes go where larger boats do not. Individually they do less damage than larger boats but, as usual, numbers are destructive, and fragile river systems should be excluded (Hardman, 1990; Rowe, 1985; M. Block, personal communication). Water-skiing, windsurfing, SCUBA-diving and the like are minor activities on rivers. When it occurs, however, water-skiing is very disruptive.

Boating, like fishing, has its own literature. Two canoeing-books are referred to above. Magazines include *Waterways World, Canal and River Boats*; books include the series on canals, several written by Hadfield (1945), *English river and canals* (with Eyre, F. Collins: London); (1955) *The canals of Southern England* (Phoenix: London); (1967) *The canals of South West England* (David & Charles: Newton Abbott), etc.; L.T.C. Rolk (1962), *Landscape with canals* (Penguin: London); (1969) *Navigable Waterways* (Narie & Wilson: London); and many more.

There are many other boat sports. Rowing-races became popular in the nineteenth century (see Fig. 12.6f). The Cambridge Boat Races started in 1827 as organised College races (in 1825 there were races between just two Colleges), and these races still take place. The University Boat Race, between Oxford and Cambridge crews, on the Thames, is a national sporting event. The first town regatta in Cambridge was in 1909, rather late (Greenhaugh, 1980). Regattas are boat festivals with races and riverside spectators. They ranged from village events (as at Hemingford) to the Henley Royal Regatta, still a major social, though not now royal, event. Regattas were introduced from Venice to the Thames in 1775. This first regatta was a splendid affair, with seats available, a procession with the Lord Mayor's barge, a race of boats and entertainment on shore. With the decline of simple local boating, most regattas died out. Regrettably this has proved desirable, with the increase of dirty rivers causing disease to those falling in — a risk, therefore, which should only be taken knowingly.

Rivers have been the scene of state occasions and other spectacles down the ages. On the Thames, this was mostly between Plantagenet and Hannoverian times. Some events have been described earlier in this book. They may be occasions for display alone, or to emphasise the seriousness or importance of an occasion. In 972, for instance, Edgar the Peacable — perhaps — had himself rowed on the Welsh Dee after his (belated) coronation, by three kings (Scots, Cumbria and the Isles) and five princes (of Wales). 'Then may my successors, the Kings of England, glory when they shall do the like', as he may have said (e.g., *Anglo-Saxon Chronicle*).

Processions on the Thames to honour the City of London (The Lord Mayor's Procession) and great and royal personages were traditionally frequent, e.g. Pepys recorded on 23 August 1662: 'Queen's coming to town, from Hampton Court, many boats and barges, two pageants, one of a King and one of a Queen. Ten thousand boats and barges, I think, for we could see no water for them, nor discern the King nor Queen.' James II had fireworks on the Thames for his coronation (a stupendous torrent of fire, 1685), and his son's birth (with 100,000 spectators) (Bryant, 1938). Funeral processions were frequent, for Admirals and the Great. Nelson's was a major national occasion With the general abandonment of European rivers such processions are now sparse. The Victory Day Fireworks on the Thames (after the Second World War) were long remembered. The last state procession on the Thames was Churchill's funeral, in January 1965. They continue elsewhere. The 1988 Olympic Games in Seoul, South Korea, had an opening ceremony on the river, with 500 coloured boats, water-skiers and windsurfers with 160 coloured flags for the 160 competing nations, 88 boats for 1988, 24 for the 24 Olympiads, and so on — a colourful occasion, designed to honour televised sport. The state was honoured only indirectly: by achieving television coverage. In 1989 the Seine at Paris bore a procession in honour of the late General de Gaulle. In 1990 the Prince and Princess of Wales, leaving Nigeria, were given a river procession on their departure.

# 14

# Holy and Healing Waters

## Introduction

Fig. 14.1 From sacred to secular (M. Bolaney).

Fig. 14.1 sums up, but exaggerates, the change in man's view of water: from goddess to supermarket bottle. The sacredness and mystery of waters and their sources go back beyond written history. Religious and magic powers and properties were associated with the water, so important was it for comfort, civilisation and survival. Water, like the sun, is numinous (inspiring awe, as if in the presence of God), but is more mysterious than the sun, obeying less obvious laws. It cleans, so making fit to appear before gods; it cures: it is both holy and healing.

> All ye who hither come to drink,
>> rest not your thoughts below;
> Remember Jacob's Well and think,
>> whence living waters flow.
>> (On an English holy well, Trubshaw, 1990)

Down the centuries the sacredness, consecration, of water has been lost, lost with both technology (mains tapwater, polluted rivers) and with changes in culture. The first and fourth verses in Table 14.1 show (irrespective of date) the pagan strangeness Christianised and made understandable. The first is numinous, the fourth is rustic jollity in a Christian framework. The next stage in this series is to change religion for morality; for Longfellow's girl standing with reluctant feet,

*Table 14.1*
*Water, the Lady and the numinous*

**(1)**
Alas the moon should ever beam
To show what man should never see
I saw a maiden on a stream
and fair was she
I staid to watch, a little space
Her parted lips if she would sing
The waters closed above her face
with many a ring
I know my life will fade away
I know that I must vainly pine
For I am made of mortal clay
but she's divine

(cited in Frazer, 1890)

**(2)**
O what can ail thee, Knight at arms
Alone and palely loitering;
The sedge has withered from the lake,
And no birds sing....

I met a lady in the meads
Full beautiful, a fairy's child;
Her hair was long, her foot was light,
And her eyes were wild....

She took me to her elfin grot,
And there she wept, and sighed full sore
And there I shut her wild wild eyes
With kisses four....

I saw pale kings, and princes too,
Pale warriors, death-pale were they all;
They cry'd 'La belle Dame sans merci
Hath thee in thrall!'

(From Keats, 'La Belle Dame sans Merci')

**(3)**
Willows whiten, aspens quiver,
Little breezes dusk and shiver
Thro' the wave that runs for ever
By the island in the river
Flowing down to Camelot.
Four grey walls and four gray towers
Overlook a space of flowers
And the silent isle embowers
The Lady of Shalott....

There she weaves by night and day
A magic web with colours gay.
She has heard a whisper say,
A curse is on her if she stay
To look down to Camelot....

She look'd down to Camelot.
Out flew the web and floated wide;
The mirror crack'd from side to side;
'The curse is come upon me', cried
The Lady of Shalott....

Down she came and found a boat
Beneath a willow left afloat,
And round about the prow she wrote
*The Lady of Shalott....*

Under tower and balcony,
By garden wall and gallery,
A gleaming shape she floated by,
Dead-pale beneath the houses high,
Silent into Camelot.
Out upon the wharfs they came
                          *[wharf in the town centre]*
Knight and burgher, lord and dame
And round the prow they read her name,
*The Lady of Shalott*

(From Tennyson, 'The Lady of Shalott')

*[The Lady is still the numinous Lady, on her Isle in the river — whether or not Tennyson was conscious of the derivation.]*

**(4)**
Here we bring new water
From the well so clear,
For to worship God with,
This happy New Year.

Sing levy-dew, sing levy-dew
The water and the wine;
The seven bright gold wires
And the bugles they do shine.

Sing reign of Fair Maid,
With gold upon her toe,
Open you the West Door *[funerals]*,
And turn the old Year go.
Sing reign of Fair Maid,
With gold upon her chin,
Open you the East Door *[the altar]*,
And let the New Year in.
(Folk song, cited in *The Athenaeum*, 1848, from
Hadfield & Hadfield, (1961)).

*[No numinous; Christianised and jolly, with ancient and forgotten elements.]*

**(5)**
Galadriel Galadriel
Clear is the water of your Well
(from J.R.R. Tolkien, *The Lord of the Rings*)

*[A modern myth, numinous, not Christian, with only few and vague associations with water.]*

**(6)**
Maiden! with the meek brown eyes
In whose orbs a shadow lies...

Standing, with reluctant feet,
Where the brook and river meet,
Womanhood and childhood fleet!...

Deep and still, that gliding stream
Beautiful to thee must seem
As the river of a dream...

O, thou child of many prayers!
Life hath quicksands — Life hath cares!
(from Longfellow, 'Maidenhood')

*[This is a moral, philosophical approach only, nothing sacred. For other moral uses, see Table 13.1.]*

where the brook and river meet. Finally, the numinous connection disappears completely. In this chapter we move from the mysterious and sacred, to the mundane and ordinary.

## Holy waters

The Lady of the Fountain is Celtic, but can usefully describe a much wider range. (In Hungary she was called the Woman of the Wells.) Most river entities are female: most collection of domestic water has been done by women. The Egyptian Ra, however, watered the Nile plain (to destroy his human enemies: but relented and withdrew the flood, leaving floodwater and fertilising silt). There were also water-gods in Greek (Alphaeus), Norse and Russian, but these are unusual. Most water-spirits are young women (though the Indian Mother Ganges in a different culture is older). Anahita started as the goddess of the Oxus, but her cult moved west. Najads lived near water; they would marry mortals, but returned to the hills though keeping in touch with their children. (They could also kidnap mortal children, making it dangerous to visit springs.)

Egeria was the nymph of the cascade at Le Mole (Frazer, 1890). Springs (fountains) were sacred children of the ocean and the land. They might be dedicated to Demeter, as in Attica. In Virgil's *Georgics*, the Shepherd Aristasus lost his bees (see Chapter 4) and called to his nymph mother by the sacred fountain of the rising river. The river nymph conveyed him beneath the river to visit his mother's place. (Nymphs might entice mortals to drowning, e.g., in ancient Greece and France: Brewer, 1881.)

Celtic lore has similar Ladies, though wrapped in Celtic mystery and complexity. There is an Otherworld under or beyond the water which may be entered through a well, over a river, or by a magic boat, and underwater bridge, etc. The way may be guarded by a giant, a shield, etc. Wonderful travels and adventures can be had in the Otherworld, where is the Isle of Glass, and the rivers flowing with wine, oil, milk, honey and jewels. Time there does not correspond to earth time. Magic objects and fountains do many wonderful things. Here the Lady lives.

Celtic literature is much concerned with water. It is often said the Celts worshipped springs. Perilous bridges abound (easy to see why!), wells give water on specified days of the week (because they take time to replenish?), or may shine at night (with luminescent bacteria?), water may be transformed to blood (with an alga such as *Haematococcus*?); fountains may run with wine (which they did, genuinely (see Chapter 3) — and a lapse of a few Dark Age centuries would make it mythical). There are many taboos, rituals which if broken bring misfortune, streams forbidden to certain people, or required bathing for other people, water which may only be drunk if brought by specified cup-bearers, etc. Trout, salmon, also swans and cranes (among river animals), were of importance, since they could change their shape. Fish, particularly trout and salmon, could give advice, convey magic powers if eaten, or be made of jewels. Trout in the fountain and salmon in the river were special. (See for the last two paragraphs, Rodgers 1947-8; Cross, undated; Frazer, 1890; Thompson, 1932. For Norse lore, similar but more down to earth, see Rausmaa, 1973.)

Much water lore is pre-Christian, and the saints who frequently intervene in men's affairs could also be Christianised earlier holy men. However, there are legends of wells that break forth at the birth of Christ: in the wet west, where water was abundant, even superfluous!

Later, various search-type fairy tales have talking fish, and assume that the land within the well is unchancy, perhaps good, perhaps not. Other fairy stories have girls (not boys) entering, being tested, and rewarded according to their deserts.

So, among much else, there is an Otherworld with a supernatural Lady, which is reached via water, and where the Lady, if present, is in charge and orders events. The Arthurian cycle develops the theme and this Matter of Britain has captured the imagination of writers down the centuries, flowering about the twelfth century and, for England, culminating in Malory's *Le Morte D'Arthur*, published in 1485. New interpretations continue — Tennyson's *Idylls of the King*, T.S. Eliot's *The Waste Land*, T.H. White's *The Once and Future King*, Mary Stewart's trilogy starting with *The Crystal Cave*. The Matter exerts a continuing fascination, but the place of water in it varies. Malory has far more fountains than his predecessors; knights and others sit by them, put pavilions by them, guard them, meet others by them, and joust by them. Bridges are, in Malory, more military, enemy knights being encountered on them. (As a note on common drinks and water purity, when Sir Lancelot went mad he drank only water for two years — and failed to die of a water-borne disease.)

In the *Mabinogion* (fourteenth century) Owein goes to the Lady's country by the fountain. He finds a fountain under a tree, and a silver bowl attached by a silver chain to a marble slab. When water is thrown on the slab there is thunder, a cold shower and hail — and the tree is leafless. Birds arrive on the tree and sing; a knight in black arrives, whom Owein defeats. Owein later marries the knight's widow, and keeps the fountain himself — defending the land. He goes off on other adventures and forgets the Lady, and though there is a happy ending it is irrelevant to the fountain. In fact the fountain is a digression, a wonder, not an integral part of the story.

Moving down the centuries and across nations, the Celtic Otherworld Lady becomes a mortal and loses her control over events. Earlier she or her maid were at the river to meet the knight, the fountain or river was the way into a magic land, and strange journeys happened within, including trips in boats controlled by the Lady. The author of *Owein* has modernised the story for his (later) readers. The knight does nothing so silly as to jump into the fountain; he crosses a bridge defended by another knight. The Lady and her country are now of this world.

In Chretien de Troye's *Yvain* the matter has again been altered, this time to give a religious allegory: French, not British. The fountain behaves slightly differently from Owein's — the water boils and is cold; leaves stay on the tree (variants of the Celtic). The fountain must be defended by ancient (unspecified) custom and to prevent damage — control of the kingdom includes control of the fountain. Yvain returns twice, marking stages in his development, and the fountain is central to the ending of the tale.

Early Celtic tales had a supernatural framework, later Welsh ones, a medi-aeval outlook, and the French used the religious allegory. Malory combines the lot in a very English way, but the fountain elements are separated, not being in one single story. The young woman by the stream is a persistent image, though she becomes more ordinary and more passive as time passes. The Lady is not lost, however.

In 1061, Lady Richoldis de Favarches, at the little English village of Walsingham, saw a Lady by, probably, a couple of wells (Fig. 14.2). The Lady identified herself as the Virgin Mary, appeared three times, and requested the building of a house like that at Nazareth. Richoldis' first effort was moved by night (magically? Well...). The two wells in the Abbey gardens are wishing-wells of later tradition. This suggests that someone objected to a Christian chapel being built by pre-Christian holy wells. (The writer learnt how quickly transport can become miraculous, when shown a holy picture in Crete, twice taken by the Nazis, and twice — miraculously—returned. By 1945, the brave Resistance retrievers might have been named!) Our Lady's Holy Well, outside the Abbey area (in the present Church of England shrine), still has some eleventh century stonework.) Walsingham became an important place of pilgrimage and healing, until Henry VIII's break with Rome and dismantling of Catholic shrines. It has had a revival in the twentieth century. There are twice-weekly sprinklings at the holy well. (Walsingham publicity literature; Whittaker, 1921). When emphasising the increase of the mundane, Fig. 14.2c can be cited — surely no previous century would have holy water so bleak and unornamented!

Eight centuries later, in 1858, Bernadette Soubirous, aged fourteen, saw a Lady in a remote village in the Pyrenées (Lourdes). The Lady was in a cave by the river (Fig 14.3), identified herself as the Immaculate Conception, considered by the Catholic Church as the Virgin Mary and, after several appearances, directed Bernadette to wash herself in a non-existent spring. The spring broke forth afterwards (see below) and was quickly recognised as miraculous and healing, and Lourdes, and St Bernadette, are now world-famous. Several score of healings are officially deemed miraculous in that they were instantaneous, and carefully verified before and after — like the blind

Fig. 14.2 Our Lady of Walsingham, England. a) The old, once-wishing wells in the Abbey grounds. Lily pool perhaps once a pilgrim's wash place. b) The present holy well. c) Dispenser of holy water — late twentieth-century style.

woman who could see when
the eye specialist could still
clearly demonstrate that
this was impossible (the eyes
later became normal).
Lesser improvements are
many, and most sick return
home with fresh cheerful-
ness and strength. Because
of these recent and well-at-
tested cures, similar ones
reported at earlier shrines

Fig. 14.3 a) Our Lady of Lourdes,
France — souvenir medal. b) St
Erik's fountain, Uppsala.

should not be dismissed out
of hand. Of course many
cures — particularly in the
past, when the pilgrimage lasted longer and the countryside was more various —
would be due to change of air, water and diet. Others would be due to mind over
matter and to falsification of data by those wanting to attract the then tourists, the
pilgrims. But some again might be attributed to divine powers.

As mentioned in Chapter 3, in pre-drainage days the ground was much wetter,
and in suitable places altering the hydraulics by, e.g. much trampling, would allow
small springs, like that at Lourdes, to break forth. The spring at Uppsala, said to
have risen where St Erik was killed, could be another example (Fig. 14.3b).

St Winifred's Well (Fig. 14.4) had well-reputed cures quite recently (a 1910
paper, N. Wales branch of the British Medical Association, stated several cures
were authentic (Heath, 1911). This well is much too large to have started with St
Winifred, by tradition a seventh-century saint. Defoe (1724-7) gives a characteris-

Fig. 14.4 a) St Winifred's Well, Wales. b) Holy
Well, Somerset, England — recent dedication to
the Baptism, but adjacent church is to St Mary
the Virgin. Note 'serpents' (Asclepius?). Both
are 'wells' in the old sense, with a flow of water.

tically sceptical account: '... The stories of this Well of S. Winifrid, are that the pious virgin, being ravished and murthered, this healing water sprung out of her body when buried; but this smells too much of the legend, to take up any of my time; the Romanists indeed believe it, as 'tis evident, from their thronging hither to receive the healing sanative virtue of the water, which they do not hope for as it is a medicinal water, but as it is a miraculous water, and heals them by virtue of the intercession and influence of this famous virgin, St. Winifrid; of which I believe as much as comes to my share.

'Here is a fine chapel cut out of a solid rock, and was dedicated to this holy virgin; and numbers of pilgrims resort to it, with no less devotion than ignorance; under this chapel the water gushes out in a great stream, and the place where it breaks out, is form'd like a basin or cistern, in which they bathe: The water is intensely cold, and indeed there is no great miracle in that point, considering the rocks it flows from, where it is impregnated by divers minerals, the virtue of which, and not of the saint, I suppose, work the greatest part of the cures.

'There is a little town near the well, which may, indeed, be said to have risen from the confluence of the people hither, for almost all the houses are either publick houses, or let into lodgings; and the priests that attend here, and are very numerous, appear in disguise: Sometimes they are physicians, sometimes surgeons, sometimes gentlemen, and sometimes patients, or any thing as occasion presents. No body takes notice of them, as to their profession, tho' they know them well enough, no not the Roman Catholicks themselves; but in private, they have their proper oratory's in certain places, whither the votaries resort and good manners has prevail'd so far, that however the Protestants know who and who's together; no body takes notice of it, or enquires whether one another goes, or has been gone....'

Others, more plausibly, say Winifred was (only) decapitated, and her head rolled near the well (Heath, 1911). (St Winifred's Wells' own literature, though, states she was a nun, her story being mixed up with an earlier one of decapitation. The mixed version is in *The Catholic Encyclopedia*.) The well became a renowned place of pilgrimage before the Reformation (King Henry V went there), and it continued since, on a minor scale, as in Defoe's time. Seventeenth-century roads in the vicinity still converged on the local village.

The healing powers of waters, removed from religion and magic, will be described below, but those where the two are mixed are included here. From early times magic drinks and magic wells could give cures and give life, wisdom, supernatural information, love, protection and immortality. The wells might be presided over by Ladies or nymphs. Some wells were bad, able to cause drowning. Some were testing: in the Well of Life and Death, one side killed, one protected from disease (Cross, undated). Wells could overflow to predict death (Brampton, Northamptonshire), give dreams before an important event (Oundle), or cure only when drunk in the early morning (Fiddlers' Well. (n.b., doing something difficult and striking gives a boost to, or cures, many ills). It is rare to find a bad well, but one near Dundee had a monster in it who ate nine maidens (Thompson, 1932). Running freshwater protected from bad magic. Magicians, witches and evil spirits could not cross it.

Merlin, however, the British magician *par excellence*, was a guardian of springs and wells in spite of being male.

Tonttus, small Finnish fairy folk, live under bridges: so arrived there after bridges were built. Riversides could be places of prayer, e.g., Acts (16.13): And on the sabbath we went out of the city by a river side, where prayer was wont to be made.

When St Augustine of England was sent by the Pope to evangelise England, instructions sent to him in 601, recorded in Bede in 731, stated that existing temples were (apart from idols) to be kept, purified and re-dedicated, and be retained as places of holiness and festivity. Thanks to this wise policy, many holy wells and other places were preserved. Ancient wells are still found near monuments or churches, and it is often probable that the spring determined the original position (Heath, 1911).

Many Celtic and Anglo-Saxon (Christian) saints were hermits and therefore would have lived near a fountain, establishing new Christian wells to add to Christianised earlier ones. English holy wells are particularly frequent in Cornwall (Heath, 1911). St Chad, Bishop of Lichfield, died in 672 (Bede, 731). St Chad's Well is in a small garden near the church with traditionally an Ascension Day procession of the clergyman, children, etc., to decorate the well with flowers and branches. In 1792 a Lichfield doctor listed the diseases benefited by the milky-looking water of the well (Heath, 1911) (which in Bede's time was renowned for healings). All over Europe wells were noted for holiness, healing or both. Various English ones extant in the twentieth century are listed in the Geological Survey memoirs on water supply. In Leicestershire, Richardson (1931) notes Golden Well (Sapcote, slightly chalybeate, i.e., iron-rich), formerly for nervous, consumptive, scorbutic (scurvy) and scrophulous complaints; currently used for rheumatism. It had a bath-house erected in 1806, decayed in the 1920s. Soap Well had remarkably soft water, said to wash without soap. In Hampshire, Whittaker (1910) notes wells visited to late last century for eye and other disorders, some being holy (St Boniface's Well and St Laurence's Well, in particular). These tended to be chalybeate. In Herefordshire Richardson (1921) found

'55 named wells,                    Where ailments noted,
13 holy,                            7 eyes,
13 saints' names,                   2 rheumatism,
4 lady,                             1 each skin, bone and crookedness.'
11 lady plus holy (female/saints).

The association between Lady and holiness in wells is strong. St Peter's Wells were three: two good for eyes, and a large one for rheumatism. The number of eye wells, here and elsewhere (Heath, 1911; Thacker, 1909, etc.) is considerable. Sore eyes are not now a common complaint. When washing was infrequent, sore eyes were presumably commoner, and regular washing with clean water would be beneficial.

Glastonbury, in Somerset, with its ancient legends of Christianity (Joseph of Arimathæa, and the source of 'And did those feet in ancient time/walk upon Englands' mountains green?' from Blakes' Jerusalem) and the Matter of Britain

(Isle of Avalon) has, of course, its holy well, the Chalice Spring well, with water rust-coloured from iron. Drinking water comes through a Lion's Head fountain: but of course!

St Bride, St Brigid, St Bridget (Fig. 14.5), the founder of many Christian communities in Ireland, became in legend the midwife to the Virgin, probably acquiring many characteristics from the Celtic goddess Brigantia (Brigit), who granted fertility to women. (Note how the goddess of fertility changed over to midwife.)

Wishing-wells are considered holy wells turned to superstitious uses — in turn perhaps derived from Celtic ones of peculiar, even prophetic, repute (in prophetic wells the water level or flow changes to 'answer' the question). Such wells may require an offering, such as a crooked pin, or a coin. The wishing could be restricted (e.g., to time of day or type of wish), and the granting unchancy.

Downpatrick, in Ireland, has wells dedicated to St Patrick, where Midsummer Eve rituals were performed, and where cures were hoped for (Heath, 1911).

Churchyard wells may often have been baptismal fonts. An ancient Northumbrian well (Holystone) is inscribed: 'Paulinus the Bishop [later Archbishop of York]

Fig. 14.5 St Bride.

baptised three thousand Northumbrians, Easter DCXXVII [627]. Few Anglo-Saxon fonts exist, and it seems likely that wells were used instead (these are often under the wall and near an entrance). There is a long-held belief that harm befalls those who harm wells (Heath, 1911).

The Romans decorated their springs with flowers in honours of the nymphs and were no doubt not the first to do so (Heath, 1911).

> ... the shepherds at their festivals...
> Throw sweet garland wreaths into her stream
> Of pansies, pinks and gaudy daffodils.        (Milton)

Simple well-decorating like this was widespread, often on or near Ascension Day (e.g. Thacker, 1914; Heath, 1911; and for Germany, Granville, 1841). In Tissington, Derbyshire the ceremony was started (or restarted?) as a thanksgiving for plenteous water after an exceptional drought in 1615, recorded in the parish register. There was almost no rain between 25 March and 4 August, which left the crops burnt up, both corn and hay (Heath, 1911). This practice was specifically a Christian one. Developed in Tissington and spread to other villages near, it gave rise to a distinctive kind of well-dressing (Fig. 14.6). Large boards are covered with wet puddled clay, and thousands of petals, leaves, etc., are pressed on to give complex and beautiful designs. Most have a Christian theme, such as 'We thank thee Lord, for this fair earth'; the Good Samaritan, etc. The dressings may now be placed at taps, or even in eye-catching positions where there is no water.

There were many enactments against the folly and superstition of worshipping at wells and hoping for cures. For each respectable place of healing there were

Fig. 14.6 Well-dressing, Derbyshire, England (The Good Shepherd).

many stupidities. Scots, as late as 1657 were being publicly rebuked at Kirk Session for having gone to Christ's Well (Falkirk) to seek their health (Heath, 1911). Results from 'healing water' depend on how and why! Clean water was free and could perhaps do much more good than a visit to a seventeenth-century doctor? Though not in the eyes of strict Presbyterians on the look-out for popery!

Wells of good repute had elaborate enclosures built round them (e.g., Fig. 14.4): wellhouses, often with chapels. A famous holy well would attract many visitors. Some might develop into the eighteenth-century spas (see below), with pump room (for the water) and assembly room (for social gathering). Malvern was one such site. An early seventeenth-century rhyme (Heath, 1911) went:

> A thousand bottles there
> Were filled weekly
> And many costrils rare
> For stomachs sickly
> Some of them into Kent
> Some were to London sent
> Others to Berwick went
> O praise the Lord

This is healing water, with remaining holy associations! In 1654 John Evelyn wrote that the (Malvern) wells were said to heal infirmities such as the King's Evil and Leprosy (meaning another skin disease?) (Heath, 1911). Clean water benefits skin ailments! Now Malvern Spring water, under that name and as Schweppes (from Primeswell Spring) goes even further, and in many more than a thousand bottles per week.

Fig. 14.7 The cave-church of St Paul, Malta. a) Nineteenth century print (gorge exaggerated). Note water — and path above water. b) Church built over, site made 'ordinary'. Public access to upper part of cave (for position, compare a)). c) Detail of upper part: Madonna and child in fake grotto. Contrast the genuine a) and Fig. 14.6.

In St James Church, Clerkenwell, in London, a tablet records that the nearby spring supplying the pump was anciently the site of sacred plays (Clerk's Well) and the water was much esteemed by the local clergy, Templars and Benedictine nuns (Heath, 1911).

Sacred caves contained wells or springs; some have curative attributes. Fig. 14.7 shows a remarkable chapel in a river gorge in Malta (the gorge is exaggerated). Regrettably it has been conserved by

b

having a church built around it. The cave is now two-partite. The upper part has a shrine to Our Lady — in a fake grotto. The artificial is too often preferred to the rough and authentic. At least the Lady is there (returned from classical times?).

Before leaving wells, another possible trail is that Celtic supernatural wells could contain magic trout. Mediaeval holy wells could, by custom, contain a trout or two. Later fountains could bear fish. Are goldfish ponds descended from magic ones?

c

While wells were usually beneficent and passed under Christian influence, rivers — which after all are more likely to drown people — are more often thought to be malevolent. On the whole, though, the English water-spirits are kindly and helpful, like the rivers themselves. (The (Cheshire) Dee was sacred in pre-Christian times. 'Deva' means goddess, holy river. The Trent had Aegir, a kindly god (note, not goddess) who stilled storms and calmed seas. The Dart, though, was unkind — 'River of Dart, river of Dart, Every year thou claimest a heart.' The Tees and Ribble also required sacrifice. In France, the dragon of flood was vanquished in the Seine by St Roma, in the Rhône by St Martha (Brewer, 1881). Some rivers are haunted by ghosts; in the Swale by an escaped highwayman who was drowned in it; on Abingdon Bridge (Thames) by one in white (who also walks in the street) and in the past said 'Revenge', but later only hissed like a snake (Rodgers, 1947-8).

Rodgers (1947-8) recounts another nice legend. Egwin, Bishop of Worcester-shire, founded Evesham Abbey where he and his swineherd had a vision of the Virgin Mary. Egwin became Abbott, but was later involved in a scandal. In consequence, he manacled his legs and threw the key into the Avon, and went off to Rome to clear his name. There he bought a salmon, and lo and behold, his key was inside, and he and his monastery were honoured by the Pope. A Christian variant of a fairy tale.

Rain-making rituals are only marginal to this subject of rivers. Frazer (1890) describes many, including troubling a sacred spring, touching or laughing at a (Munster) fountain, catching water in tankards and throwing it on a nearby slab (Brecilieu, France). This last fountain is very like that of Owein and Yvain, described above. A birch could be dressed in woman's clothes and thrown into a river (Russia), and a statue be taken to a river, and be both prayed to and threatened with a ducking (St Peter, France).

The use of water in ritual purity was important in classical times. Roman Christians put fountains in church courtyards — as copied in mosques. The Old Testament makes frequent use of water, as a metaphor of strength, whether comforting or terrible (Table 14.2). There is also the idea that waters can be used to bless and curse. The strong monotheism of the Old Testament contrasts sharply with the Celtic. The Lord is not in, but above, nature and has not just power, but might greater even than the waters. The folklore holy man, Lady or magic fish, of the Celts pretends to no such power.

The Jordan was a special river. In II Kings 5, Naaman, the Captain of the host of Syria, was a leper. He took gifts to Elisha, asking for a cure. Elisha sent a message to say he must wash seven times in the Jordan. Naaman was indignant that he was not given better treatment — 'Are not Abana and Pharpar, rivers of Damascus, better than all rivers of Israel?' His servants pointed out that Naaman would have done anything difficult required by Elisha, so he should equally do something simple. He did so and was cured. The Jordan became more renowned when:

> On Jordan's bank the Baptist's cry
> Announces that the Lord is nigh.

John baptised many, in the Jordan and baptism, of course, came to be the entry into most Christian Churches. The Coptic service described by Morton (1938) from Cairo, is among the most ancient now known. A stone font has been built into a

Table 14.2
*Some Biblical descriptions*

| | |
|---|---|
| And he shall be like a tree planted by the rivers of water,<br>that bringeth forth his fruit in his season<br>(Ps. 1) | I am come into deep water, where the floods overflow me....<br>Let not the waterflood overflow me (Ps. 69) |
| The LORD is my shepherd;...<br>He leadeth me beside the still waters<br>(Ps. 23) | Thou carriest them away as with a flood<br>(Ps. 90) |
| As the hart panteth after the water brooks,<br>So panteth my soul after thee, O God.<br>(Ps. 42) | The floods have lifted up, O LORD,<br>The floods have lifted up their voice;...<br>The LORD on high is mightier<br>Than the noise of many waters (Ps. 93) |
| A fountain of gardens,<br>A well of living water,<br>and streams from Lebanon.<br>(Song of Solomon 4) | So two or three cities wandered unto one city,<br>To drink water; but they were not satisfied:<br>Yet have ye not returned unto me,<br>saith the LORD (Amos 4) |
| Behold I will extend peace to her *[Jerusalem]*<br>like a river,<br>And the glory of the Gentiles like a flowing stream. (Isaiah 66) | But let judgement run down as waters,<br>And righteousness as a mighty stream.<br>(Amos 5) |
| For in the wilderness shall waters break out,<br>And streams in the desert.<br>And the parched ground shall become a pool,<br>And the thirsty land springs of water<br>(Isaiah, 35) | He bindeth the floods from overflowing.<br>(Job 28)<br><br>For my people have committed two evils;<br>They have forsaken me,<br>The fountain of living *[running]* waters,<br>And hewed them out cisterns,<br>Broken cisterns, that can hold no water.<br>(Jeremiah 2) |
| And he shewed me a pure river of water of life, clear as crystal, proceeding out of the throne of God and of the Lamb. (Revelation 22) | |

corner of a side chapel and, in the middle of the general service, the mother is purified here. Then, addressing the baby as an adult, the priest prays that all remains of the worship of idols be cast out of its heart, and the baby be worthy of the new birth coming. The baby is anointed, the godparents — and the baby by proxy — renouncing evil, and there is a second (complex) anointing. Oil is put in the font, incense is burned, and the priest breathes thrice on the water, his breath making the sign of the cross. Chrism is poured on the water. The priest then breathes on the naked baby to exorcise any evil spirit (as described by Tertullian in the second century). He plunges the baby into the water three times, each time deeper (the third time it is a ducking), in the Name of the Father, Son and Holy Spirit. The water is then deconsecrated, the baby is anointed for the third time, and is breathed on: 'Receive the Holy Ghost.' The priest lays hands on the child and blesses it, and the mother dresses it in new clothes. As the baby is confirmed too, it is given Communion — water being dashed on its face to make it gasp, and a drop of wine inserted in its open mouth. Finally at the end of the whole service, the deacon pours water on the priest's hands, who tosses it to the roof three times, while the people scramble to catch drops. The early elements are clear.

Rivers also have been used for Christian baptism — Bede (731) describes baptising in the rivers Swale, Glen and Trent. Fig. 14.8b shows a Baptist village baptism in the late nineteenth century. (Note that enough boats are present for safety and that rivers were still reasonably clean.)

The Jordan was also hallowed by pilgrimage; people were bathing there by 333 A.D., and, in 1172, 60,000 were noted bathing (Morton, 1934). This is a very large number, particularly considering it was after the

Fig. 14.8 a) The Baptism of Christ. Sixteenth-century German woodcut. b) Baptising (Baptist Church) in a Cambridgeshire river, redrawn from nineteenth century (M. Bolaney).

rise of Islam, so that Christians were sparser in the region.

The Kings of France and England touched for the King's Evil for nearly eight centuries. (The custom started in France.) In the beginning water was used by the King in the ceremony — Edward the Confessor of England and Charles VI of France sprinkled the sufferers with water, signing the Cross. By the seventeenth century Charles II of England and Louis XIV of France were instead washing themselves after the ceremony —

from religion to hygiene. Charles II, at least, recommended sufferers to wash frequently, which, in those dirty days, may have been curative without other aid, for various skin, etc., troubles (Crawfurd, 1911).

The church of St Paul of the Three Fountains, outside Rome, is on the traditional site of St Paul's martyrdom. It is said his head bounced three times, drawing the three springs (Morton, 1936). An earlier version of Lourdes was at the place where St Mena died in the third century near Alexandria. A spring emerged near his grave, which cured first sheep and then humans, including the daughter of the Emperor of Constantinople (cf. Lourdes, which reportedly cured the son of the Emperor of France). The importance of this spring peaked from the fifth century to the seventh century (until the rise of Islam). Spring-water was taken away in flasks of clay stamped with pictures of St Mena and the two camels who refused to move his body further (Morton, 1938).

St Christopher became the patron saint of ferries (see Chapter 7 and Fig. 7.3), St Bartholomew of bridges, St Nicholas of travellers. In 1254 Queen Marguerite of France promised a silver ship for a safe journey (at Luneville where ships were made: see Chapter 9). St Andrew was, of course, patron of fishermen, St Simon of tanners, St James the less of fullers —among many other patron saints. St John Nepamuk, a political priest (Fig. 14.9), is the patron saint of structures in rivers in Czechoslovakia, where he was thrown into the river in the fourteenth century, and his statue is frequent by bridges. (He was the saint of the Hungarian Fire Brigade also: Y. Bower, personal communication.)

Fig. 14.9 St John Nepamuk, guarding a bridge in Czechoslovakia.

The author of the Book of Revelation describes in the City of God, a pure river of water of life, clear as crystal. In classical times Charon ferried the dead across a river. John Bunyan's seventeenth-century pilgrim story has a river of death, through which all must pass before reaching the Heavenly City. The river varies in depth and difficulty. Welcome awaits, a welcome like that for Mr Valiant-for-truth: all the trumpets sounded for him on the other side.

## Healing waters

Spas, named from Spa in the Belgian hills, started to flourish in the eighteenth century — the Age of Reason rather than that of Faith. When painkillers and surgery were negligible, those who could afford it toured the Continental Baths in search of ironwater or other water to relieve the pain, for instance, of gallstones, and were certainly doing so in the sixteenth century (R.M. Haslam, personal communication). To visit a spa and take the waters was neutral; it did not imply pilgrimage and the invocation of divine blessing (though the site might well be a holy well, these being thick on the ground and often already known — see Malvern above). The waters, with change of air, diet and pleasant surroundings, could be effective and taking the waters became fashionable.

Bath (Fig. 14.10), the Aqua Sulis of the Romans, was, very properly, dedicated by them to Sulis Minerva (a combined Celtic and Roman divinity). The hot spring

Fig. 14.10 The King's Bath, seventeenth century, Bath, England.

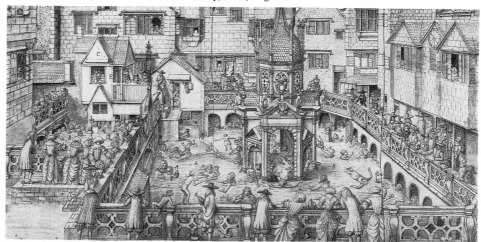

gushes at 46.5°C, meaning it comes rapidly from a great depth in the earth (some is, by carbon 14 dating, up to 100,000 years old, most is probably about 10,000 years old; it is not yet polluted!). The Romans constructed a fine bathing-place, shrine and ancillaries here. They piped water (through lead pipes) into a series of baths, remains of the Great Bath still being there. Offertory coins are mostly A.D. 43-260, decreasing by about 400. (*The Times* newspaper in an article on the excavations, adds that recently a bunch of violets with 'Thank you, Sulis, for the cure' was found on the spring.) Regrettably, curse tablets were also found during recent excavations, invoking divine vengeance for petty theft and such-like.

The baths were abandoned by the Anglo-Saxons, and not restored until the twelfth century, when the sick visited to see and bathe in its health-giving waters. The first hospital dated from then. The baths were again decayed in the fifteenth century and were restored at its end. A sixteenth-century description is: 'five dirty baths open to the sky'. Nevertheless, notables, like Lord Burghley, sought health there. Queen Anne of Denmark (wife of James I) went in the mid-seventeenth century, Queen Anne (of Britain) a little later. Pepys, in 1668, wrote, of the Cross Bath: 'methinks it cannot be clean to go so many bodies together into the same water'. He found the water hot, too hot for feet, even in this cooler bath. He stayed two hours, went home wrapped in a sheet to sweat in bed, 'and music comes to play'. Defoe, a little later again (1724-7) describes Bath as being earlier for cripples, crutches being hung up in thanksgiving for cures, but in his time it had become a place for the diversion of those in sound health. He describes young ladies in smocks bathing in the Cross Bath, with floating dishes in front of them for handkerchiefs, nosegays (against infection), etc. The sexes mingled more in the King and Queen's Bath. Anciently, he says, there was bathing only, but now water is drunk also, and the cures seem to be equal. Colic, ill-digestion and scurvy are specially benefited.

In the eighteenth century, good public buildings were built, and well-bred manners fostered. Drinking was considered more important than bathing. In mid-century the Royal Mineral Water Hospital was founded to provide spa treatment for the poor. It is still open, treating rheumatic disorders.

In 1841 Granville, a doctor, considered Bath a good town but a poor spa, the waters being mis-managed, though there were douches, baths, etc. He considered that drinking should be in the morning and that limbs, paralysis, rheumatism, gout and hypochondria were helped.

The spa later decayed. In 1976 the National Health Service withdrew its support from the hot bath. A revival is planned, at least for tourists. (Granville, 1841; Heath, 1911; Wilton-Smith, 1988; original sources; and descriptions of excavations in the media).

Two other smaller and differing English watering-places will be described, before moving to general principles.

Matlock, on the south of the Pennine hills, had a small but noted success, based on an old well. Defoe describes the hot bath and hot springs in several places, which run into ditches. However, the accommodation was decayed. The waters varied chemically, being mineral-rich and iron-rich, the former aiding rheumatic, scorbutic and scrofulous ills, the latter aches, nervous pains and skin complaints, and a mixture of the two helping diabetes and bloody urine. Granville (1841) confirms Defoe's view that the water at 68°F (20°C) did not feel hot, and the accommodation was still decayed. It was restored, but too late to become a major health centre. It still, though, has the unmistakeable air of a watering-place.

Wellingborough (Northamptonshire) is even more decayed as a watering-place but has recovered and diversified. It is named for its many wells, including the Red Well, White Well, Stan Well, Burymoat Well and Rising Sun Well. Wells are on the borough's Arms, showing their early significance. At the turn of the seventeenth century Wellingborough became known as a Watering-Place, and visits by royalty (1628, 1637) promised well for the future. Unfortunately the royalty were Charles I and Queen Henrietta Maria, and an executed King is no immediate recommendation. The woollen industry also decayed, but recovery over the past few centuries has been in craft — lace, boots, shoes, steel, brewing, matting, silk, tanning, bricks, clothes and box-making.

It was early recognised that there are many different kinds of spring: hot, sulphur, mineral of various kinds (high in iron, magnesium, etc.) salt, solute-low, cold, etc. The Etruscans turned to their hot springs for health; the Romans copied: e.g., *fontes clusini, aquae populinae*, baths of Caldona. Bede (731) wrote that Britain had salt springs and hot springs, used for bathing.

Like canals, spas continued to flourish on the Continent in the nineteenth, and into the twentieth, century. As with the canals, the main reason for British decline seems to be lack of will — lack of funding, modernisation and general wish to please the customer. Granville (1841) speaks as highly of the health-giving properties of English as of German spas — having previously written a book on German ones. He points to the decay, though, and to its being due to mis-management of the medical side and lack of comfortable, amusing and pleasant surroundings for social benefit. He points out that the cold mineral waters of Germany have much carbonic acid gas, those of England very little (warm waters containing little gas anyway). Bubbly waters are pleasanter to taste and easier to digest, and can contain more minerals in solution. The range and levels of minerals are less in England. Table 14.3 shows places recommended by Granville and the ills they benefit.

*Table 14.3*

*English spas in the mid-nineteenth century*

(*Extracted from Granville (1841)*)

Chemical composition can be inferred from cures reported, and vice versa.

Originally cold springs were primarily used for drinking, hot for bathing, but by 1840 most were used for both, cold water sometimes being heated. Granville approves of bottled water only if the spring is cold, and without sulphur or other substances that are lost on storage. Water that is naturally heated underground is, he considers, far more beneficial than ordinarily-heated water.

These are restricted to large springs (not just wells) and entirely secular.

| spa | temp.(°C.) | water type | recommended for | comments |
|---|---|---|---|---|
| Buxton | 28 | Close to pure[1] | Rheumatic, gout, paralytic affections and weakness after. Faulty internal organs. Debility. Not for inflammation. | May be heated to 36°. Effect due to heat. |
| Matlock | 20; 15.5 | Slightly calcareous, close to pure | Dyspeptic and nephritic affections? | |
| Monkswell, Lincoln | 10.5 | Chalybeate[2] | Dyspepsia with acidity, green sickness, female debility, glandular disorders, muscle torpor | Patients drink at spring-head. Iron 'untraceable' after first day. Cold baths. |
| | 4.5 | No iron | | |
| Woodhall Spa, Lincoln | 11.5 | Iodine, bromine, brine, some CO$_2$ (champagne-like) | Scrofula, glandular affections, disordered digestion, some rheumatism, gout | |
| Ashby-de-la-Zouch | 16.5 | (Uncertain) | Internal diseases, rheumatic and paralytic affections | Water brought to town from colliery for bathing |
| Willoughby Spa, Rugby | 9 | Sulphurated saline? | Female complaints, (?) certain children's maladies | Water is for drinking |
| Salt Wells, Dudley | 10 | Salt, muriates[3] of lime, magnesium, iron | Weakness of limbs, palsy (if non-inflammatory), glandular and scrofula affections | Probably better than Cheltenham |
| Tenbury | 9 | Salt, muriate of lime, trace iodine, bromine; water is sparkly | Glandular swellings, internal trouble, scrofula, scurvy, gout, rheumatic gout, paralytic affections, worms, skin troubles | Can be bottled and sent away |
| Leamington Spa | 9 | Saline, sulphuretted | Several moderate virtues for drinking | |
| Malvern | 10 | Pure | | Pure water, healthy site on hill |
| Cheltenham | 10 | Muriates, sulphate of soda, etc. Proportions vary with depth. | Chronic derangements of stomach and liver | Declined as Spa, grown as town. Water is for drinking. |
| Gloucester | 9.5 | Saline, iodine | | Water is for drinking |
| Clifton | 23 | Slightly saline | Irritative fever, phthisical complaints. Various. Not for lungs. | Benefit is from heat. In the past patients were too often sent who could not recover. |
| Bath | up to 46.5 | High mineral, iron, some CO$_2$ | Stimulates skin, strengthens muscles, joints, limbs, quickens circulation. Wide range. Paralysis, rheumatism, gout. Female complaints. As drink, diuretic, diaphoretic, not purgative. Only for some. | Temperature lowered for bathing. Cannot be bottled |
| Tunbridge Wells | 10 | Poor chalybeate | | Undeserved fame. Now a social town only. If water was sparkly, would be excellent. As good chalybeate can be found at any turnpike in Yorks. |
| Harrogate | 11.5-15.5 | Pure chalybeate, saline chalybeate, saline, sulphur. Vary in strength. | Wide variety. Glandular, scrofulous and digestive complaints. Especially slow-acting skin diseases. (Not fever or inflammation.) | Different wells have different effects. Water is for bathing in (and drinking). Should be heated before drinking. |
| Knaresborough | 11 | Sulphuretted hydrogen, less saline, more muriates and carbonate than the last (there is another well, which is chalybeate) | Better than Harrogate for many irritable skin diseases. | Water is for drinking and bathing in |

| spa | temp. (°C.) | water type | recommended for | comments |
|---|---|---|---|---|
| Aldfield Spa | 11 | Sulphur, in between the last two | | |
| Thorpe Arch | 9.5 | Saline | Diuretic, like Harrogate. | |
| Malton | — | Saline-chalybeate | Many chronic diseases, liver, digestion, debility. | |
| Scarborough | 10.5 | Saline-chalybeate lime, etc. | Digestive and varied complaints (debility, skin disorders, etc.) | Water is for drinking. There is also marine bathing. |
| Croft | 10.5 | Saponaceous alkaline Strong sulphur | Diuretic drink Sulphur baths (not for drinking), refreshing various complaints | |
| Dinsdale | 10.5 | Sulphuretted | As other sulphur ones | Water is for bathing in and drinking. Sulphur remains after heating. |
| Guisborough | 10 | Slightly sulphuretted, low mineral | Not much use (too dilute) | Water is for bathing |
| Butterby | 10 | Near-pure (lime carbonate); sulphur and muriates; iron and saline (in middle of Wear: unusable unless enclosed) | Alterative [improving the metabolism] | |
| Shotley Bridge | 9 | (Alterative) chalybeate, muriates, $CO_2$, etc. | Weakness and obstruction in circulation, indigestion, skin diseases and, in warm bath, rheumatism | Differs from other British waters. Water is for drinking (and bathing in). |
| Gilsend Spa | 10.5 | Sulphuretted, strongly | As other sulphur waters | |
| Skipton Spa | 10.5 | Alkaline sulphuretted | Warms stomach, intestines, muscle joints; improves vitality; relieves female complaints | |
| Horley Green Spa | 10.5 | Chalybeate, strong (sulphate of iron) | As other chalybeate | Water is for bathing and drinking. |
| Ilkley Spa | 8.5 | Muriates of lime and magnesia (2:1), $CO_2$ | Scrofula, eye inflammation, atrophy, mesenteric diseases, stiff joints, muscles, stomach irritability, chronic weakness, some female complaints | After bath, rub, exercise or have a hot drink until the skin feels warm |

[1] Pure = solute low
[2] Chalybeate = iron
[3] muriate = chloride

Granville comments that waters must be drunk at source — that if a warm water is cooled and reheated and turns milky, it is not in the same state (which is true). The 'genuine article' is superior to that made up by chemists (who do not know, so cannot copy, the micro-constituents). (A friend of the writer was recently offered a spa bath in a hotel: artificially bubbling water was the only thing provided!) Spas should be recommended on the basis of climate, soil, land use and housing (with exact instructions on where to go) as well as the waters. Diet is important also. Harrogate is recommended, as the visitor can dip his cup himself in the fountain head and know the water is pure and strong, with no interference by pipe or pump. The High Village is chalybeate (iron-rich), the Low, saline without sulphur, and sulphur. There is also expensive pumped-up water. Germans do not pump their water, which Granville considers correct. Harrogate has 60°F (15°C) baths, but they are imperfect. Granville thinks there ought also to be mud baths. Liver, glands, rheumatism, boils, etc., are helped.

There are plenty of descriptions of Continental spas by sick English; of a great room with liquid mud instead of a floor from which a lot of heads looked out, each with a little board floating before him with pocket handkerchiefs, coffee cups and newspapers; or of rows of pinewood boxes in a vault, containing rusty water (iron), each with a shelf for one's head and a lid closing to the chin.

Elizabeth Barrett Browning's brother, recovering from measles in London in the 1840s, went to the Public Baths 'for purification' and was then considered free of infection. This old element became lost when baths became common in houses.

The last phase of healing waters in Britain was the hydropathic hotels the 'Hydros' of around the early twentieth century, e.g., at Pitlochry. These never took off. The watering-places at the sea grew and spread in the nineteenth century and here — as so often with developing, rather than developed, English enterprises, pains were taken to provide what the visitor wanted and enjoyed. The therapeutic result of a seaside holiday was considered as due to the sun, air, break from work, etc., sea-bathing being a minor factor (sea-bathing never had the medical publicity given to the inland spas).

On the Continent, however, there are — as well as were — the spas. Whether in Portugal, Switzerland, Hungary, Russia or Germany, they abound. They range from large watering-places, with plenty of tower-block hotels, to quiet local places like the Health Wall in Chapter 2 (Fig. 2.3). In parts of Germany they were especially numerous. There are eight just south and west of Hannover, for example (Bad Nenndorf, Bad Münder. Bad Salzuflen, Bad Salsdetfurth, Bad Bymat, Bad Gandersheim, Bad Oynhausen, Bad Meinburg) (and see Table 14.4 and Fig. 14.11). Some spas are household names: Spa itself in Belgium, Baden Baden in Germany, and Aix-la-Chapelle in France, for instance. Modern spa hotels still have bathing in the waters: the waters being in their natural state, whether warm or cold, fizzy or still.

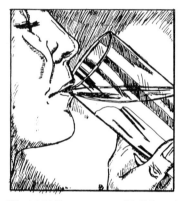

Fig. 14.11 Spa treatment (M. Bolaney).

But these hotels may also have

| | |
|---|---|
| underwater jet massage, | swimming and aquatic group exercises, |
| mud baths or packs, | drinking the water, |
| bathing of part of the body, | peat baths (if relevant), |
| sauna baths, | breathing in air from the spring, etc. |

Also provided are many treatments not connected with water, but on the same general spa principles:

| | |
|---|---|
| exercise, | massage, |
| sunbathing, | manicures. |
| skin treatments, | |

Then there may be specific treatments added to cure or alleviate

| | |
|---|---|
| heart trouble, | rheumatic and arthritic complaints, |
| nerves, | lung ailments |

and many more.

Doctors can be in attendance to give qualified treatment on a large range of disorders, with or without waters. People are encouraged to go for holidays — and many firms, particularly German ones, will send employees there to keep them in good health (though some employers feel that this is too expensive and that they are just paying for pleasant holidays). Pleasantness is and should be a key element;

Table 14.4
*Bavaria's spas and health resorts*

| | resorts providing dry-diet treatment | medicinal spring (mud-bath) treatment centre | climatic health resort | Kneipp (hydropathic) health resort (spa) | moorland spa | mineral (thermal) spa | height above sea-level (metres) | skin diseases (e.g. acne, psoriasis) | diseases of the kidneys and urinary ducts | women's illnesses | eye ailments | respiratory disturbances | conditions of nervous exhaustion/stress symptoms | cardiac and circulatory disorders | rheumatic, articular and vertebral ailments | abdominal, intestinal, hepatic and bilious complaints | metabolic disorders (e.g. diabetes, gout) |
|---|---|---|---|---|---|---|---|---|---|---|---|---|---|---|---|---|---|
| Bad Abbach | | | | | ✗ | ✗ | 356 | | | | | | | | ● | ● | |
| Bad Adelholzen | | ✗ | | | | | 657 | | | | ● | | | | ● | | ● |
| Bad Aibling | | | | | ✗ | | 498 | | ● | ● | | | | | ● | | |
| Bad Alexandersbad | ● | | | | ✗ | ✗ | 590 | | | | | | | ● | ● | ● | |
| Bayersolen | | ✗ | | | | | 800 | | | ● | | | | | ● | | |
| Bayrischzell | | | ✗ | | | | 802 | ● | | | | | ● | ● | ● | ● | ● |
| Berchtesgadener Land | | | ✗ | | | | 480-1170 | ● | | | | | ● | ● | ● | ● | ● |
| Bad Berneck | | | | ✗ | | | 400 | | ● | | | | ● | ● | ● | ● | |
| Bad Birnbach | | | | | | ✗ | 350 | | | | | | | | ● | | |
| Bad Bocklet | ● | | | | ✗ | ✗ | 230 | | ● | | | | | ● | ● | ● | |
| Bad Brückenau | | | | | ✗ | ✗ | 300 | | ● | ● | | | | ● | ● | ● | ● |
| Bad Endorf | | | | | ✗ | ✗ | 525 | | ● | | | ● | | | ● | ● | |
| Bad Feilnbach | | | | | ✗ | | 540 | | ● | | | | | ● | | ● | |
| Füssen-Bad Faulenbach-Hopfen | ● | | | ✗ | ✗ | ✗ | 800 | | ● | | | | ● | ● | ● | ● | |
| Bad Füssing | | | | | | ✗ | 324 | | ● | | | | | | ● | | |
| Garmisch-Partenkirchen | | | ✗ | | | | 710 | ● | | | | | ● | ● | ● | | |
| Bad Gögging | | | | | ✗ | ✗ | 350 | ● | ● | | | | | ● | ● | | |
| Bad Griesbach | | | | | | ✗ | 525 | | ● | | | | | | ● | | ● |
| Grönenbach | | | ✗ | | | | 680 | | ● | | | ● | ● | ● | ● | ● | ● |
| Bad Heilbrunn | | | | | | ✗ | 680 | | ● | | ● | ● | ● | ● | ● | | |
| Hindelang - Bad Oberdorft | ● | ✗ | ✗ | ✗ | | | 850 | | ● | | | | ● | ● | ● | ● | ● |
| Keilberg | | ✗ | | | | | 450 | | | | | | ● | ● | ● | ● | ● |
| Bad Kissingen | | | | | ✗ | ✗ | 201 | | ● | | | | ● | ● | ● | ● | ● |
| Bad Konigshofen | | | | | | ✗ | 277 | | ● | | ● | | | | ● | | ● |
| Bad Kohlgrub | | | | | ✗ | | 900 | | ● | | | | ● | | ● | | |
| Kreuth | | | ✗ | | | | 800 | | | | | | ● | ● | ● | ● | ● |
| Krumbad | | ✗ | | | | | 550 | | | | | | ● | ● | ● | ● | |
| Murnau (Ludwigsbad) | | ✗ | | | | | 700 | ● | ● | ● | | | ● | | ● | ● | |
| Bad Neustadt/Saale | | | | | ✗ | ✗ | 234 | | ● | | | | ● | ● | ● | | ● |
| Oberstaufen | ● | | ✗ | ✗ | | | 800 | ● | ● | | | ● | ● | ● | ● | ● | |
| Oberstdorf | ● | | ✗ | ✗ | | | 843 | | ● | | | | ● | ● | ● | ● | |
| Ottobeuren | | | ✗ | | | | 660-800 | | ● | | | | ● | ● | ● | ● | |
| Oy-Mittelberg | | | ✗ | | | | 960 | | ● | | | | ● | ● | ● | ● | |
| Prien am Chiemsee | | | ✗ | | | | 518-620 | | ● | | | | ● | ● | ● | ● | ● |
| Bad Reichenhall | ● | | | | ✗ | ✗ | 470-1613 | ● | ● | | | ● | ● | ● | ● | | |
| Rodach | | ✗ | | | | | 300-404 | | | | | | | | ● | | |
| Rottach-Egern | | | ✗ | | | | 746 | | | | | | ● | ● | | | |
| Scheidegg | ● | | ✗ | ✗ | | | 800 | | ● | | | ● | ● | ● | ● | ● | ● |
| Schwangau | | | ✗ | | | | 800 | | | | | | ● | ● | ● | ● | |
| Bad Steben | | | | | ✗ | ✗ | 600 | | ● | | | | ● | ● | ● | ● | |
| Tegernsee | | | ✗ | | | | 732 | | ● | | | ● | ● | ● | ● | ● | |
| Bad Tölz | | | ✗ | | | ✗ | 670 | | ● | | | ● | ● | ● | ● | | |
| Weiler-Simmerberg | ● | ✗ | | | | | 630-900 | | | | | | ● | ● | ● | ● | ● |
| Bad Wiessee | | | | | | ✗ | 735 | ● | | | | ● | ● | | ● | | |
| Bad Windsheim | | | | | | ✗ | 314 | | ● | | | | ● | ● | ● | ● | ● |
| Bad Wörishofen | | | | ✗ | | | 630 | | ● | ● | | ● | ● | ● | ● | ● | ● |

(From *Landes fremden verkehrs-verband. Bayern e.V.* (no date))

it helps the sick anyway. It was largely for its lack that the British spas died. To take the Cure is part of Continental life and persists because it benefits (if it was just the hotel which was beneficial, only the hotel would come to be provided). With all these extra skills and variations in surroundings, the choice of which bath to visit is determined by the patient's need of treatment as well as by the waters themselves

—but still, though a general 'pick-me-up' cure exists in most places, different spas have their different specialities.

The waters still, as always, differ in their composition. How much has been lost when they are amalgamated, blandly, at the waterworks and in the tap!

Britain has a few health farms, mainly advertised for weight loss and beauty care. The difference between that and taking the Cure at a Watering-Place is great. The former are likely to be using water not from an ancient Baths but from the tap. (also to have a controlling 'You are here to do what we say and get healthy' attitude.) Spa principles are not the main medical practices there, though hydrotherapy can be included.

Damp cloths for inflammation are ancient and effective and work perfectly well with tapwater. For other ills, there are also similar hydropathic treatments. Water treatments are likewise used for animals (e.g., standing horses in running water for laminitis: Y. Bower, personal communication).

A recent advertisement read: 'Despite the progress achieved in today's medical science, the bathing cure, a many thousand year old therapy, has lost none of its significance.... The cure in its various applications affords the physiological stimuli that are necessary to stir up the curative power within the body.' Those in charge of healing wells down the ages would surely agree, within their own terminology. It would be interesting to compare statistically cures from spas and from (ordinary) doctors for the same type of complaint!

Bottled drinking-water is the last aspect to be considered here. The French, with their tradition of spa cures, have drunk bottled waters, such as Vichy, for a long time (even though much of the virtue, according to some writers, is lost by the bottling). Although originally spread for medical reasons, the waters could be equally drunk for their pleasant taste and — as relevant — sparkle. In Britain, by about 1900, without the indigenous spa tradition and with well-acclaimed, clean tapwater, bottled water did not 'catch on' except as, e.g., tonic water or soda water to mix with cocktails. Special waters are, of course, famous for producing the best taste in certain drinks, e.g., Highland Scotland for whisky, Ireland for Guinness.

In the past two decades, the position has changed dramatically. Nitrates, pesticide residues and other micro-organics are appearing in mains water over much of Europe, and gastric bugs are still not eliminated from Mediterranean coasts, whither enormous numbers of tourists now go. To satisfy this distrust of tapwater (a distrust repeatedly denied by Governments), bottled water has in the past decade or so become a standard item in any grocer's shop from Britain to Malta, not just in places of recent spa tradition. The waters come from famous springs, such as Vichy, Evian, Malvern, Spa itself, from the less famous (e.g., the Chiltern hills) and from places never before heard of, like Highland Spring and Bahrija: anywhere spring-water can be got which can be guaranteed (or hoped!) free of extra nitrates and organic poisons, etc.

The important words are 'free of'. The waters are not being drunk for their divine properties, or for their healing ones. They are being drunk as being free from harm, a very negative — though necessary — virtue.

Perhaps more people than ever before believe in the virtues of spring waters, but rate that virtue lower than ever before.

# 15

# Conclusions

The power of man has grown in every sphere except over himself. (Churchill)

It is time the human ecology of rivers, a fascinating record of human ingenuity and endeavour, was rediscovered, and re-appreciated. Indeed, if it is not to be lost under redevelopment, its rightful importance must be recognised, and quickly. This is no plea for museum status for each and every river in the land. It is a plea for the understanding, appreciation and appropriate conservation of the rich heritage of rivers.

Over these pages it has been shown how man's dependence on the river has changed, so that it is no longer immediate, but distanced. Instead of water being drunk from the spring or stream, it is drunk from a tap leading from supplies from far away — and maybe from many different supplies at that. The tap is not thought of as being part of the river.

Instead of supplying fish and fowl for the table, the river's main role in food is to drain crop land: again how many think of this as the work of the river? The river is used less for passenger transport — except for the innumerable leisure craft. But then leisure is not considered to be in the mainstream of life. Millwheels rarely turn for water power: the fact that more water than ever before is used in power generation, is known to but few.

There is a gap, a distance, between man and the use of the river, so that the river has been set aside, indeed vandalised, in the name of progress. Compare the rivers in Fig. 15.1! Few notice, and fewer complain, about the bad — they are just an ordinary part of background. What else can be expected? The river is in the foreground only to special-interest groups — odd bods like anglers, canoeists, academics and children.

The river is relegated to history — but without the benefit that that has brought to, say, castles. Rivers can be destroyed without public protest — but the public outcry over destroying a castle would be overwhelming. Parker (1975) describes a thousand years of the Village Stream, ending when it was piped underground in the 1960s. This loss should be stopped! The distancing of man and the river has led to lack of knowledge and so of appreciation. No castle would have been wantonly pulled down in the 1960s!

Rivers show how man lived, worked and thought in the past. Much of our present is rooted in that past and only by understanding it, is the present understood. The river adds another dimension. Here boats arrived with coal and malt, there lay the holy well which helped sore eyes, the supply channel, the fishponds, the flood-protection works, the mill — in whose field the present industrialists still go daily to work. The riverside is not static, but whereas gradual changes, from path to lane, or from mill to factory unit, maintain the ancient pattern, wholesale change destroys that which can never come again.

The river is endangered. It is no longer a symbol of purity, but of pollution — 'Put your boots on before you paddle; dear, don't touch the water.' This could and should be stopped. Creative thinking and work (and the willingness to pay taxes to support these) could restore the rivers to chemical health. The river is no longer in good physical shape. Look at Fig. 15.1! Certainly there are places where constriction and lining are needed: man's welfare comes first, but his greed and idleness should not come even second, and much of the river length could easily be in adequate physical shape for the river's health, and in good shape for man's purposes. Good chemical and physical health lead to good plant and animal life.

Conservation of nature and of man's history is the aim for rivers. If this book can do something towards that, its aim will have been achieved.

Fig. 15.. 'Good' and 'bad' rivers, in country, village and city.

The river full of life, plenty of different plants and animals, trees by the waterside, gentle banks form a good habitat. *(P. A. Wolseley in Haslam 1990).*

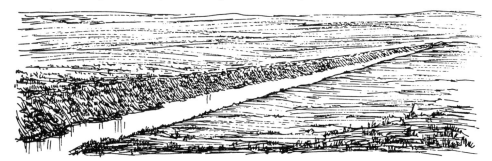

Monoculture around, no trees, straight trapezoid channel: poor habitat, even if clean.

Fig. 15.1 contd.

A good village. Beauty of river and river structures enhancing qualify of (human) life. Quite good habitats.

A bad village. Horrendous 'improvements', but hardly to the quality of life. Rank vegetation around, bad habitat within. Note concrete bed.

Fig. 15.1 contd.

A good town. Lovely buildings fronting on river. Trees and parkland on near bank. Fair river habitat in urban setting.

A bad town. No use made of river — it is an unwanted river, polluted. A bad habitat with poor life.

# Appendix

*Pollution Assessment by Macrophytes (larger plants)*

(For method in full, see Haslam & Wolseley, 1981 (semi-popular), and Haslam et al., 1987 (academic).)

1. Learn identification at nearby streams, using any book with good pictures of vegetative parts, or Haslam *et al.* (1982). (Wade and use grapnel or weighted hook on rope.) Table 1 (see below) provides a summary.
2. Look up the undamaged reference-vegetation for the site in Table 2 (see below). For accuracy, refer to Haslam & Wolseley (1981) (Britain); Haslam (1987) (West Europe); or, better, survey to obtain the current reference vegetation for the locality. (If books are out of print, the writer can probably send photocopies on request.)
3. Survey when the vegetation is fully grown (in central latitudes from mid-June to mid-September) and without storm flow or, for deep water, other temporary causes of poor visibility.
4. Select sites where (mostly) the whole cross-section is visible (bridges, vantage points, both banks).
5. Record stream width, depth, clarity (approximate), flow (slow, moderate, fast, rapid), substrate (which one is prominent: mud plus silt, sand, gravel, stone, rock).
6. For the stream bank, record height above water level, slope (approximate), habit and type of vegetation (grazed grass, shading, trees, etc.).
7. Record (obvious) management and damage factors.
8. Record cover to the nearest 10% in water up to 1m deep (or, if none, that in bands at sides).
9. Record species partly or wholly in water. (In turbid water, check with, for example, grapnel until experience shows which habitats tend to have non-visible species. Enter shallow streams to check on small and doubtful species until experience shows where this is necessary.) Record frequency. Convert to two-point scale (much, little) for analyses. N.b., safety advice is omitted: see Haslam *et al.* (1987).
10. Determine rock type either by observation or, for Britain, using the 1:250 000 Geological Survey or Haslam & Wolseley (1981); for other countries, use relevant maps (Haslam, 1987, gives small-scale maps for Western Europe).
11. Using data from procedures 2, 9 and 10, determine the damage rating from Table 3 (see below). Using data from procedures 6 and 7, and any other available, convert to Pollution Index (see Tables 3-7).

N.b., Reference-vegetation fluctuates with weather and other medium-type habitat variables. It should be re-established by surveys every few years. Reference-vegetation is the best available under the most nearly ancient management (subject, of course, to this being up to the standards of Table 2).

Width and depth are usually correlated for any one stream type, and width, being less variable, is preferable for general use. Vegetation is governed more by depth, and when depth is abnormal for width, the site should be classed according to depth.

For general assessment of a river on one rock type and on typical topography, beginners should record, for a river that is, e.g., 30 kilometres long, 20 separate sites spread over main river and tributaries, that is two-thirds of the number of kilometres of the main stream. With experience, fewer are needed to classify stream type. More are always needed in special circumstances, such as estimating recovery from pollution, studying the effect of changes in rock type, assessing much physical damage. Beginners should never interpret from a single site.

**To those who find this method too fearsome, a rough guide can be given. Be able to identify Potamogeton pectinatus and Blanket weed (Fig. 11.4). Note a common site diversity of streams of size ii (Fig. 1) is 6; of size iii, 7; and of size iv, 8. Count the species present. If there are at least this number, the cover in water up to 1m deep is at least 60% and if neither P. pectinatus nor Blanket weed are prominent, there is not much wrong (probably *a* or *b*, perhaps *c*, rarely *d*). The lower the diversity and cover, excluding P. pectinatus, Blanket weed, and the more the pollution-favoured species, the worse the rating — except, of course, that no vegetation is the worst of all. (Remember that water force reduces vegetation in the hills!) It is important to remember that damage does not necessarily mean pollution. The sewage works must not be blamed for vegetation harmed by boats!**

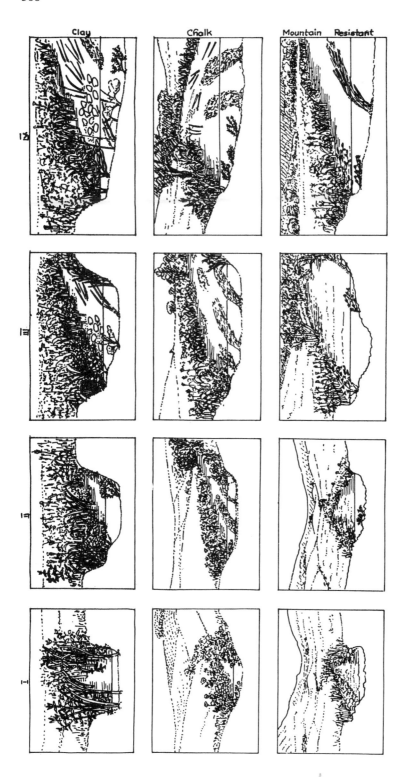

Appendix Fig. 1 River variation with stream size and rock type. Note the differences in channel outline, bank, water depth and flow, and in the vegetation type, diversity and cover. Size i, up to 3m wide, no water-supported species. Size ii, up to 3m wide, at least one water-supported species. Size iii, 4-8m wide. Size iv, 10+m wide (here mostly 10-25m) (P.-A. Wolseley in Haslam, 1987).

## Table 1  A key to the commoner species of rivers (From Haslam et al., 1982)

The further a European country is from lowland Britain (latitude being more important than distance), the more likely it is that other species will also be common.

Specimens should be carefully compared with good illustrations as rare species may be locally abundant.

1. Leaves (or leaf-like shoots) simple, over 4mm
   wide, strap-like, grass-like or cylindrical          2
   Not as above                                        17

2. Mainly emergent                                      3

   Mainly in or on water                                9

3. Plant dark green, cylindrical  *Scirpus lacustris*
   Plant with flat leaves                               4

4. Stem bearing grass-like leaves
   well above water level                               5

   Leaves arising from base
   of plant, usually under water                        7

5. Leaves parallel sided,
   bright or yellowish green  *Glyceria maxima*

   Leaves wider in centre, tapering,
   bluish-green                                         6

6. Hairs present where leaf blade
   joins the sheath          *Phragmites communis*

   A membranous ligule     *Phalaris arundinacea*
   present where the leaf
   blade joins the sheath

7. Leaves almost triangular
   in cross section         *Sparganium erectum*

   Leaves flat or
   V-shaped in section                                  8

8. Leaves iris-like, V-shaped     *Iris pseudacorus*
   below

   Leaves flat throughout,
   not V-shaped (leaves less
   than 7mm wide,
   *T. Angustifolia*:
   leaves over 7mm
   wide, *T. latifolia*)                        *Typha*

9. Leaves grass-like                                   10

   Leaves strap-like                                   15

10. Tall erect reed-like plant with wide leaves
    (often more than 10mm wide)                        11
    Stems trailing in water, often with short,
    erect branch-shoots, not reed-like; leaves
    usually less than 10mm wide, somewhat
    blue-green                                         13

11. Ligule (at base of blade, on
    upper surface) a dense
    eyelash-like fringe of hairs,
    leaves bluish-green     *Phragmites communis*
    Ligule membranous, conspicuous                     12

12. Leaves flat, tapering above,
    blue-green; leaf sheaths
    without keel; ligule over
    6mm long               *Phalaris arundinacea*

    Leaves channelled,
    parallel-sided for much of
    their length, bright green;
    leaf sheaths keeled on the
    back; ligule less than
    6mm long                     *Glyceria maxima*

13. Youngest leaf rolled
    in shoot, which is
    thus cylindrical          *Agrostis stolonifera*

    Youngest leaf folded
    in shoot, which is thus
    laterally compressed                               14

14. Leaf blades tapering for much
    of length, up to 8mm wide
    (submerged leaves
    (may be parallel-sided)     *Catabrosa aquatica*

    Leaf blades parallel-sided
    nearly to tip usually
    above 5 mm wide            *Glyceria fluitans*

15. Leaves long-tapering, bending in current from
    junction of blade and sheath  *Scirpus lacustris*

    Leaves parallel-sided almost to the tip, bending
    in current from the base                           16

16. Leaves usually over 1cm wide, separated; veins at the leaf-tip few, well separated   *Sagittaria sagittifolia*

Leaves usually under 1cm wide, grouped into shoots; veins at the leaf-tip many, crowded   *Sparganium emersum*

17. Plant 2-3mm wide, floating   *Lemna minor*

Plant composed of stems and leaves, rooted   13

18. Plant submerged and leaves thread-like   19
Leaves not submerged, or leaves not thread-like   23

19. Leaves opposite   15

or alternate

Leaves whorled   22

20. Leaves finely divided   *Ranunculus* spp (*Batrachian*)

Leaves entire   16

21. Leaves usually opposite   *Zannichellia palustris*

Leaves alternate   *Potamogeton pectinatus*

22. Leaves pinnately divided   *Myrophyllum spicatum*

Leaves forked   *Ceratophyllum demersum*

23. Leaves over 12cm long and wide, submerged or floating   *Nuphar lutea*

Not as above   24

24. Leaves divided into leaflets   25

Leaves simple   28

25. Leaves over 20cm long, much-divided segments, not ovate   *Oenanthe fluviatilis*

Leaves less than 20cm long, once pinnate; segments ovate   26

26. Terminal leaflet larger than the lateral ones   *Rorippa nasturtium-aquaticum* agg.

Terminal leaflet not larger than the lateral ones   27

27. When the leaf is held up to the light, a dark line (septum) is visible across the stalk, below the lowest pair of leaflets   *Berula erecta*

No septum is visible below the lowest pair of leaflets   *Apium nodiflorum*

28. Leaves in whorls of three   *Elodea canadensis*

Leaves alternate or opposite   29

29. Leaves opposite, pale green; floating leaves (if present) less than 2cm long; submerged leaves notched at the tip   *Callitriche*  30

Leaves alternate; floating leaves (if present) longer than 2cm, submerged leaves not as above   34

## *Callitriche simple identification*
(Keying out more specimens as *C. platycarpa* than belong to this species)

30. Leaves translucent   *C. hermaphroditica*
(Living) leaves not translucent, though sometimes pale and thin   31

31. At least some of the
    parallel-sided
    lower leaves with a
    spanner-like
    tip. Usually in acid water        *C. hamulata*

    Lower leaves with a notched,
    but not spanner-like, tip                        32

32. Floating leaves with leaf
    outline angular, leaves ribbed
    above, often blue-green; lower
    leaves often parallel-sided        *C. obtusangula*

    Floating leaves with rounded
    outline; leaves smooth above,
    usually mid-green                                 33

33. Floating broad leaves nearly      *C. stagnalis*
    circular, smooth above
    Lower leaves broad or long
    and narrow, widest towards
    tip, seldom parallel-sided;
    shoots sometimes bronzed;
    common

    Floating broad leaves narrower.
    Lower leaves usually
    parallel-sided, widest in
    mid-leaf; infrequent               *C. platycarpa*

34. Leaves less than 1.5cm long,
    translucent                        Various mosses
    Leaves more than 1.5cm long                      35

35. Ovate, floating leaves present                   36

    Only submerged leaves present, sometimes at
    surface of water, but never ovate                38

38. Floating leaves with pinnate
    side veins

                                       *Polygonum amphibium*

Floating leaves
with sub-parallel
veins                                                28

37. Submerged leaves linear,
    opaque; widespread

                                       *Potamogeton natans*

    Submerged leaves ovate,
    translucent                                      38

    (*P. x sparganifolius* is abundant in some
    Scottish rivers; it has submerged leaves,
    narrow, strap-shaped and translucent)

38. Leaves more or less oblong;
    margins with small teeth;
    leaves often curly (crisped)

                                       *Potamogeton crispus*
    Leaves ovate, margins entire,
    sometimes wavy but not curled                    39

39. Leaf base
    clasping stem

                                       *Potamogeton*
                                       *perfoliatus*

    Leaf base not clasping stem                      40

40. Leaves (when free
    of mud) pale
    shining green,
    tapering at base;
    mainly southern          *Potamogeton lucens*

    Leaves dark green,
    less tapering;
    mainly northern

                                       *Potamogeton alpinus*

## Table 2 Reference for undamaged vegetation: minimum diversities, covers and nutrient-status bands of communities.

(For different countries, see Haslam, 1987.) When two figures are given, these apply to two variants (for example, variable hill steepness; with or without monodominant monocotyledons). D, diversity; C, percentage cover. NSB, nutrient status band. Stream sizes ii, iii and iv, as in Fig.1. Nutrient status bands from low to high: Br, Brown; Or, Orange; Y, Yellow; B, Blue; P, Purple; R, Red.

| | | stream sizes | | | | | | | | |
|---|---|---|---|---|---|---|---|---|---|---|
| | | ii | | | iii | | | iv | | |
| **rock type** | **landscape** | **D** | **C** | **NSB** | **D** | **C** | **NSB** | **D** | **C** | **NSB** |
| limestone | lowland | 6 | 50,80 | B | 6,8 | 80 | BP | 9 | 80 | BP,P |
| limestone | upland | 3,5 | 40,80 | Or(B) | 4 | 50(20) | B(P) | 5 | 40 | B,BP |
| limestone | mountain and alpine | 0 | | YB | 0 | | YBP | 0,1 | | Y(BP) |
| clay | lowland | 2,6 | 20,40 | BP | 8 | 60 | P,P(R) | 9 | 60 | PR,R |
| clay | upland | 4 | 20 | B,BP | 6 | 20 | B,BP | | | |
| clay | hill | 0 | | | 0 | | | | | |
| sandstone | lowland | 6 | 50 | B(BP) | 7 | 60 | BP | | | |
| sandstone (New Forest) | lowland | 1,4 | 10,50 | Or,B | 5,7 | 60 | B,P | | | |
| sandstone | upland | 4(3) | 40(20) | B | 4 | 40(20) | B,BP | 5(7) | 25(20) | BP,P |
| sandstone | mountain | 0 | | YB | 0,2 | | YB | 0,5 | 0,20 | B,BP |
| sandstone | alpine | 0 | | Y,B | 0 | | Y,B | | | |
| resistant | lowland bog | 4 | 40 | Br(BrOr) | 5 | 5 | Br,BrOr | 6 | 1 | Or |
| resistant | lowland moor | 5 | 40 | Or,Y | 7 | 40 | Y(Or,Br) | 4 | 5 | OrY |
| resistant | lowland farmland | 2,5 | 5,40 | Y,B | 4,7 | 10,20 | B,BP | 4,8 | 5,30 | BP |
| resistant | upland | 3 | 20 | B(Y) | 2 | 10 | B, etc. | 1 | 5 | B etc. |
| resistant | mountain | 1 | 1 | YB | 1,3 | 1,25 | Y,B(BP) | 0,4 | 0,25 | YBP |
| resistant | alpine | 0 | | Y | 0 | | OrY | 0 | | Y |
| alluvium (streams) | plain | 6 | 80 | BP | 7 | 80 | P,PR | 3,9 | 80 | PR,R |
| alluvium (dykes) | plain | 6 | 100 | BP | 8,9 | 100 | P,PR | 3,9 | 100 | PR |

## Table 3 Calculation of stream damage rating for British streams

1.  Species diversity allowance*
    number of species present**      0      1-2    3-4    5-6    7-8    9+
    assign figure of:                5      4      3      2      1      0

2.  Decrease in diversity: difference between expected and actual number of species=

3.  Percentage decrease in percentage vegetation cover
    % loss in cover in water up to 1m deep=†      100   80-95 60-75 40-55 20-35 0-15
    assign figure of:                             5     4     3     2     1     0

4.  Change in colour band (Tables 2 and 4 list habitats; Table 5 lists species)
    change      over one band        one, or change      half    dubious      no change
                to uncertain or
                nil
    assign figure of:    4           3                    2       1            0

5.  Percentage of pollution-tolerant species. Add score of 1 for each tolerant species (and 1 if one or more land species are rooted in streams of sizes iii and iv), a half for each semi-tolerant species (Table 6).
    % tolerant spp.    nil spp.      100   75-95 50-70 30-45 15-25 0-10
    assign figure of:  5             5     4     3     2     1     0
    Assign 4 if only sensitive spp. are present but the number present is not over one-sixth of those expected, and 3 if one-quarter of those expected are present.

6. Weighting for special species
   much *Potamogeton pectinatus*    sparse *P. pectinatus*   the only sp.   much Blanket weed
   assign figure of: 4 (2 if intermediate)       1              2

7. Britain only. Weighting for clay, etc., in lower reaches and lowlands

   clay, size iv }                      clay, size iii, slower
   clay (mix), size iv } subtract 2     flatter sandstone, size iii-iv } subtract 1
                                        clay-mix, size iv, and size iii if flat }

   Add the numbers for criteria 1-7. The damage rating is then:

   | total | damage rating |
   |-------|---------------|
   | 0-4   | a |
   | 5-7   | b |
   | 8-10  | c |
   | 11-13 | d |
   | 14-16 | e |
   | 17-18 | f |
   | 19-21 | g |
   | 22+   | h (*g* if channel has over 15% cover) |

   *   Use aggregates for *Ranunculus* spp., *Callitriche platycarpa / obtusangula / platycarpa* and mosses.
   **  Mosses restricted to man-made structures (Bridge piers, concrete slopes, etc.) should be disregarded.
   †   A negative number is recorded as 0.
   ††  Or in bands the side if the water is all deep or turbid.

Convert to Pollution Index of *A-H* if no physical damage present. If physical damage eliminates vegetation, irrespective of pollution, the site is unclassable, *U*. If physical damage is mild, a rating of *d* will have an index of *C*, *B*, or *A*, i.e. *C+*. Sites with an *a* rating but with yellow or flaccid species (below) are *B*.

   Yellow leaves: *Agrostis stolonifera, Apium nodiflorum, Callitriche* spp., *Catabrosa aquatica, Glyceria maxima, G.* spp., short-leaved, *Myosotis scorpioides, Phalaris arundinacea.*

   Flaccid or over-lush species: *Agrostis stolonifera, Apium nodiflorum, Glyceria maxima, Gspp.,* short-leaved, *Phalaris arundinacea, Potamogeton crispus, Sparganium erectum.*

---

**Table 4** Macrophyte species in approximate nutrient status order (and order of presentation, on river maps).

The contractions used on the maps are listed in the order in which they are placed on the site lists on the river maps. This is roughly in nutrient-status order. The order is roughly the same for each country, but no country is exactly like any other. Therefore, for easy comparison in these maps, the order given here resembles that of each country but is not exactly the same as any. Additionally, species may behave differently in unusual habitats within a country. (See Haslam, 1987, for detail and evidence.) Other species on the maps are unbanded - not precisely associated with a nutrient status band.

**(Brown)**

| | |
|---|---|
| Sphag | *Sphagnum* spp. |
| Dros | *Drosera* spp. |
| Erioph | *Eriophorum angustifolium* |
| Litt | *Littorella uniflora* |
| Meny | *Menyanthes trifoliata* |
| Pot. poly | *Potamogeton polygonifolius* |
| Car. ros | *Carex rostrata* |
| Ran. (flamm) | *Ranunculus flammula* |

**(Orange)**

| | |
|---|---|
| Ran. hed | *Ranunculus hederaceus* |
| Ran. omi | *Ranunculus omiophyllus* |
| Myr. alt | *Myriophyllum alterniflorum* |
| Call. ham | *Callitriche hamulata* |
| J. art | *Juncus articulatus* |
| El. ac | *Eleocharis acicularis* |
| Sc. fl | *Eleogiton (Scirpus) fluitans* |
| J. bulb | *Juncus bulbosus* |
| G. fluit | *Glyceria fluitans* (long leaves) |

**(Yellow)**

| | |
|---|---|
| Pot. alp | *Potamogeton alpinus* |
| Phal | *Phalaris arundinacea* (hills and nutrient-poor areas) |
| Moss | Mosses (hills only) |
| Bl. wd | Blanket weed (sparse in hills only) |
| Oen. cr | *Oenanthe crocata* |
| Caltha | *Caltha palustris* |
| Pet | *Petasites hybridus* |

**(Blue)**

| | |
|---|---|
| Mim | *Mimulus guttatus* |
| L. tri | *Lemna trisulca* |
| Cerat. s | *Ceratophyllum submersum* |
| Ver. b | *Veronica beccabunga* |
| Ber | *Berula erecta* |
| Bid | *Bidens cernua* |
| Call | *Callitriche* spp. other than *C. hamulata* |
| Moss | Mosses (lowlands) |
| Ment | *Mentha aquatica* |
| Ran | *Ranunculus* spp. (Batrachian) |
| Hydroch | *Hydrocharis morsus-ranae* |
| Iris | *Iris pseudacorus* |
| Ror. n (Ror) | *Rorippa nasturtium-aquaticum* (*Nasturtium officinale*) agg. |
| Sol | *Solanum dulcamara* |
| Ap | *Apium nodiflorum* |
| Myos | *Myosotis scorpioides* |
| Pot. nat | *Potamogeton natans* |
| Ver. a | *Veronica anagallis-aquatica* agg. |
| Sp. er | *Sparganium erectum* |

**(Purple)**

| | |
|---|---|
| Elod | *Elodea canadensis* agg. |
| Pol. hydr, Pol. | *Polygonum hydropiper* agg. |
| pers | |
| C. acut | *Carex acutiformis* agg. |
| T. ang | *Typha angustifolia* |
| T. lat | *Typha latifolia* |

| | |
|---|---|
| Phrag | *Phragmites communis* |
| Pot. perf | *Potamogeton perfoliatus* |
| Polyg. a | *Polygonum amphibium* |
| Bl. wd | Blanket weed (except as above) |
| Groenl | *Groenlandia densa* |
| Zann | *Zannichellia palustris* |
| Oen. fl | *Oenanthe fluviatilis* |
| G. max | *Glyceria maxima* |
| Alis. p | *Alisma plantago-aquatica* |
| Pot. luc | *Potamogeton lucens* |
| M. spic. | *Myriophyllum spicatum* |
| Pot. cris | *Potamogeton crispus* |
| Phal | *Phalaris arundinacea* |
| Ac | *Acorus calamus* |

**(Red)**

| | |
|---|---|
| Epil | *Epilobium hirsutum* |
| But | *Butomus umbellatus* |
| Cerat | *Ceratophyllum demersum* |
| Sp. em | *Sparganium emersum* |
| Enter | *Enteromorpha* sp. |
| Sag | *Sagittaria sagittifolia* |
| Pot. nod | *Potamogeton nodosus* |
| Pot. pect | *Potamogeton pectinatus* |
| Rum | *Rumex hydrolapathum* |
| Ror. a | *Rorippa amphibia* |
| S. lac | *Scirpus lacustris* |
| Nuph | *Nuphar lutea* |

## Table 5 Pollution-tolerant species of rivers of different countries

(For different countries see Haslam, 1987.)

**Tolerant:** *Potamogeton crispus, P. pectinatus, Scirpus lacustris, Sparganium emersum, Sp. erectum, Enteromorpha* sp., Blanket weed (*Apium nodiflorum,* small clay lowland, *Mimulus guttatus,* some small hilly).

**Semi-tolerant:** *Agrostis stolonifera,* small *Glyceria* spp. (short leaves), *Butomus umbellatus, Glyceria maxima, Lemna minor* agg., *Nuphar lutea, Rorippa amphibia,* (*Phalaris arundinacea* hilly).

## Table 6 The effects of different types of damage on the components of the stream Damage Rating

The typical, not the sole type of response is shown. Symbols: ++ strong effect; + mild effect; ? doubtful effect; - negligible effect.

| type of damage | diversity | cover | NSB[a] | % tolerant spp.[a] | Blanket weed | *Potamogeton pectinatus* | notes |
|---|---|---|---|---|---|---|---|
| dredging | ++ | ++ | ? | ? | ++ | - | |
| cutting | + | ++ | ? | ? | + | - | |
| shade | + | ++ | - | - | - | - | |
| herbicides, on emergents | - | + | ? | - | ? | - | |
| herbicides, on channel | ++ | ++ | ++ | ++ | ++ | - | |
| boats | + | ++ | ? | ++ | - | + | Delicate spp. lost first |
| disturbance | + | ++ | - | + | ? | - | Channel spp. lost first |
| drought | + | + | + | + | ++ | - | Submergents lost first. Land |
| storm flow, etc. | + | ++ | ? | - | ? | - | spp. scored in % tolerant |
| eutrophication | - | - | ++ | ? | ? | - | |
| turbidity | + | + | - | + | - | - | |
| salt | ++ | + | - | - | ? | ++ | Submergents lost first |
| town effluent | ++ | ++ | ? | ++ | ++ | ++ | |

a These criteria have provisions for scoring even if all vegetation is lost (see Table 3). Such scores are not included in this table.

# Bibliography

This bibliography is short, because it does not list the hundreds of pictures (illuminations, woodcuts, paintings, old photographs) studied as reference material. Many sources have been examined, including:

London        National Gallery
              Tate Gallery
              Victoria and Albert Museum

Cambridge     Fitzwilliam Museum
              Public Library
              University Library
              Libraries of various Colleges (particularly Kings, St Catharine's and Trinity)

Norwich       Norfolk and Norwich Museum

Cathedral museums, various

Malta         Museum of Fine Arts
              Mdina Museum.

Almestrand, A. (1984). 'Rönneå'. In *Ecology of European Rivers*, ed. B.A. Whitton. Blackwell: Oxford. Pp. 553-76.

*Anglo Saxon Chronicle*, (1954). Everyman, J.M. Dent & Sons: London.

Anon. (1979). *The Fisherman's guide to coarse fishing*. Marshall Cavendish: London.

Archer, F. (1969). *Under the parish lantern*. Coronet, Hodder: London.

Ashley, M. (1973). *General Monck*. Jonathan Cape: London.

Athie, D., & Cerri, C.C. (eds.) (1987). 'The use of macrophytes in water pollution control'. *Water Science and Technology* **19**, 10.

Austen, J. (1811). *Sense and sensibility*. Clarendon Press: Oxford, 1923.

Baldock, D. (1984). *Wetland drainage in Europe*. Institute for European Environmental Policy. The International Institute for Environment and Development.

Bartlett, N. (1965). *The gold seekers*. Jarrolds: London.

Beaglehole, J.C. (1974). *The life of Captain James Cook*. Adam & Charles Black: London.

Bede (731). *A history of the English Church and people*. Penguin: Middlesex, 1955.

Bennett, G. (1970). 'Bristol floods 1968. Controlled survey of effect on health of local community disaster'. *Brit. Med. Journ.* **3**, 454-8.

Bennett, G. (1972). *Nelson the commander*. B.T. Batsford Ltd: London.

Beresford, M.W., & St Joseph, J.K.S. (1979). 2nd ed. *Medieval England, an aerial survey*. University Press: Cambridge.

Berrie, A.D., & Wright, J.F. (1984). 'The winterbourne stream'. In *Ecology of European Rivers*, ed. B.A.Whitton. Blackwells: Oxford. Pp. 179-206.

Bond, C.J. (1981a). 'The marshlands of Malvern Chase'. In *The evolution of marshland landscapes*. University Department for External Studies: Oxford. Pp. 95-112.

    (1981b). 'Otmoor'. In *The evolution of marshland landscapes*. University Department for External Studies: Oxford. Pp. 113-35.

Boyer, A. (1703-13). *The history of the reign of Queen Anne. Digested into annals*: London.

Boyes, J., & Russell, R. (1977). *The canals of eastern England*. David & Charles: Newton Abbott.

Brewer, E.C. (1881). *A dictionary of phrase and fable*. 12th ed. Cassell: London.

Broads Authority (1985). *Waterside parks and recreation areas*. BADG4.

Brooks, N.P. (1981). 'Romney Marsh in the early middle ages'. In *Evolution of marshland landscapes*. University Department of External Studies: Oxford. Pp. 74-94.

Bryant, A. (1938). *Samuel Pepys: the Saviour of the Navy*. University Press: Cambridge.

Bryant, A. (1971). *The Great Duke*. Collins: London.

Bunyan, J. (1682). *The Pilgrims Progress*. Jarrold: London.

Burton, E. (1967). *The Georgians at home 1714-1830*. Longmans: London.

Cadbury, G.D. (1929). *Canals and inland waterways*. Pitman: London.

Caesar, Gaius Julius. *The conquest of Gaul and Germany*. Penguin: Harmondsworth, Middlesex,1951.

Camden, W. (1789). *Camden's Britannia*, ed. of R. Gough; ed. G.J. Copley, 1977. (Original ed. in Latin 1587; 1st English ed. 1610.)

Cameron, H.S. (1932). 'The viability of *Brucella abortus*'. *Cornell. Vell.* **22**, 212.

*Canal and Riverboat* (Magazine). A.E. Morgan: Epsom.

*Canterbury Psalter*. 12th century.

Chadwick, O. (1884). *Report on the water supply of Malta*. Government Printing Office: Malta.

Chanin, P. (1985). *The natural history of otters*. Croom Helm: London.

Chapman, H.W. (1953). *Mary II. Queen of England*. Jonathan Cape: London.

Charlesworth, Mrs (1956). *Ministering Children*. Sealey, Jackson & Halliday: London.

Chaucer, G. (13th century). *The Canterbury Tales*. Penguin Books: Harmondsworth, Middlesex, 1981.

Chiaudani, C., & Marchetti, Pr. (1984). 'Po'. In *Ecology of European Rivers*. ed. B.A. Whitton. Blackwells: Oxford. Pp. 401-36.

Clarke, J.A. (1854-5). 'On trunk drainage'. *J. Roy. Agric. Soc.* (1st series), **15**, 1-73.

*Coarse Angler*, (Magazine).

Cobbett, W. (1838). *Rural rides*. Penguin: Harmondsworth, Middlesex, 1967.

Coles, J.M., & Orme, B.J. (1980). *Pre-history of the Somerset Levels*. Somerset Levels Project.

Collinson, J. (1791). *The history and antiquities of the county of Somerset*. Crettwell: Bath.

Cory, R.H. (1948-9). 'Memorial of the silent river'. *East Anglia Magazine*, **8**, 518-24.

Council for British Archaeology (1978). *Excavations at Little Waltham*. Research Report 26.

Crawfurd, R. (1911). *The King's Evil*. Clarendon Press: Oxford.

Crisp, D.T. (1989). 'Some impacts of human activity on trout, *Salmo trutta*, populations'. *Freshwat. Biol.*, **21**, 21-34.

Crocker, E.G. (1913). 'The drainage of the River Ouse Basin'. *Proc. Inst. Mech. Eng.*, **13**, 805-29.

Cross, T.P. (undated). *Motif index of early Irish literature*. University Publications, Folklore Series 7: Bloomington, Indiana.

Crossley, D.W. (ed.) (1981). *Medieval Industry*. CBA Research Report 40, Council for British Archaeology.

Crossley, D.W. (1981). 'Medieval iron smelting'. In *Mediaeval Industry*, ed. D.W. Crossley. CBA Research Report 40, Council for British Archaeology. Pp. 29-41.

Cunningham (Archdeacon)(1916). 'The problem as to the changes in the course of the Cam since Roman times'. *Proc. Camb. Antiq. Soc.*, with communications, **8 N.S.**, 74-85.

Darby, H.C. (1968). *The draining of the Fens*. University Press: Cambridge.

(1983). *The changing fenland*. University Press: Cambridge.

de Buitlear, E. (1985). *Irish rivers*. County House: Dublin.

Decamps, H., Capblang, J., & Tonseng, J.N. (1984). 'Lot'. *Ecology of European Rivers*, ed. B.A. Whitton. Blackwells: Oxford. Pp. 207-35.

Defoe, Daniel (1724-7). *A tour through the whole island of Great Britain*. Everyman, J.M. Dent: London,1974.

Descy, J.P., & Empain, A. (1984). 'Meuse'. In *Ecology of European Rivers*, ed. B.A. Whitton. Blackwells: Oxford. Pp. 1-23.

Dickens, C. (1839). *Nicholas Nickleby*. Sherratt: Altrincham, 1948.

(1865). *Our Mutual Friend*. Nelson: London.

Drury, P.J. (1978). *Excavations of Little Waltham*. Chelmsford Excavation Committee and the Council for British Archaeology.

Eden, P. (1972). *Waterways of the Fens*. Privately printed, University Printing House: Cambridge.

Edwards, L.A. (1950). *Inland waterways of Great Britain and Northern Ireland*. Imrey, Laurie: London.

Edwards, P.R. (1981). 'Drainage operations in the Weald Moors'. In *Evolution of Marshland Landscapes*. University Department for External Studies: Oxford. Pp. 130-43.

Edwards, R.W., & Brooks, M. (1984). 'Wye'. In *Ecology of European Rivers*. ed. B.A. Whitton. Blackwells: Oxford. Pp. 83-111.

Edwards, R.W., Williams, P.F., & Williams, R. (1984). 'Ebbw'. In *Ecology of European Rivers*, ed. B.A. Whitton. Blackwells: Oxford. Pp. 83-111.

Ekwall, E. (1960). *The concise Oxford dictionary of English place-names*. University Press: Oxford.

Eliot, G. (1860). *The Mill on the Floss*. Chatto & Windus: London, 1951.

Elliott, J.M. (ed.) (1989a). 'Wild Brown Trout: the scientific basis for their conservation and management'. *Freshwat. Biol.*, **21**(1).

Elliott, J.M. (1989b). 'Wild brown trout *Salmo Trutta*: an important national and international resource'. *Freshwat. Biol.*, **21**, 1-6.

*Encyclopedia Britannica 1910-11*. 11th ed. University Press: Cambridge.

Ewing, J.H. (1876). *Jan of the windmill*. Society for Promoting Christian Knowledge: London.

Eyre, F. & Hadfield, E.C.R. (1945) *English rivers and canals*. Collins: London.

Faulkner, A.H. (ed.) (1972). *Fenland barge traffic*. Robert Wilson: Kettering.

Faulkner, A.H. (1977). 'The River Lark'. *The Easterling*, **2**, 4-10.

(1979). 'The Little Ouse'. *The Easterling*, **2**, 5-8.

Ferguson, R.I. (1981). 'Channel forms and channel changes'. In *British Rivers*, ed. J. Lewin. Allen & Unwin: London. Pp. 90-125.

Fowler, G. (1934). 'The extinct waterways of the Fens'. *The Geographical Journal* LXXXIII (**83**), 30-9.

Frazer, J.G. (1890). *The golden bough*. Macmillan: London.

Friedrich, G., & Müller, D. (1984). 'Rhine'. In *Ecology of European Rivers*. ed. B.A. Whitton. Blackwells: Oxford. Pp. 265-315.

Gaskell, E.C. (1848, describing 1839). *Mary Barton*. Smith, Elder: London. 1906.

(1857). *Life of Charlotte Brönte*. Everyman, J.M. Dent: London, 1974.

Gelling, M. (1984). *Place names in the landscape*. Dent: London.

Geoffrey of Monmouth (c. 1136). *The history of the kings of England*. Penguin: Harmondsworth, Middlesex, 1966.

Giles, N. (1989). 'Assessing the status of British wild brown trout, Salmo trutta, a pilot study utilising data from game fisheries'. *Freshwat. Biol.*, **21**, 125-39.

Grant, M. (1972). *Cleopatra*. Weidenfeld & Nicolson: London.

Granville, A.B. (1841). *Spas of England.* . 2nd ed. Adams & Dart: Bath, 1971.

Green, D. (1970). *Queen Anne*. Collins: London.

Greenhaugh, J.G. (1980). 'The present use of the River Cam in relation to its historical perspective'. M.Litt. Thesis, University of Cambridge.

Greever, T.A.P. (1981). 'The archaeological potential of the Devon tin industry'. In *Mediaeval Industry*, ed. D.W. Crossley. CBA Research Report 40, Council for British Archaeology. Pp. 85-95.

Gregory, K.J. (1983). *Background to Palaeohydrology. A perspective*. Wiley: Chichester.

Hadfield, C. (1955). *The canals of Southern England*. Phoenix: London.

(1967). *The canals of South West England*. David & Charles: Newton Abbott.

Hadfield, M., & Hadfield, J. (1961). *The twelve days of Christmas*. Cassell: London.

Haldane, C. (1970). *Madame de Maintenon: uncrowned queen of France*. Constable: London.

Hall, A.R., Kenward, H.K., William, D., & Grieg, J.R.A. (1983). *Environment and living conditions of Anglo-Scandinavian sites*. York Archaeological Trust by Council for British Archaeology.

Hardman, R. (ed.), (1990). *Canoeists guide to the east of England*. British Canoe Union. Sports Council.

Haslam, R.M. (1989). 'Raglan and after'. *Country Life*. London, November.

Haslam, S.M. (1978). *River Plants*. University Press: Cambridge.

(1982). 'A proposed method for monitoring river pollution using macrophytes'. *Envir. Tech. Lett..*, **3**, 19-34.

(1987). *River plants of Western Europe*. University Press: Cambridge.

(1990). *River pollution: an ecological perspective*. Belhaven: London.

Haslam, S.M., Harding, J.P.C., & Spence, D.H.N. (1987). (Authors not listed on title page). *Methods for the use of aquatic macrophytes for assessing water quality 1985-6. Methods for the examination of water and associated materials*. Her Majesty's Stationery Office: London.

Haslam, S.M., Sinker, C.A., & Wolseley, P.A. (1982). *British water plants*. Field Studies Council (repr. with addns).

Haslam, S.M., & Wolseley, P.A. (1981). *River vegetation: its identification, assessment and management*. University Press: Cambridge.

Head, L. (1985). *River fishing*. Crawood: Marlborough.

Heath, S. (1911). *Pilgrim life in the middle ages*. Kennikat Press: London. 1971.

Hellawell, J.M. (1980). *Biological indicators of freshwater pollution and environmental management*. Elsevier: London.

Heise, P. (1984). 'Gudenå'. In *Ecology of European Rivers*, ed. B.A. Whitton. Blackwells: Oxford. Pp. 25-49.

Herold, J.C. (1959). *Mistress to an age: the life of Madame de Stael*. Hamish Hamilton: London.

Heuff, H., & Harkan, K. (1984). 'Caragh'. In *Ecology of European Rivers*, ed. B.A. Whitton. Blackwells: Oxford.

Hills, J.W. (1924). *A summer on the Test*. 2nd ed. Hodder & Stoughton: London, 1941.

Holland, D.C., & Harding, J.P.C. (1984). 'Mersey'. In *Ecology of European Rivers*, ed. B.A. Whitton. Blackwells: Oxford. Pp. 113-44.

Holmes, P. (1974). *That alarming malady*. Cambridge Education Authority: Ely.

Horkan, K. (1984a). 'Shannon'. In *Ecology of European Rivers*, ed. B.A. Whitton. Blackwells: Oxford. Pp. 345-62.

Horkan, K. (1984b). 'Suir'. In *Ecology of European Rivers*, ed. B.A. Whitton. Blackwells: Oxford. Pp. 384-400.

Hoskins, W.G. (1953). *The making of the English landscape*. Penguin: London.

(1973). *English landscapes. How to read the man-made scenery of England*. BBC publication: London.

Howard, D. (1980). *The architectural history of Venice*. Batsford: London.

Hudson, K. (1984). *Industrial history from the air*. University Press: Cambridge.

Humfrey, C. (1829). *A report upon the present state of the River Cam*. W. Metcalf: Cambridge.

Hunt, B. (1982). The ancient history of the valley'. In *The Deverill Valley*, ed. F. Myatt. Deverill Valley History Group. Pp. 21-30.

Hutyra, M.J., Marek, J., & Manninger, R. (1938). *Special pathology of domestic animals*, vol. 2. 4th ed. Baillière, Tindale & Cox: London.

Hynes, H.B.M. (1960). *The biology of polluted waters*. University Press: Liverpool.

Jansen, P. Ph., Bendegom, L. van, Berg, J. van den, Vries, M. & de, Zanen, A. (1979). *Principles of river engineering*. Pitman: London.

Jenyns, L. (1846). *Observation in natural history*. John van Voost: London.

Jones, J.M. (1963). 'Local river as sources of power'. *Proc. Birm'n. Nat. Hist. Phil. Soc.* **20**, 22-36.

Kawecka, B., & Sycesny, B. (1984). 'Dunajec'. In *Ecology of European Rivers*, ed. B.A. Whitton. Blackwells: Oxford. Pp. 499-525.

Kerr, R. (Anon. 1862). *The Nene in Danger*. London.

Kickuth, R. (1976). 'Degradation and incorporation of nutrients from rural waste waters by plant rhizosphere under limnic conditions. In *Utilisation of Manure by land spreading*. Commission of the European Communities. Pp. 335-47.

(1984) Das Wurzelraumverfahren in der Praxis. *Landsch. Stadt*, **16**, 148-59.

Kohler, A., Abt, K., & Zelesny, H. (1989). 'Das grünlandgebiet des württembergischen Allgäu aus der sicht der Landschaftsökologie'. *Informationen für der Landwirtsch-aftsberatung in Baden Württemberg*. Baden: Württemberg, **6**, 49-69.

Kuklik, K. (1984). *Ceské a Moravske Rybriky (Bohemian and Moravian Ponds)*. CTK - Pressgota: Praha.

Lachat, B. (1988). 'Le cours d'eau: conservation, entretien et aménagement'. Unpublished report, Council of Europe: Strasbourg.

Lambrick, G., & Robinson, M. (1979). *Iron Age and Roman riverside settlements at Oxfordshire*. Oxfordshire Archaeology Unit and the Council for British Archaeology. Oxfordshire Archaeological Unit Report 2. CBA Research Report 32.

*Landesfremden verkehrsverband Bayern (Let's go to Bavaria.)* (no date).

Lane Fox, R. (1973). *Alexander the Great*. Omega: London.

Langford, T.E. (1983). *Electricity generation and the ecology of natural waters*. University Press: Liverpool.

Larandien, P., & Décamps, H. (1984). 'Estarag'. In *Ecology of European Rivers*, ed. B.A. Whitton. Blackwells: Oxford. Pp. 237-68.

Lawson, G.J. (1985). *Cultivating reeds ('Phragmites australis') for root zone treatment of sewage*. Institute of Terrestrial Ecology: Grange-over-Sands.

*Laxdaela Saga*, (1245). Penguin: Harmondsworth, Middlesex, 1969.

Leech, R.H. (1981). 'The Somerset Levels in the Romano-British period'. In *Evolution of Marshland Landscapes*. University Department of External Studies: Oxford. Pp. 20-51.

Lewin, J. (ed.), (1981a). *British Rivers*. Allen & Unwin: London.

Lewin, J. (1981b). 'Contemporary erosion and sedimentation'. In *British Rivers*, ed. J. Lewin. Allen & Unwin: London. Pp. 35-58.

Lewis, J. (1983). 'A new look at river management'. *Natural World*, **8**, 10-13.

Limbrey, S. (1983). 'Archaeology and Palaeohydrology'. In *Background to Palaeohydrology*, ed. K. J. Gregory. John Wiley & Sons Ltd: Chichester.

Lovegrove, R., & Snow, P. (1984). *River birds*. Columbus Books: London.

*Mabinogion, The*, (14th Century or earlier). Everyman, J.M. Dent & Sons: London, 1949.

McNight, H. (1975). *The Shell book of inland waterways*. David & Charles: Newton Abbott.

*Magna Carta* (1215).

Malory, T. (c. 1470). *Le Morte d'Arthur*. Everyman, J.M. Dent & Sons: London, 1906.

Mawle, G.W., Winstove, A., & Brooker, M.P. (1986). 'Salmon and sea trout in the Taff, past, present and future'. *Nature in Wales*, NS **4**, 36-45.

Meirion-Jones, G.E. (1975). 'The history of the River Stour 1760-1860'. M.A. Thesis: Canterbury.

Miller, S.H., & Skertahly, S.B.J. (1878). *The Fenland, past and present*. Leach: Wisbech.

Modrow, B. (1989). 'Die Wassenkünste und wasseranlagen im bergpark, Wilhelmshöhe'. *Wasser Abwasser Abfall*, Kassell, **5**, 320-35.

Morrah, P. (1976). *Prince Rupert of the Rhine*. Constable: London.

Morton, H.V. (1934). *In the steps of the Master*. Methuen: London.

(1936). *In the steps of St Paul*. Methuen: London.

(1938). *Through the lands of the Bible*. Methuen: London.

Myatt F. (ed.), (1982). *The Deverill Valley*. Deverill Valley History Group.

Myatt, F. (1982). 'The valley in modern times'. In *The Deverill Valley*, ed. F. Myatt. The Deverill Valley History Group. Pp. 151-8.

Netherlands Central Bureau of Statistics: Environmental Statistics (1987). *Environmental Statistics of The Netherlands*. The Hague, 1987.

Newhold, C., Purseglove, J. & Holmes, N.T.H. (1983). *Nature conservation and river engineering*. Nature Conservancy Council: London.

*Niebelungenlied, The* (c. 1200). Penguin Harmondsworth: Middlesex, 1965.

*Njals Saga* (13th Century). Penguin Harmondsworth: Middlesex, 1960.

Norden, J. (1610). *The Surveiors dialogue, very profitable for all men to peruse*. Montagu: London, 1738.

Norwich, J.J. (1967). *The Normans in the south*. Longmans: London.

*Nuremberg Chronicle* (1493). Schedel, H. Liber cronicarum: Nuremburg.

Pannett, D.J. (1981). 'Fish weirs of the River Severn'.In *Evolution of marshland landscapes*. University Department of External Studies: Oxford. Pp. 144-57.

(1987-8). 'Fish weirs of the River Severn'. *Folk Life*, **26**, 55-69.

Parker, G. (1977). *The Dutch revolt*. Allen Lane: London.

Parker, R. (1975). *The common stream*. Collins: London.

Peddie, J. (1982a). 'Men, women and manors'. In *The Deverill Valley*, ed. F. Myatt . Deverill Valley History Group. Pp. 51-63.

(1982b). 'A new England', *Ibid*. Pp. 131-49.

Pepys, S. (1660-9). *Diary* 1st ed., 1825. Bell & Hyman: London, 1978.

Pinter, I., & Backhaus, D. (1984). 'Neckar'. In *Ecology of European Rivers*, ed. B.A. Whitton. Blackwells: Oxford. Pp. 317-44.

Porter, E. (1969). 'The river trade of old Cambridgeshire'. *Cambs. Hunts. and Peterborough Life*. October 1969. Pp. 24-6.

Potter, T.W. (1981). 'Marshland and drainage in the classical world'. In *Evolution of Marshland Landscapes*. University Department for External Studies: Oxford. Pp. 1-19.

Prat, N.F., Puig, M.A., Gingaley, G., Tost, M.F., & Estrada, M. (1984). 'Llobregat'. In *Ecology of European rivers*, ed. B.A. Whitton. Blackwells: Oxford. Pp. 527-52.

Priestley, J. (1969). *Navigable rivers, canals and railways throughout Great Britain*. David & Charles: Newton Abbott, 1969.

Prothero, F.E., & Clark, W.A. (1896). *A new oarsman's guide to rivers and canals*. Phillips: London.

Rakty, P.A. (1981). 'Medieval Milling'. In *Mediaeval Industry*, ed. D.W. Crossley. CBA Research Report 40, Council for British Archaeology. Pp. 1-15.

Rausmaa, P.L. (1973). *Catalogues of Finnish anecdotes and historical, local and religious legends*. NLF Publications No. 3. Nordic Institute of Folklore: Turku.

Ravensdale, J.R. (1974). *Liable to floods. Village landscape on the edge of the fens. AD 450-1850*. University Press: Cambridge.

Reddy, K.R., & Smith, W.H. (eds.), (1987). *Aquatic plants for water treatment and resource recovery*. Magnolia: Orlando, Florida.

Reid, K.C. (1959). *Water-mills and the landscape*. Society for the Protection of Ancient Buildings. Wind and Water Mill Section. Booklet 6.

Richardson, L. (1921). *Wells and springs of Herefordshire*. Memoirs of the Geological Survey, England. His Majesty's Stationery Office: London.

(1931). *Wells and springs of Leicestershire*. Memoirs of the Geological Survey of England. His Majesty's Stationery Office: London.

Roberts, B.K. (1977). *Rural Settlement in Britain*. Studies in Historical Geography. Dawson Archon: Folkestone.

Robb, N.A. (1962, 1966). *William of Orange*. 2 vols. Heinemann: London. 1966.

Rodgers, J. (1947-8). *English rivers*. Batsford: London.

Rolk, L.T.C. (1962). *Landscape with canals*. Penguin: London.

(1969) *Navigable waterways*. Narie & Wilson: London.

Rowe, R. (ed.), (1985). *Canoeing handbook*. British Canoe Union: Nottingham.

Sanders, F. (1970). *The cactus king*. Hodder & Stoughton: London.

Sayers, D. (1934). *The nine tailors*. Victor Gollancz: London.

Scherman, K. (1976). *Iceland: daughter of fire*. Victor Gollancz: London.

Schmitz, A., Gommes, R., Vander Borght, P., & Vets, A. (1982). 'L'épuration en marais naturel: Cossigny'. In *Studies on aquatic vascular plants*, ed. J.J. Symoens, S.-S. Hooper, P. Compère. Royal Botanical Society of Belgium: Brussels. Pp. 353-87.

Sears, J. (1989a). A review of lead poisoning among the River Thames mute swan *cygnus onor* population. *Wildfowl* **41**, 151-2.

(1989b). A better alternative. R.S.P.B. Birds Magazine **12**, 53-5.

Skulberg, O.M., & Lilliehammer, A. (1984). 'Glåma'. In *Ecology of European Rivers*, ed. B.A. Whitton. Blackwells: Oxford. Pp. 469-98.

Spencer, E. (1580-94). *The Faerie Queen*, vol. 1. Everyman, J.M. Dent & Sons: London. 1910.

Sterluson, S. *King Harold's saga*. Penguin, Harmondsworth: Middlesex, 1960

Steward, R.J. (ed.), (1987). *The book of Merlin*. Blandford Press: Poole.

Stott, K.G. (1959). *A review of the brisket basket willow growing industry.* Long Ashton Research Station, Report.

Stratton, R. (1982). 'Farming in the Upper Deverills'. In *The Deverill Valley*, ed. F. Myatt. The Deverill Valley History Group. Pp. 83-97.

Streeter, D. (1985). 'Tomorrow is too late: natural grasslands'. *Natural World,* **23** (April), 28-9.

Stuart, M. (1979). *The colour dictionary of herbs and herbalism.* Orbis: London.

Stuckey, R.L., & Roberts, M.L. (1979). 'Distribution patterns of selected aquatic and wetland vascular plants in relation to the abandoned canals of Ohio'. *Ohio Journ. Sci.,* **79**, 18.

Summers, D. (1973). *The Great Ouse.* David & Charles: Newton Abbott.

Taylor, C.C. (1981). 'The drainage of Burwell Fen, Cambridgeshire 1840-1950'. In *Evolution of Marshland Landscapes*, University Department for External Studies: Oxford. Pp. 158-77.

Thacker, F.S. (1909). *The stripling Thames.* Fred S. Thacker: Holborn, London.

    (1914). *The Thames highway.* Fred S. Thacker: Dyer's buildings, Holborn, London.

Thompson, S. (1932). *Motif index of folk literature,* vol. 1. A-CFF Communications 106, Academia Scientarcen Fennice: Helsinki.

Thurston, H., & Attwater, D. (eds.), (1986). *Butler's lives of the Saints.* Burns & Oates: London.

Ticehurst, N.F. (1957). *The mute swan in England.* Cleaver Hume: London.

*Tourist Guide* (1986). Friesland, Holland. Frisian Tourist Office VVV: The Netherlands.

Toynbee, A. (1955). *A study of history.* Abridgement of vols. 7-10 by D.C. Somervell. University Press: Oxford.

Trollope, A. (1869-70). *The Vicar of Bulthampton.* The Worlds Classics. University Press: Oxford. 1924.

*Trout, Rod and Line* (Magazine).

*Trout Fisherman, The* (Magazine).

*Trout and Salmon* (Magazine).

Trubshaw, B. (1990). *Holy Wells and Springs of Leicestershire and Rutland.* Heart of Albion Press, Loughborough.

Turngren, A. (1945). *Flaxen braids.* Penguin: Middlesex & W. Yorks.

Tylecote, R.H. (1981). The medieval smith and his methods'. In *Mediaeval Industry*, ed. D.W. Crossley. CBA Research Report 40, Council for British Archaeology. Pp. 42-50.

Urk, G., van (1984). 'Lower Rhine-Meuse'. In *Ecology of European Rivers*, ed. B.A. Whitton. Blackwells, Oxford. Pp. 437-68.

Vaughan, R. (1970). *Philip the Good.* Longmans: London.

Victoria County History. (1902-14). Constable: London. *A History of the County of Hertfordshire*, 3 vols.
    (1900-12). *A History of the County of Hampshire and the Isle of Wight*, 5 vols.
    (1908-32). *A History of the County of Kent*, 3 vols.

Vince, J. (1970). *Discovering watermills.* Shire publications: Tring, Herts.

Walker, L.F. (ed.) (1963). *The complete fly-fisher.* Herbert Jenkins: London.

Walling, D.E., & Webb, B.W. (1981). 'Water quality'. In *British Rivers*, ed. J. Lewin. Allen & Unwin: London. Pp. 126-72.

Walton, I. (1653). *The compleat angler.* Folio Society: London, 1949.

Ward, R.C. (1981). 'River systems and river regimes'. In *British Rivers*, ed. J. Lewin. Allen & Unwin: London. Pp. 1-34.

Warren, C.E. (1971). *Biology and water pollution control.* W.B. Saunders: Philadelphia.

Water Research Centre (1977). *Water purification in the EEC. A state-of-the-art review.* Pergamon Press of the Commission of the European Communities.

Water Research Centre (1984, with 1987 Addendum). *An inventory of polluting substances which have been identified in various freshwater effluent discharges, aquatic animals and plants, and bottom sediments.* Concerted action analyses of organic micropollutants in water (COST 64b). Compiled by Water Research Centre, Stevenage, Commission of the European Communities.

Waters, B. (1979). *Severn streams.* Dent: London.

*Waterways World* (Magazine). Waterways Productions Ltd: Burton-on-Trent.

Watkin, B. (1982). 'Industry in the Deverill'. In *The Deverill Valley*, ed. F. Myatt. Deverill Valley History Group. Pp. 113-29.

White, G. (1788). *The natural history of Selbourne.* Penguin: Harmondsworth, London, 1977.

Whittaker, W. (1921). *The water supply of Hampshire.* Memoirs of the Geological Survey. Her Majesty's Stationery Office: London.

Whitton, B.A. (ed.) (1984). *Ecology of European Rivers.* Blackwells: Oxford.

Whitton, B.A., & Crisp, D.T. (1984). 'Tees'. In *Ecology of European Rivers*, ed. B.A. Whitton. Blackwells: Oxford. Pp. 145-78.

Whyle, L. (1962). *Medieval technology and social change.* University Press: Oxford.

Widdowson, E.M. (ed.) (1977). *Cam or Rhee.* Barrington Local History and Conservation Society: Sindall, Cambridge.

Willan, T.S. (1936). *River navigation in England, 1600-1750*. London.

Williams, M. (1970). *The draining of the Somerset Levels*. University Press: Cambridge.

Williamson, C., & Williamson, A.N. (1907). *The botor chaperon*. Methuen: London.

Wilson, D.R. (1971). *Air photointerpretation for archaeologists*. Batsford: London.

Wilson, J.K. (1965). *A study of the fenland waterways and barge trade over the past 2,000 years*. School of Navigation: Warsach.

Wilton-Smith, J. (1988). *Bath*. Pitkin Pictorials: Andover.

Winter, M., & Kickuth, R. (1985). 'Elimination of nutrients (sulphur, phosphorus, nitrogen) by the root zone process and simultaneous degradation of organic matter'. *Utrecht Plant Ecology News Report*, 4, 123-40.

(1988). 'Elimination of sulphur compounds from sewage by an ecotechnological treatment process'. *Dechema*, 2, 457-67.

(1989). 'Elimination of sulphur compounds from waste water by the root zone process. 1 performance of a large-scale purification plant at a textile finishing industry'. *Wat. Res.*, 23, 535-46.

(1991, in Press). 'Synecology of a *Phragmites-sulfuretum*'.

Wolseley, P.A. (1987). Contribution to S.M. Haslam, *River Plants of Western Europe*. University Press: Cambridge.

Wood, T.R. (1981). 'River Management'. In *British Rivers*, ed. J. Lewin. Allen & Unwin: London. Pp. 173-95.

Yonge, C.M. (1886). *Chantry House*. Macmillan: London.

Zammit, T. (1931). *The water supply of the Maltese islands*. Government Printing Press: Valletta.

# Index